Instructor's Answer Manual
to Accompany

Mathematical Ideas
Sixth Edition

Charles D. Miller

Vern E. Heeren
American River College

E. John Hornsby, Jr.
University of New Orleans

ISBN 0-673-47955-2.

3 4 5 6 - EBL - 94 93 92

CONTENTS

3 NUMERATION SYSTEMS

4 NUMBER THEORY

5 THE REAL NUMBERS

6 MATHEMATICAL SYSTEMS

7 EQUATIONS, INEQUALITIES, AND PROBLEM SOLVING

8 GRAPHS AND FUNCTIONS

9 GEOMETRY

10 COUNTING METHODS

11 PROBABILITY

12 STATISTICS

13 CONSUMER MATHEMATICS

14 COMPUTERS

15 MATRICES AND THEIR APPLICATIONS

ANSWERS TO EXERCISES

An Introduction to Calculators (page xvii)

1. 104.596 **2.** 653.327 **3.** 14,904.754 **4.** 18,264.589 **5.** 1857.777

6. 1224.825 **7.** 7.676 **8.** 733.443 **9.** 1.202 **10.** 7.595 **11.** 56.511

12. 6.217 **13.** 369.019 **14.** 58.901 **15.** 25.801 **16.** 25.600

17. 1.889 **18.** .857 **19.** .003 **20.** .005 **21.** 4.227 **22.** 4.017

23. .458 **24.** 4 **25.** 12.959 **26.** .975 **27.** .665 **28.** .691

29. .833 **30.** .667 **31.** 1.267 **32.** 1.139 **33.** 4.917 **34.** 3.9

35. 7.733 **36.** 2.393 **37.** .524 **38.** .485 **39.** 2.033 **40.** 1.164

41. 5/6 **42.** 2/3 **43.** 19/15 **44.** 41/36 **45.** 11/21 **46.** 16/33

47. 61/30 **48.** 64/55 **49.** $86.72 **50.** $68.61 **51.** $134.42

52. $189.23 **53.** $11 **54.** $47 **55.** $20 **56.** $2 **57.** $.16

58. $.24 **59.** $99 **60.** $88 **61.** $24 **62.** $178

In Exercises 63-78, the number of digits displayed will vary depending on the model of calculator used.

63. 54 **64.** 79 **65.** 23.58 **66.** 236.5 **67.** 5776 **68.** 59,536

69. 11.9025 **70.** 613.0576 **71.** 166,375 **72.** 33,554,432

73. 912,618,650,000 **74.** 82,995,965.93 **75.** .125 **76.** .0625

77. .0434783 **78.** .03448275862 **79.** 1, 2, 3, 4, 6, 7, 8, 9

80. 1, 3, 4, 5, 6 **81.** 2, 3, 5, 8, 9 **85.** For example, suppose the date of birth is October 12, 1949, and the trick is being performed in 1990. (a) 1949 (b) 1949 - 10 = 1939 (c) .656059 (d) 41 (e) The person will be 41 years old in 1990.

CHAPTER 1

Section 1.1 (page 6)

1. {12, 13, 14, 15, 16, 17, 18, 19, 20} **2.** {8, 9, 10, 11, 12, 13, 14, 15, 16, 17}
3. {1, 1/2, 1/4, 1/8, 1/16, 1/32} **4.** {3, 9, 27, 81, 243, 729}
5. {17, 22, 27, 32, 37, 42, 47} **6.** {74, 68, 62, 56, 50, 44, 38}
7. {1, 2, 3, 4, 5} **8.** {8, 9, 10, 11, 12, 13, 14} **9.** {1, 2, 3, 4}
10. {3, 4, 5, 6, 7, 8, 9, 10} **11.** {4, 6, 8, 10, 12, ...}
12. {1, 2, 3, 4, 5, 6, 7, 8, 9, 10, 11, 12} **13.** {9, 11, 13, 15}
14. {1, 3, 5, 7, 9, 11, 13, 15} **15.** Finite **16.** Infinite **17.** Infinite
18. Finite **19.** Infinite **20.** Finite **21.** Infinite **22.** Infinite
23. 5 **24.** 7 **25.** 1000 **26.** 2000 **27.** 50 **28.** 26
29. {x|x is an odd counting number between 6 and 18}
30. {x|x is a counting number less than 7}
31. {x|x is a counting number multiple of 10}
32. {x|x is a counting number multiple of 25} **33.** {x|x is a season of the year}
34. {x|x is one of the twelve months} **35.** Well defined **36.** Well defined
37. Not well defined **38.** Not well defined **39.** Not well defined **40.** Not well defined **41.** Well defined (There are none.) **42.** Well defined (There are none.)
43. $\in$ **44.** $\in$ **45.** $\notin$ **46.** $\notin$ **47.** $\in$ **48.** $\notin$ **49.** $\notin$ **50.** $\notin$
51. False **52.** False **53.** True **54.** True **55.** True **56.** True
57. True **58.** True **59.** False **60.** False **61.** True **62.** True
63. True **64.** True **65.** True **66.** True **67.** False **68.** False
69. False **70.** False **71.** True **72.** False **73.** {1, 2, 3, 4, 5, 6}
74. {boy, girl} **75.** (a) {se}, {ve} (b) {se}, {ve}, {mo, li}, {se, ve}, {ve, mo}, {ve, li}, {ve, si}, {se, mo}, {se, li}, {se, si} **76.** (a) {2, 5} (b) $\emptyset$

Section 1.2 (page 14)

1. $\subseteq$ **2.** $\subseteq$ **3.** $\not\subseteq$ **4.** $\not\subseteq$ **5.** $\subseteq$ **6.** $\subseteq$ **7.** $\subseteq$ **8.** $\not\subseteq$ **9.** $\subset$, $\subseteq$ **10.** $\subset$, $\subseteq$ **11.** $\subseteq$ **12.** $\subseteq$ **13.** $\subset$, $\subseteq$ **14.** $\subseteq$ **15.** True **16.** True **17.** True **18.** True **19.** False **20.** False **21.** True **22.** True **23.** True **24.** False **25.** True **26.** False **27.** False **28.** True **29.** False **30.** True **31.** False **32.** True **33.** True **34.** True **35.** True **36.** False **37.** 8; 7 **38.** 16; 15 **39.** 32; 31 **40.** 64; 63 **41.** 1; none **42.** 64; 63 **43.** 32; 31 **44.** 8; 7 **45.** {2, 3, 5, 7, 9, 10} **46.** {1, 3, 4, 6, 8} **47.** {2} **48.** {1, 2, 4, 6, 8, 10} **49.** U **50.** Ø **51.** Ø **52.** Ø, {Ø} **53.** Ø, {0} **54.** Ø, {{0}} **55.** {low cost, high cost, pays off at death, no retirement benefits, retirement benefits} **56.** {high cost, retirement benefits} **57.** {low cost, no retirement benefits} **58.** {pays off at death} **59.** {high cost, retirement benefits} **60.** {low cost, no retirement benefits} **61.** All five must be present. **62.** DLAK, DLAS, DLKS, DAKS, LAKS **63.** DLA, DLK, DLS, LAK, LAS, DAK, DAS, AKS, LKS, DKS **64.** DL, DA, DK, DS, LA, LK, LS, AK, AS, KS **65.** D, L, A, K, S **66.** No one should be present. **67.** 1 + 5 + 10 + 10 + 5 + 1 = 32 **68.** The answer is the same. There are $2^5 = 32$ subsets of the set of the five family members.

69. (a) 15 (b) 16, since it is now possible to select no bills

70. (a) 63 (b) 64, since you can now make a "sum" of no money by selecting no coins

Section 1.3 (page 23)

1. True **2.** True **3.** False **4.** False **5.** True **6.** False **7.** False **8.** True **9.** True **10.** False **11.** True **12.** True **13.** {3, 5} **14.** {2, 3, 4, 5, 7, 9}, or U **15.** {2, 3, 4, 5, 7, 9}, or U **16.** {5, 7, 9} **17.** {2, 3, 4, 5, 7, 9}, or U **18.** {3, 5, 7, 9}, or Y **19.** {7, 9} **20.** {2, 4} **21.** Ø **22.** {7, 9}, or X′ **23.** Ø **24.** {2, 4}, or Y′ **25.** {2, 3, 4, 5, 7, 9}, or U **26.** {3, 5, 7, 9}, or Y **27.** {2, 3, 4, 5}, or X

28. {2, 4, 5, 7, 9}, or Z **29.** {3} **30.** {2, 3, 4, 5}, or X **31.** {3, 9} **32.** {15, 17} **33.** {18} **34.** {18} **35.** {3, 9} **36.** {7, 11, 15, 17}, or N **37.** $A \cap B = \emptyset$ **38.** If both A and B are equal to $\emptyset$ **39.** Always true for any set A **40.** If $A = \emptyset$ **41.** {s, d, c, g, i, m, h} **42.** {s, d, c} **43.** {i, m, h} **44.** {g} **45.** {s, d, c, g, i, m, h} **46.** {s, d, c} **47.** All students studying math and history **48.** All students over 25 who study history **49.** All students on a student loan who study math **50.** All students studying math or who are over 25 **51.** All students who do not study math and are over 25 **52.** All students who do not study math and who do not study history **53.** All students who do not study math and study history and are over 25 **54.** All students studying math or history and who are not over 25 **55.** True **56.** False **57.** True **58.** False **59.** False **60.** False **61.** True **62.** True **63.** True **64.** False **65.** True **66.** True **67.** False **68.** True **69.** True **70.** True **71.** True **72.** True **73.** False **74.** False **75.** True **76.** True **77.** True **78.** True **79.** False **80.** False **81.** False **82.** False **83.** True **84.** True **85.** True **86.** True

87. $A \times B = \{(2, 4), (2, 9), (8, 4), (8, 9), (12, 4), (12, 9)\}$;
$B \times A = \{(4, 2), (9, 2), (4, 8), (9, 8), (4, 12), (9, 12)\}$

88. $A \times B = \{(3, 6), (3, 8), (6, 6), (6, 8), (9, 6), (9, 8), (12, 6), (12, 8)\}$;
$B \times A = \{(6, 3), (8, 3), (6, 6), (8, 6), (6, 9), (8, 9), (6, 12), (8, 12)\}$

89. $A \times B = \{(d, p), (d, i), (d, g), (o, p), (o, i), (o, g), (g, p), (g, i), (g, g)\}$;
$B \times A = \{(p, d), (i, d), (g, d), (p, o), (i, o), (g, o), (p, g), (i, g), (g, g)\}$

90. $A \times B = \{(b, r), (b, e), (b, d), (l, r), (l, e), (l, d), (u, r), (u, e), (u, d), (e, r), (e, e), (e, d)\}$;
$B \times A = \{(r, b), (e, b), (d, b), (r, l), (e, l), (d, l), (r, u), (e, u), (d, u), (r, e), (e, e), (d, e)\}$

91. $n(A \times B) = 6$; $n(B \times A) = 6$ **92.** $n(A \times B) = 9$; $n(B \times A) = 9$ **93.** 210 in both cases **94.** 65 in both cases **95.** 3 **96.** 25

Section 1.4 (page 30)

1.

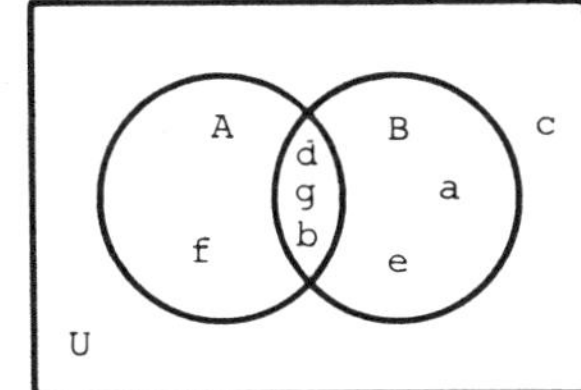

2.

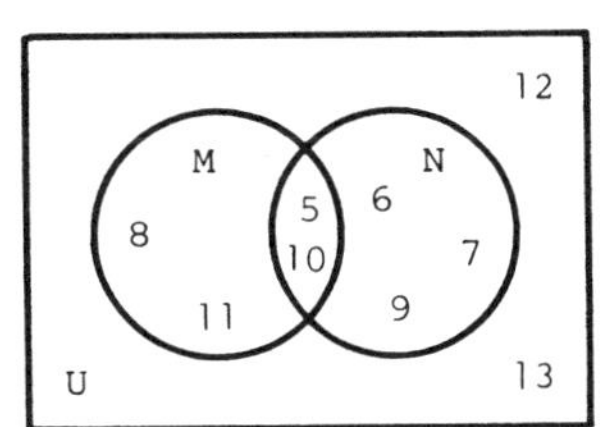

3.

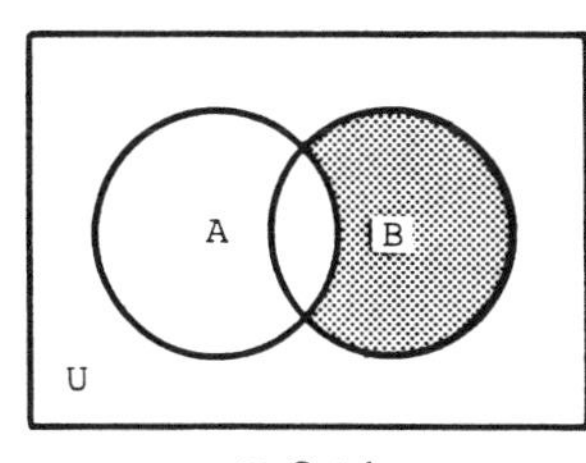

$B \cap A'$

4.

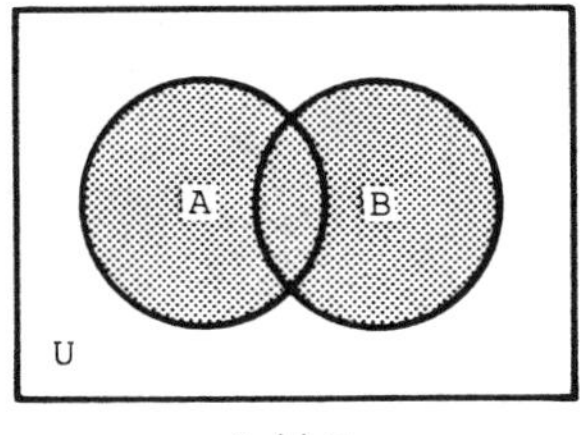

$A \cup B$

5.

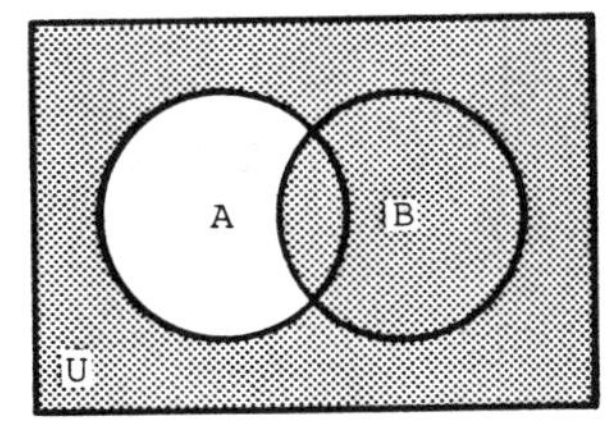

$A' \cup B$

6.

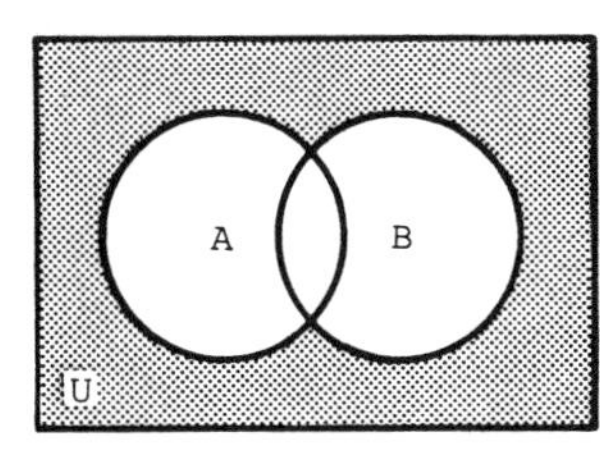

$A' \cap B'$

7.

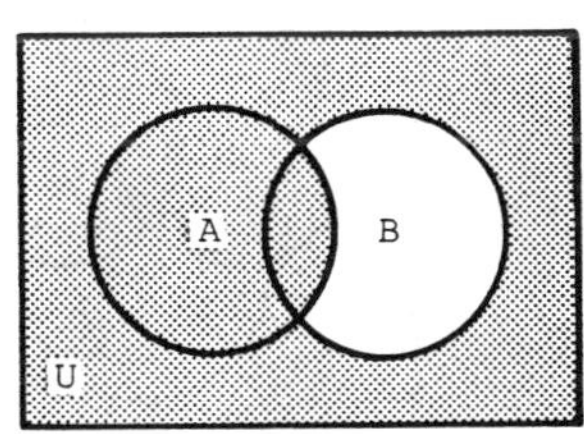

$B' \cup A$

8.

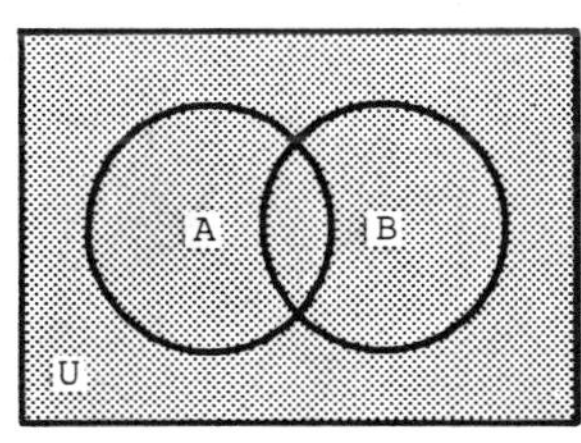

$A' \cup A$

9. $B' \cap B = \emptyset$

10.

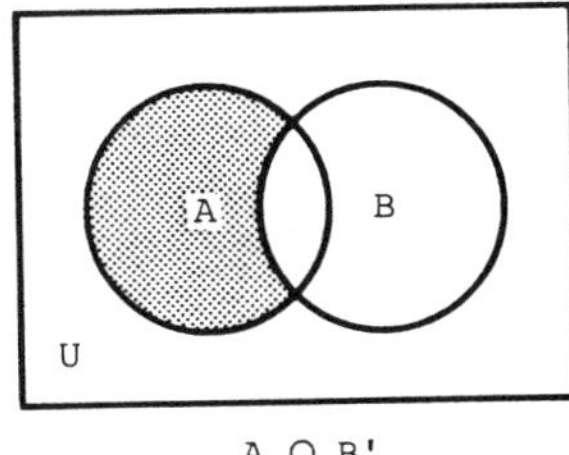

$A \cap B'$

11.

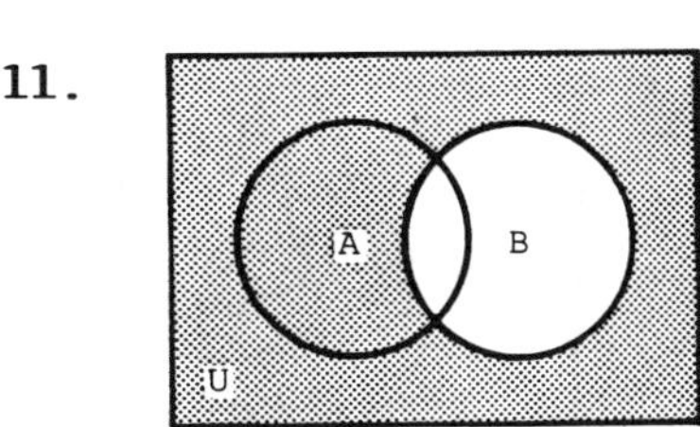

$B' \cup (A' \cap B')$

12.

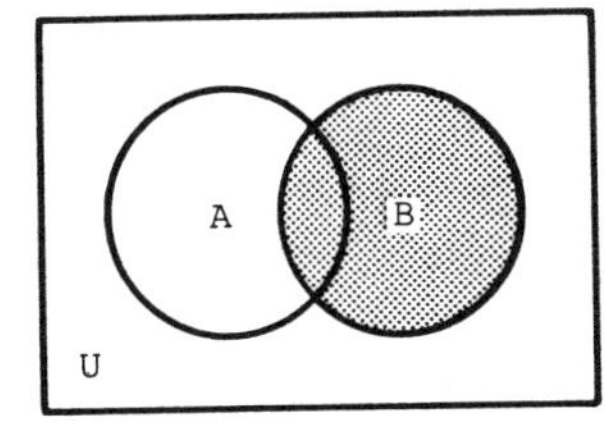

$(A \cap B) \cup B$

13. $U' = \emptyset$

14.

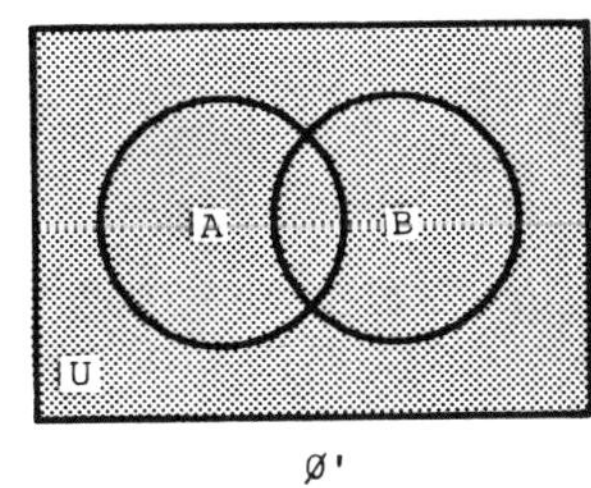

$\emptyset'$

15.

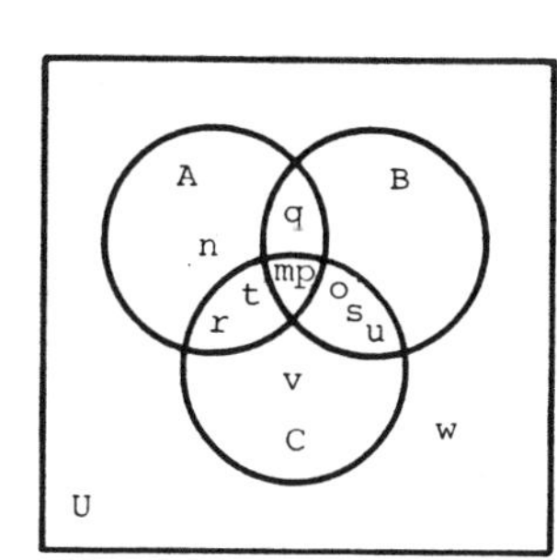

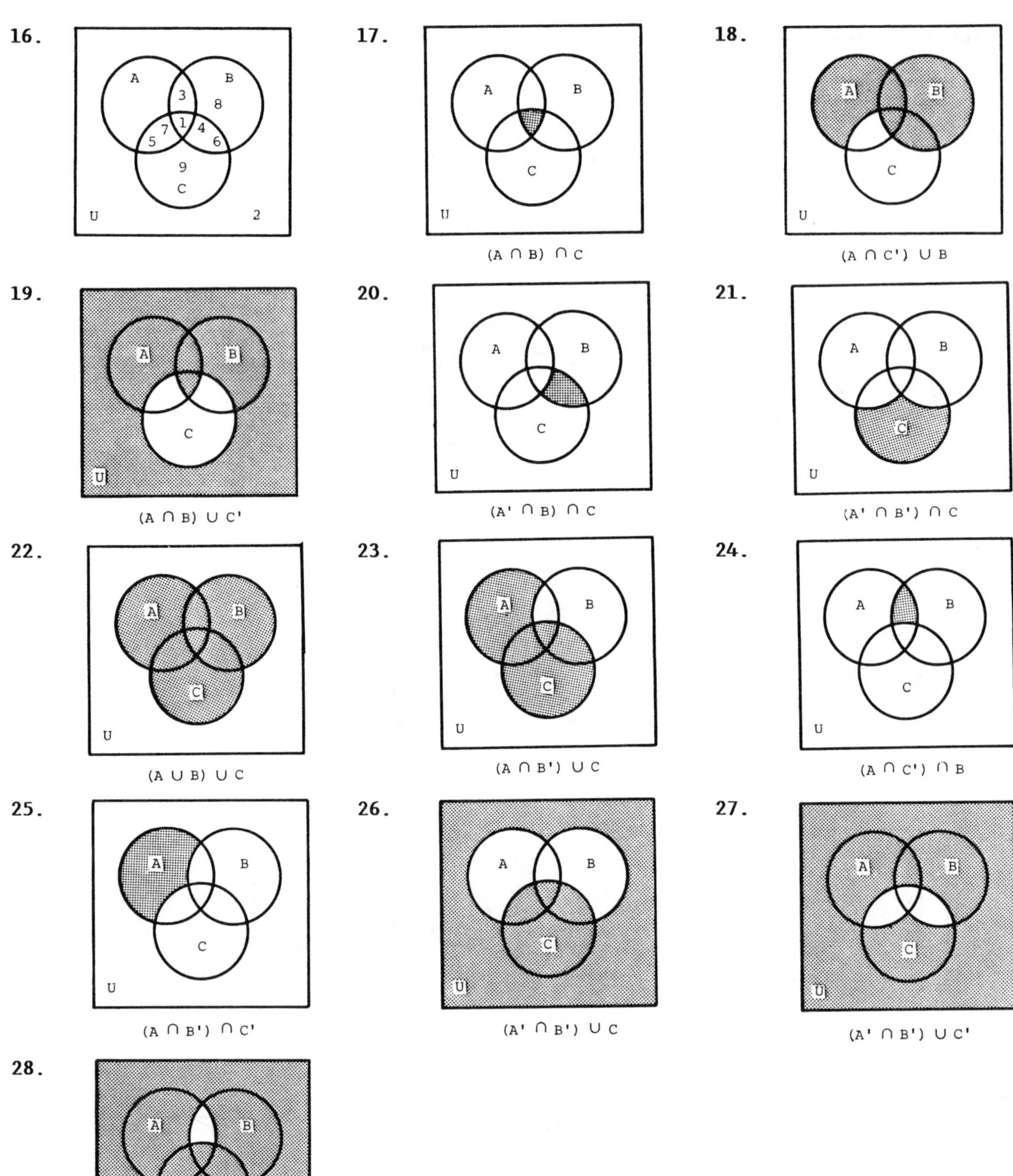

17. $(A \cap B) \cap C$

18. $(A \cap C') \cup B$

19. $(A \cap B) \cup C'$

20. $(A' \cap B) \cap C$

21. $(A' \cap B') \cap C$

22. $(A \cup B) \cup C$

23. $(A \cap B') \cup C$

24. $(A \cap C') \cap B$

25. $(A \cap B') \cap C'$

26. $(A' \cap B') \cup C$

27. $(A' \cap B') \cup C'$

28. $(A \cap B)' \cup C$

In Exercises 29-36, two possible answers are given. There may be others.

29. $A' \cap B'$ or $(A \cup B)'$ **30.** $A' \cup B$ or $U - (A \cap B')$ **31.** $(A \cup B) \cap [(A \cap B)']$ or $(A \cup B) - (A \cap B)$ **32.** $A \cap B'$ or $A - B$ **33.** $(A \cap B) \cup (A \cap C)$ or $A \cap (B \cup C)$

34. $A \cap (B \cup C)'$ or $A \cap (B' \cap C')$ **35.** $(A \cap B) \cap C'$ or $(A \cap B) - C$

36. $(B \cup C) \cap A'$ or $(B \cup C) - A$

37.

$A \cup B = B \cup A$

38.

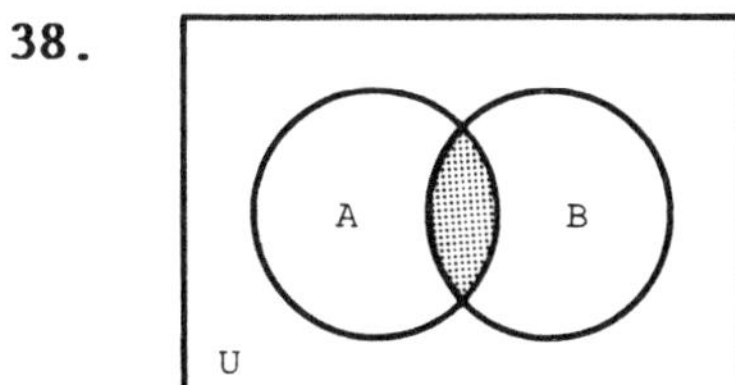

$A \cap B = B \cap A$

39.

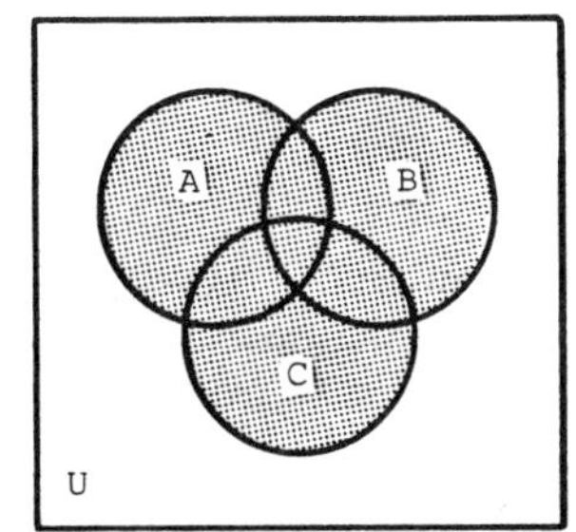

$A \cup (B \cup C) = (A \cup B) \cup C$

40.

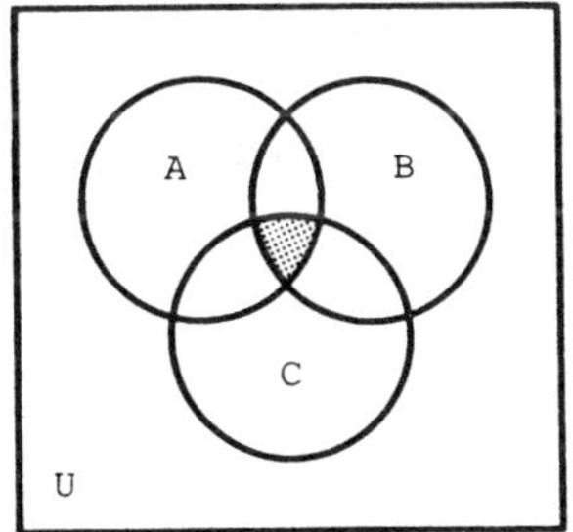

$A \cap (B \cap C) = (A \cap B) \cap C$

41.

$A \cup \emptyset = A$

42.

$A \cap U = A$

43.

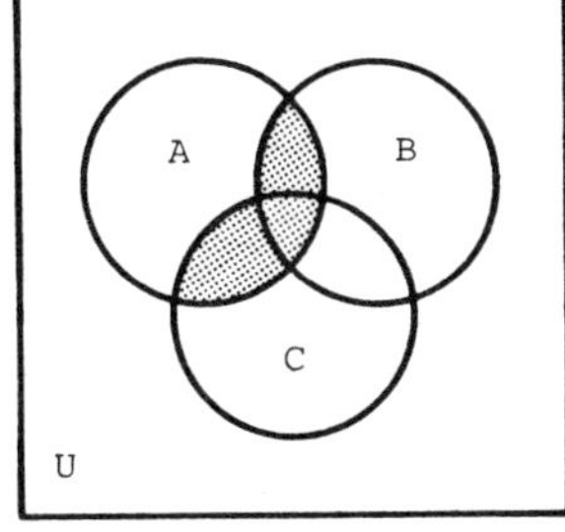

$A \cap (B \cup C) = (A \cap B) \cup (A \cap C)$

44.

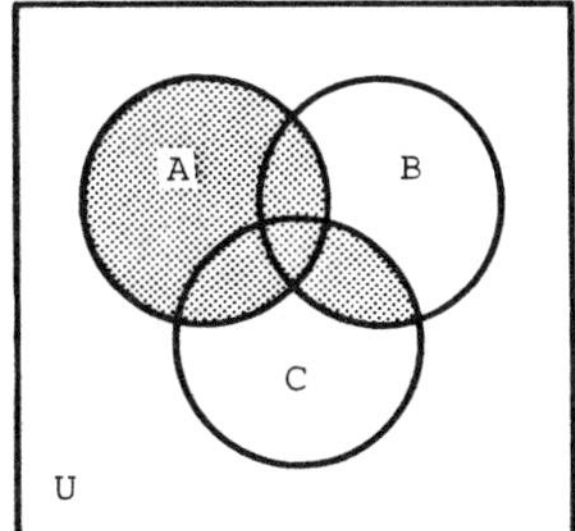

$A \cup (B \cap C) = (A \cup B) \cap (A \cup C)$

45. True

46. False

47. True

48. False

49. False

50. False

51. Each set is equal to $\{1, 2, 3, 4, 5, 9, 10\}$. **52.** Each set is equal to $\{5, 9\}$.

53. Each set is equal to $\{5\}$. **54.** Each set is equal to $\{1, 2, 3, 4, 5, 9, 10\}$.

55. Each set is equal to $\{1, 2, 3, 5\}$. **56.** Each set is equal to $\{1, 2, 3, 4, 5, 9\}$.

57. Each set is equal to $\{2, 5, 9, 10\}$. **58.** Each set is equal to $\{1, 3, 5, 9\}$.

59. Normal rate, regular rhythm, p wave precedes r wave **60.** Normal rate, irregular rhythm, p wave precedes r wave **61.** Non-normal rate, regular rhythm, p wave precedes r wave **62.** Non-normal rate, irregular rhythm, p wave precedes r wave **63.** Normal rate, regular rhythm, p wave precedes r wave **64.** Normal rate or p wave precedes r wave, and regular rhythm **65.** 4, 8, 16 **66.** 1 **67.** 1, 2, 3, 4, 5, 6, 7, 8, 9, 10, 11, 12, 13, 14, 15 (all except 16) **68.** 1, 2, 3, 4, 5, 9, 11 **69.** 5, 8, 13 **70.** $2^5 = 32$; 2^n

Section 1.5 (page 35)

1. (a) 12 (b) 20 (c) 6 (d) 10 (e) 48 **2.** (a) 0 (b) 4 (c) 3 (d) 0 (e) 6 **3.** Yes; his data adds up to 142 people. **4.** (a) 12 (b) 18 (c) 37 (d) 97 **5.** (a) A-negative (b) AB-negative (c) B-negative (d) AB-positive (e) B-positive (f) O-positive (g) O-negative **6.** (a) 54 (b) 17 (c) 10 (d) 7 (e) 15 (f) 3 (g) 12 (h) 1 **7.** (a) 37 (b) 22 (c) 50 (d) 11 (e) 25 (f) 11 **8.** (a) 51 (b) 31 (c) 18 (d) 15 (e) 33 (f) 23 **9.** (a) 40 (b) 30 (c) 95 (d) 110 (e) 160 (f) 65 **10.** (a) 2 (b) 60 (c) 8 (d) 100 (e) 27 **11.** 9 **12.** 9 **13.** 16 **14.** 27

15.

16.

17.

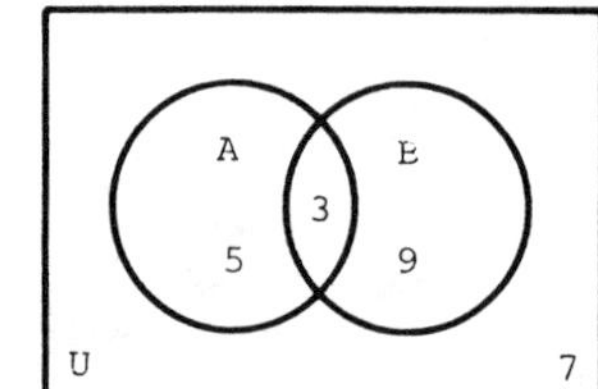

18.

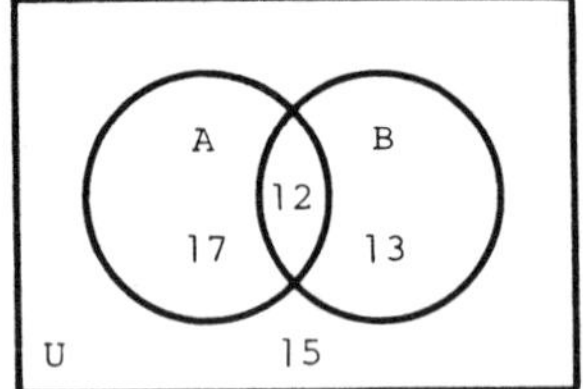

19.

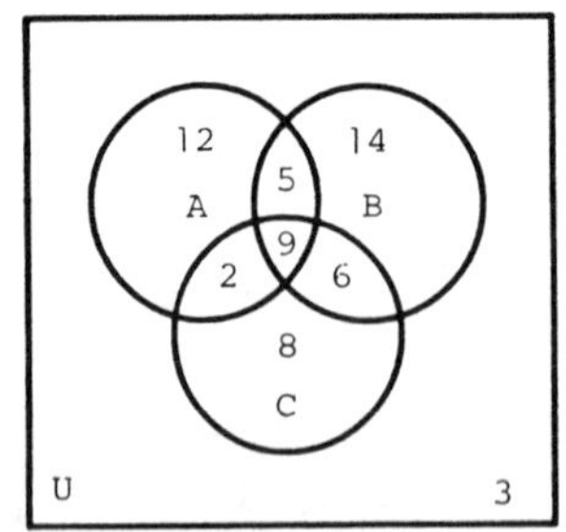

20.

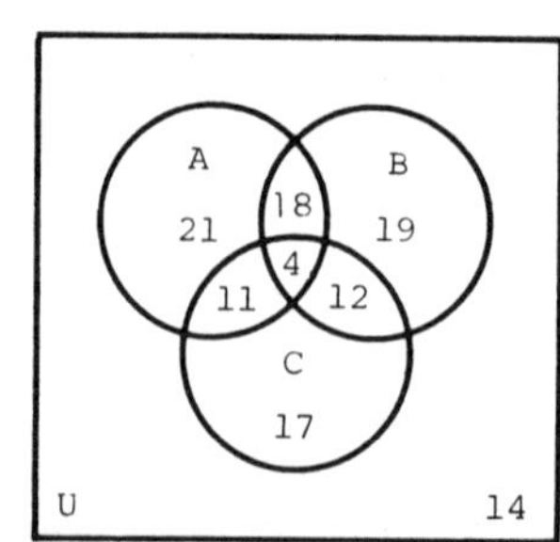

21.

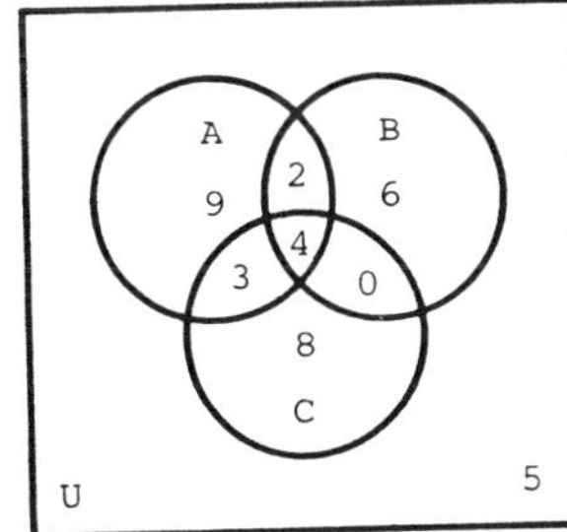

22.

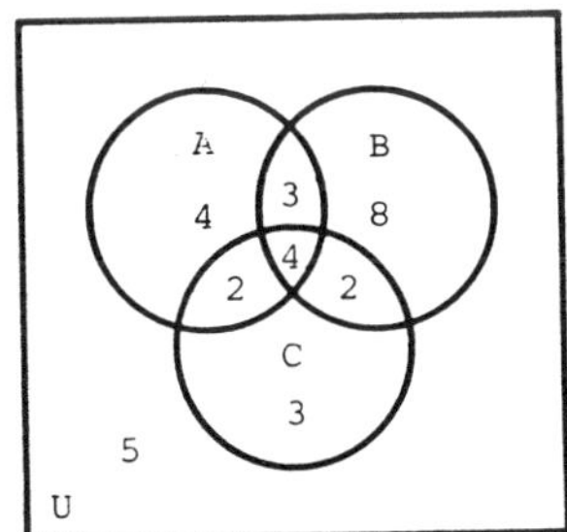

Section 1.6 (page 45)

Each of the answers to Exercises 1–4 shows only one possible one-to-one correspondence.

1. {1, 4, 9, 12} ↕ {8, 12, 16, 20}

2. {Shamus, Anna, Kerry} ↕ {□, ○, ☆}

3. Not possible

4.

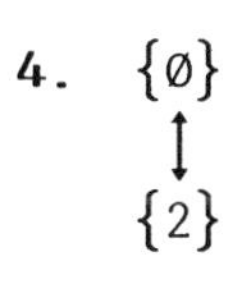
{∅} ↕ {2}

5. 5 **6.** 52 **7.** 4 **8.** 5 **9.** 1 **10.** 1 **11.** $\aleph_0$ **12.** $\aleph_0$

13. *c* **14.** *c*

Each of the answers to Exercises 15–30 shows only one possible one-to-one correspondence.

15. {5, 10, 15, 20, 25, 30, ..., 5n, ...}
↕
{1, 2, 3, 4, 5, 6, ..., n, ...}

16. {1,000,000, 2,000,000, 3,000,000, ..., $n \cdot 10^6$, ...}
↕
{1, 2, 3, ..., n, ...}

17. {2, 4, 6, 8, 10, 12, ..., 2n, ...}
↕
{1, 2, 3, 4, 5, 6, ..., n, ...}

18. {1, 3, 5, 7, 9, 11, ..., 2n − 1, ...}
↕
{1, 2, 3, 4, 5, 6, ..., n, ...}

19. {0, 2, −2, 4, −4, 6, −6, 8, −8, ..., 2n, −2n, ...}
↕
{1, 2, 3, 4, 5, 6, 7, 8, 9, ..., 2n, 2n + 1, ...}

20. {1, −1, 3, −3, 5, −5, 7, −7, ..., 2n − 1, −(2n − 1), ...}
↕
{1, 2, 3, 4, 5, 6, 7, 8, ..., 2n − 1, 2n, ...}

21. $\{2, 4, 8, 16, 32, 64, 128, \ldots\} = \{2^1, 2^2, 2^3, 2^4, 2^5, 2^6, 2^7, \ldots, 2^n, \ldots\}$

$\updownarrow \; \updownarrow \; \updownarrow \; \updownarrow \; \updownarrow \; \updownarrow \; \updownarrow \qquad \updownarrow$

$\{1, 2, 3, 4, 5, 6, 7, \ldots, n, \ldots\}$

22. $\{1/3, 1/9, 1/27, 1/81, 1/243, \ldots\} = \{1/3^1, 1/3^2, 1/3^3, 1/3^4, 1/3^5, \ldots, 1/3^n, \ldots\}$

$\updownarrow \; \updownarrow \; \updownarrow \; \updownarrow \; \updownarrow \qquad \updownarrow$

$\{1, 2, 3, 4, 5, \ldots, n, \ldots\}$

25. $\{2, 4, 6, 8, 10, 12, \ldots, 2n, \ldots\}$

$\updownarrow \; \updownarrow \; \updownarrow \; \updownarrow \; \updownarrow \; \updownarrow \qquad \updownarrow$

$\{4, 8, 12, 16, 20, 24, \ldots, 2(2n), \ldots\}$

26. $\{1, 3, 5, 7, 9, \ldots, 2n - 1, \ldots\}$

$\updownarrow \; \updownarrow \; \updownarrow \; \updownarrow \; \updownarrow \qquad \updownarrow$

$\{1, 5, 9, 13, 17, \ldots, 2(2n - 1) - 1, \ldots\}$

27. $\{1/3, 1/6, 1/12, 1/24, \ldots, 1/(3 \cdot 2^{n-1}), \ldots\}$

$\updownarrow \; \updownarrow \; \updownarrow \; \updownarrow \qquad \updownarrow$

$\{1/6, 1/12, 1/24, 1/48, \ldots, 1/(3 \cdot 2^n), \ldots\}$

28. $\{25, 50, 75, 100, 125, \ldots, 25n, \ldots\}$

$\updownarrow \; \updownarrow \; \updownarrow \; \updownarrow \; \updownarrow \qquad \updownarrow$

$\{50, 100, 150, 200, 250, \ldots, 2 \cdot 25n, \ldots\}$

29. $\{2/5, 3/5, 4/5, 5/5, 6/5, \ldots, (n + 1)/5, \ldots\}$

$\updownarrow \; \updownarrow \; \updownarrow \; \updownarrow \; \updownarrow \qquad \updownarrow$

$\{4/5, 6/5, 8/5, 10/5, 12/5, \ldots, 2(n + 1)/5, \ldots\}$

30. $\{5/9, 6/9, 7/9, 8/9, 9/9, 10/9, \ldots, (n + 4)/9, \ldots\}$

$\updownarrow \; \updownarrow \; \updownarrow \; \updownarrow \; \updownarrow \; \updownarrow \qquad \updownarrow$

$\{10/9, 12/9, 14/9, 16/9, 18/9, 20/9, \ldots, 2(n + 4)/9, \ldots\}$

31. $\aleph_0$ **32.** $\aleph_0$ **33.** $\aleph_0$ **34.** c **35.** c **36.** c

37. Each guest must move to a room having a number 1 higher than the current room number of the guest. This leaves one room available for the new guest.

38. Each guest must move to a room having twice the current room number. Thus, only the even-numbered rooms will be used by current guests. The odd-numbered rooms will be available for the new guests. **39.** Both **40.** Equivalent **41.** Equivalent **42.** Equivalent **43.** Equivalent **44.** Neither

Chapter 1 Test (page 47)

1. {2, 4, 6} **2.** {3, 7} **3.** {1, 3, 6, 7} **4.** {2, 4, 6} **5.** False

6. True **7.** False **8.** True **9.** True **10.** False **11.** False

12. True

More than one answer may be possible for Exercises 13-14.

13. {x|x is a counting number less than 7}

14. {x|x is a counting number multiple of 3 less than 19} **15.** $\subset$, $\subseteq$ **16.** $\subseteq$

17. $2^5 = 32$ **18.** A × B = {(4, 1), (4, 3), (4, 5), (8, 1), (8, 3), (8, 5)};
B × A = {(1, 4), (3, 4), (5, 4), (1, 8), (3, 8), (5, 8)} **19.** {5, 7} **20.** {6}

21.

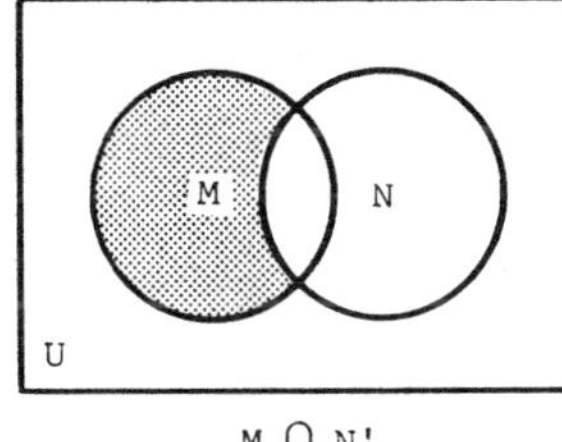

$M \cap N'$

22.

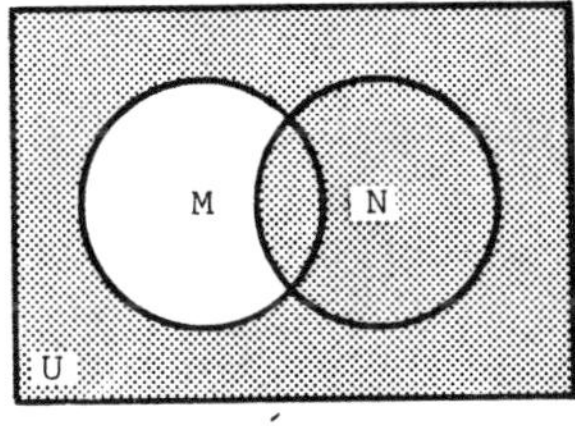

$M' \cup N$

23.

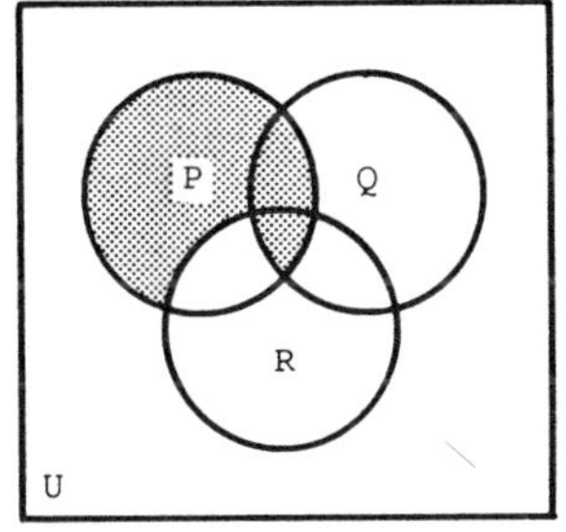

$P \cap (Q \cup R')$

24.

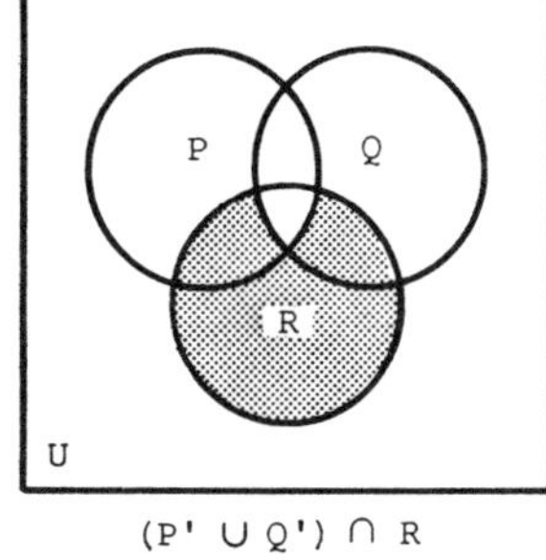

$(P' \cup Q') \cap R$

25.

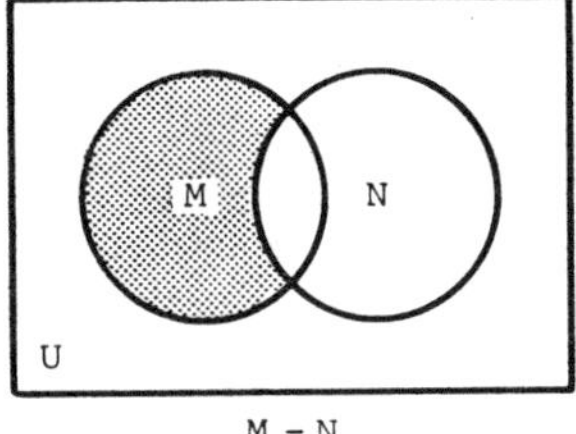

$M - N$

26.

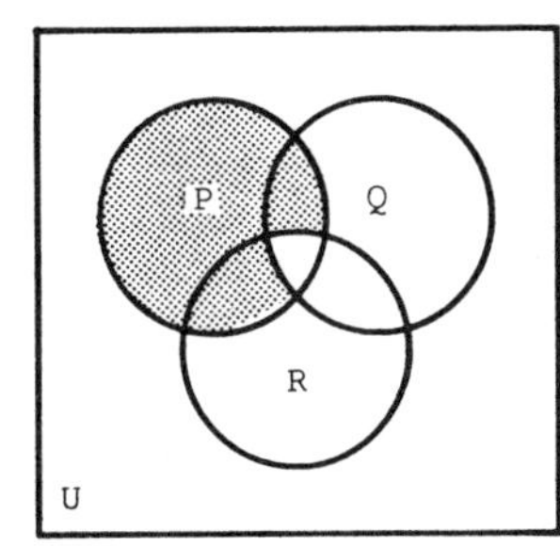

$P - (Q \cap R)$

27. {outdoor gaslight, color television, clothes dryer, central air conditioner, waterbed heater} **28.** {outdoor gaslight, frostless refrigerator, clothes dryer, central air conditioner, waterbed heater} **29.** {coffee maker, dishwasher, manual refrigerator, toaster} **30.** {outdoor gaslight, coffee maker, dishwasher, frostless refrigerator, manual refrigerator, toaster, clothes dryer, central air conditioner, waterbed heater} **31.** 8 **32.** 27 **33.** 16 **34.** 28 **35.** 43

CHAPTER 2

Section 2.1 (page 55)

1. Statement **2.** Statement **3.** Not a statement **4.** Statement **5.** Statement **6.** Statement **7.** Statement **8.** Statement **9.** Statement **10.** Statement **11.** Statement **12.** Not a statement **13.** Not a statement **14.** Not a statement **15.** Statement **16.** Statement **17.** Or **18.** Not compound **19.** Or **20.** And **21.** Not compound **22.** Not compound **23.** Not compound **24.** Not compound **25.** He does not have brown hair. **26.** He is not a student. **27.** He has brown hair and he is a student. **28.** He has brown hair or he is a student. **29.** He does not have brown hair or he is a student. **30.** He has brown hair and he is not a student. **31.** He does not have brown hair or he is not a student. **32.** He does not have brown hair and he is not a student. **33.** It is not the case that he does not have brown hair and he is a student. **34.** It is not the case that he has brown hair or he is not a student. **35.** $b \wedge f$ **36.** $b \wedge \sim f$ **37.** $\sim b \vee \sim f$ **38.** $b \vee f$ **39.** $\sim(b \vee f)$ **40.** $(b \vee f) \wedge [\sim(b \wedge f)]$ **41.** $2 < 5$ and $4 > 1$, or "2 is less than 5 and 4 is greater than 1." **42.** $2 < 5$ or $4 \not> 1$, or "2 is less than 5 or 4 is not greater than 1." **43.** $2 \not< 5$ or $4 \not> 1$, or "2 is not less than 5 or 4 is not greater than 1." **44.** $2 \not< 5$ and $4 > 1$, or "2 is not less than 5 and 4 is greater than 1." **45.** His mother's name is not Lucy. **46.** The grass does not need to be cut. **47.** Some cows were not once calves. **48.** Some dew forms in the desert. **49.** No people eat pancakes. **50.** Someone may not be seated. **51.** Sometimes I try and do not fail. **52.** No politicians are crooked. **53.** All ground squirrels are happy. **54.** Some telephone installers can play poker. **55.** All people are American citizens. **56.** Somebody doesn't like Sara Lee. **57.** Somebody likes me. **58.** Some people never love anybody. **59.** $x \geq 4$ **60.** $x < 9$ **61.** $y < -1$ **62.** $p \geq 0$ **63.** $2x + 5y \geq 1$ **64.** $3x - 7y < 21$ **65.** $9x < 7y + 3$ **66.** $5x + 3y \geq 5$ **67.** Literal meaning: Not a single person may enter the White House. Intended meaning: Unauthorized people may not enter the White House.

68. Literal meaning: No one can be an expert in mathematics. Intended meaning: Not everyone can be an expert in mathematics. **69.** Literal meaning: No one at all is on the committee. Intended meaning: Not everyone is on the committee. **70.** Literal meaning: I have tried to find a book called "How to Play the Tuba Without Success." Intended meaning: I have tried with no success to find the book. **71.** Literal meaning: This door must never be opened. Intended meaning: This door should be opened only for good reason. **72.** Literal meaning: This door must always be closed, no matter what. Intended meaning: This door must remain closed unless someone is using it.
73. Not all students park on the north side; all students park on the north side.
74. Not all citizens go to Tallahassee to complain; all citizens go to Tallahassee to complain. **75.** Not all people get their oil changed properly; all people get their oil changed properly. **76.** Not all doctors have a good bedside manner; all doctors have a good bedside manner. **77.** Against birth control **78.** No **79.** True
80. True **81.** True **82.** False; to make the statement true, replace $<$ with $>$ or $\geq$.
83. True **84.** False; to make the statement true, replace $\leq$ with $<$. **85.** False; to make the statement true, replace $= x$ with $= |x|$. **86.** True

Section 2.2 (page 64)

1. False	**2.** True	**3.** True	**4.** False	**5.** True	**6.** False
7. True	**8.** True	**9.** False	**10.** False	**11.** True	**12.** False
13. False	**14.** True	**15.** False	**16.** True	**17.** True	**18.** False
19. False	**20.** False	**21.** True	**22.** False	**23.** False	**24.** True
25. True	**26.** True	**27.** True	**28.** True	**29.** FTTT	**30.** FFTF
31. TTFT	**32.** FTTT	**33.** FTFF	**34.** TTTT	**35.** FFTT	**36.** FFFT

37. TFTT **38.** TFFF **39.** TFTTTFTF **40.** FFFFTFFF **41.** FFFTTTTT
42. FTFTTTTT **43.** FFFFFFFFTFTTFFFF **44.** TTTTTTTTTTTTFTTT **45.** 16
46. 32 **47.** 128 **48.** 64 **49.** The book is not too long or it is not boring.

50. The doctor is not in and the nurse is not out. **51.** Her BMW does not go fast and she does not know the reason why. **52.** I won't major in business and I won't work for the government. **53.** $4 \nless 9$ and $3 = 5$ **54.** $6 - 2 \neq 4$ or $8 + 5 = 12$
55. She will come or he won't go. **56.** I won't do this and you can do that.
57. The bride will not attend or the groom will not attend the wedding. **58.** Santa won't attend the Christmas party and Rudolph won't attend. **59.** Inclusive disjunction
60. False **61.** True **62.** True **63.** False **64.** FTTF **65.** TFFT
66. TFFT **67.** FFFT **68.** FFTF **69.** TFTT **70.** TTFT
71. (a) Number the tubes from left to right across the top of the photograph. One sequence of balls is 1, 2, 4, 5, 8, and 11. (b) Number the tubes from left to right. Use tubes 1, 3, 4, 5, 8, and 12. **72.** (a) $(H \vee S) \wedge {\sim}H$ (b) FFTF (c) Row 3 (d) She did it. **73.** True **74.** False **75.** True **76.** True **77.** False
78. True **79.** True **80.** False **81.** False **82.** True **83.** True
84. True **85.** False **86.** True

Section 2.3 (page 72)

Each answer for Exercises 1–24 gives only one of several possible wordings.
1. If it's Tuesday, then this must be Belgium. **2.** If you watch too much television, then you'll get a headache. **3.** If it flies, then it's a bird. **4.** If it's in *The Wall Street Journal*, then you can believe it. **5.** If it's Saturday, then Sally goes downtown. **6.** If it's dog food, then Snoopy likes it. **7.** If you're a person, then you have a head. **8.** If you're a biologist, then you love formaldehyde.
9. If it's a chicken, then it's not a teetotaler. **10.** If it's candy, then it doesn't come from Bolivia. **11.** If the city is New York, then I love it.
12. If it's a banana tree, then it won't grow here. **13.** If I study daily, then I pass my history course. **14.** If I pass my history course, then I will take more mathematics. **15.** If I will not take more mathematics, then I study daily.

16. If I don't study daily, then I pass my history course. **17.** If I do not study daily, then I will not take more mathematics. **18.** If I don't pass my history course, then I don't study daily. **19.** If I pass my history course, then I will not take more mathematics. **20.** If I will not take more mathematics, then I pass my history course. **21.** If I study daily, then I will take more mathematics and I pass my history course. **22.** If I don't pass my history course, then I will not take more mathematics or I study daily. **23.** If I study daily and I pass my history course, then I will take more mathematics. **24.** If I don't study daily or I will not take more mathematics, then I will not pass my history course. **25.** $t \to u$ **26.** $r \to t$ **27.** $u \to \sim r$ **28.** $\sim t \to \sim r$ **29.** $u \wedge (r \to \sim t)$ **30.** $t \vee (u \to r)$ **31.** $u \to r$ **32.** $\sim r \to t$ **33.** True **34.** True **35.** True **36.** True **37.** False **38.** False **39.** True **40.** False **41.** False **42.** True **43.** True **44.** False **45.** FTTT **46.** TTTF **47.** TTTT; tautology **48.** TTTF **49.** TTFT **50.** FTFT **51.** TFTF **52.** TTTT; tautology **53.** TTTTTTFT **54.** FTTTFTFT **55.** TTTFTTTTTTTTTTTT **56.** TTTTTTTTTTTTTTFT **57.** Taxes go up and I don't quit work. **58.** You overwater orange trees and they won't die. **59.** I do that and they won't do this. **60.** You can't and he can't. **61.** $x < 2$ and $y \ngtr 5$, or alternatively, $x < 2$ and $y \leq 5$. **62.** $m \ngtr 4$ and $k < 0$, or alternatively, $m \leq 4$ and $k > 0$. **63.** Taxes do not go up or I'll quit work. **64.** You don't overwater orange trees or they will die. **65.** I do not do that or they'll do this. **66.** You can or he can. **67.** $x \nless 2$ or $y > 5$, or alternatively, $x \geq 2$ or $y > 5$. **68.** $m > 4$ or $k \nless 0$, or alternatively, $m > 4$ or $k \geq 0$. **69.** If she has cash, then she can buy a stamp. **70.** If Tom has a cat, then he has mice. **71.** If it's not raining, then it's warm. **72.** If taxes are due, then it's April 15. **73.** Equivalent **74.** Equivalent **75.** Equivalent **76.** Equivalent **77.** Not equivalent **78.** Equivalent **79.** Not equivalent **80.** Not equivalent **81.** True **82.** True **83.** True **84.** False **85.** False **86.** True **87.** True **88.** False **89.** True **90.** False **91.** True **92.** True **93.** False **94.** True **95.** True **96.** False

An Extension Circuits (page 76)

1.

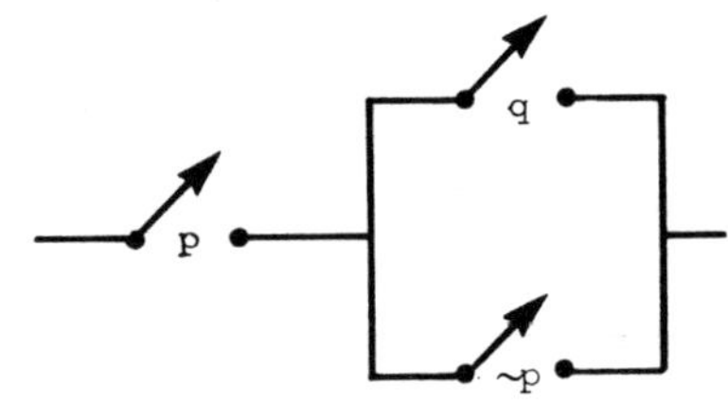

2.

3. The statement simplifies to F.

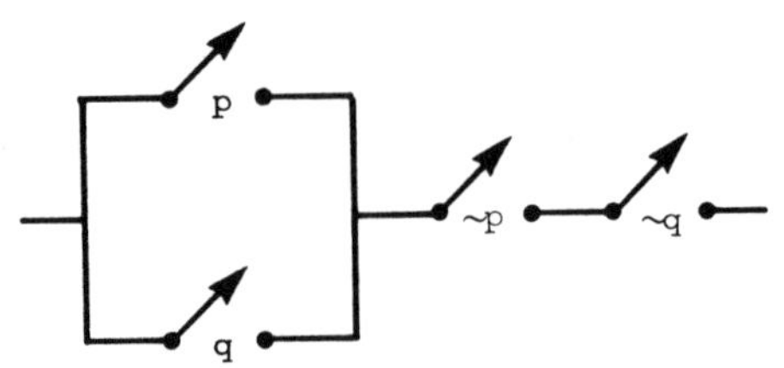

4.

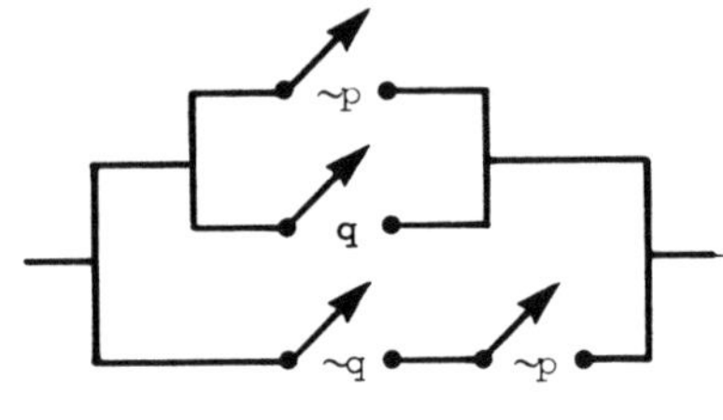

5.

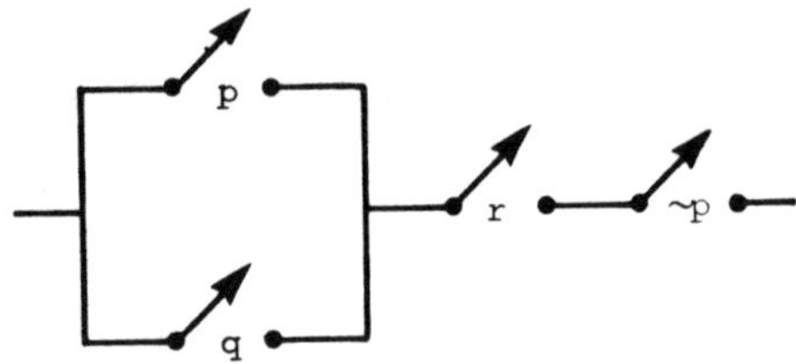

6.

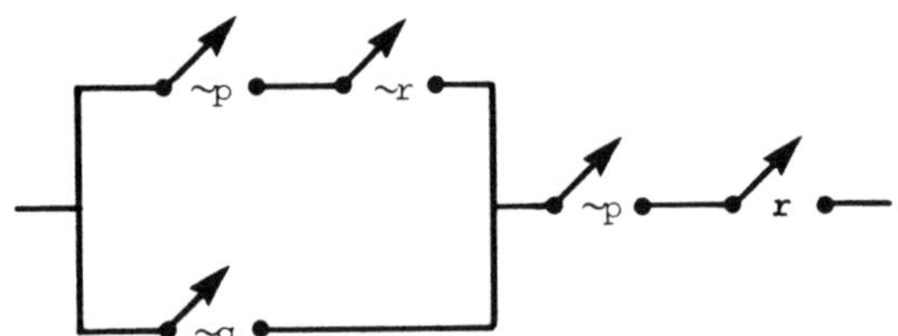

7. The statement simplifies to T.

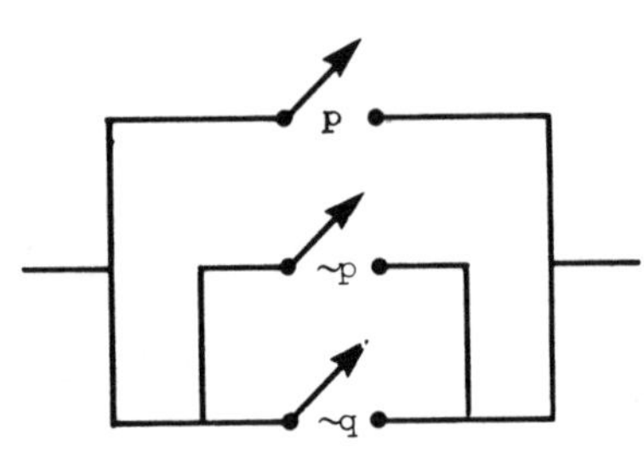

8.

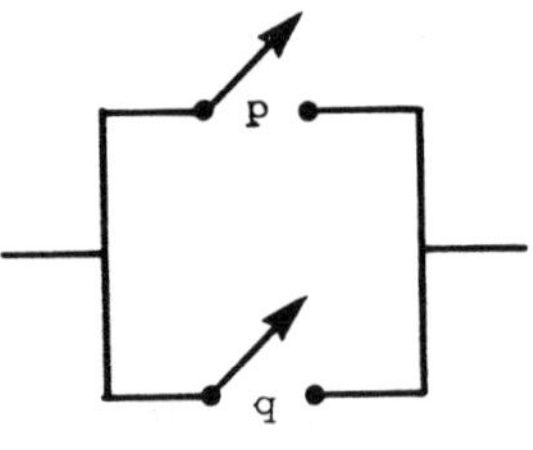

9. p 10. p ∧ (r ∨ q) 11. The statement simplifies to T.

12. q ∨ [p ∧ (q ∨ ~p)]

Section 2.4 (page 82)

1. If it rains, then I will stay home. **2.** If I go skiing, then it snows. **3.** If I pass this class, then I did homework. **4.** If I water the grass, then it will grow. **5.** If you are in Raleigh, then you are in North Carolina. **6.** If I drive fast, then I have a Porsche. **7.** If it is a cat, then it is an animal. **8.** If it is a whale, then it is a mammal. **9.** If you are elected, then you are against pollution. **10.** If I cut the grass, then it is long. **11.** If the city redevelops Eastlake, then the government approves. **12.** If I do logic, then I will be driven crazy. **13.** If I feel bad, then I lost on the slot machines. **14.** If I go from Boardwalk to Oriental, then I pass Go. **15.** If I live in West Virginia, then I like coal. **16.** If I go 65 on the highway, then I have a CB radio. **17.** If the figure is a parallelogram, then it is a four-sided figure with opposite sides parallel. **18.** If a parallelogram has a right angle, then it is a rectangle. **19.** If the figure is a square, then it is a rectangle with two adjacent sides equal. **20.** If an odd integer n is squared, then the square is odd. **21.** If the number n ends in 0 or 5, then it is divisible by 5. **22.** If a triangle has two sides of the same length, then it is an isosceles triangle. **23.** If $x = 5$, then $2x + 1 = 11$. **24.** If $2x + 1 = 11$, then $x = 5$. **25.** If $a > 3$, then $a^2 > 9$. **26.** If $m^2 < 4$, then $m < 2$. **27.** If $p = 8$, then $|p + 3| = 11$. **28.** If $|y| = 9$, then $y = \pm 9$.

The answers for Exercises 29-44 give first the converse, then the inverse, and finally the contrapositive.

29. If I need a garage, then I buy a Ford. If I don't buy a Ford, then I won't need a garage. If I don't need a garage, then I didn't buy a Ford. **30.** If I go, then she comes. If she doesn't come, then I don't go. If I don't go, then she doesn't come. **31.** If you endanger your health, then you smoke cigarettes. If you don't smoke cigarettes, then you don't endanger your health. If you don't endanger your health, then you don't smoke cigarettes. **32.** If it contains vitamin C, then it's orange juice. If it's not orange juice, then it doesn't contain vitamin C. If it doesn't

contain vitamin C, then it's not orange juice. **33.** If it has fleas, then it's a dog. If it's not a dog, then it doesn't have fleas. If it doesn't have fleas, then it's not a dog. **34.** If you have big payments, then you live in a big house. If you don't live in a big house, then you don't have big payments. If you don't have big payments, then you don't live in a big house. **35.** If they flock together, then they are birds of a feather. If they are not birds of a feather, then they don't flock together. If they don't flock together, then they are not birds of a feather. **36.** If it gathers no moss, then it's a rolling stone. If it's not a rolling stone, then it gathers moss. If it gathers moss, then it's not a rolling stone. **37.** If $3 = 2 + 1$, then $5 = 6$. If $5 \neq 6$, then $3 \neq 2 + 1$. If $3 \neq 2 + 1$, then $5 \neq 6$. **38.** If it's not gold, then it glitters. If it doesn't glitter, then it's gold. If it's gold, then it doesn't glitter.
39. $q \to \sim p$; $p \to \sim q$; $\sim q \to p$ **40.** $\sim q \to p$; $\sim p \to q$; $q \to \sim p$ **41.** $\sim q \to \sim p$; $p \to q$; $q \to p$
42. $\sim p \to \sim q$; $q \to p$; $p \to q$ **43.** $(q \vee r) \to p$; $\sim p \to \sim(q \vee r)$; $\sim(q \vee r) \to \sim p$
44. $p \to (r \vee \sim q)$; $\sim(r \vee \sim q) \to \sim p$; $\sim p \to \sim(r \vee \sim q)$ **45.** True **46.** True
47. False **48.** False **49.** True **50.** True **51.** False **52.** False
53. True **54.** True **55.** False **56.** False **57.** True **58.** True
59. True **60.** False **61.** False **62.** True **63.** False **64.** False
65. Contrary **66.** Consistent **67.** Contrary **68.** Contrary **69.** Consistent
70. Consistent **71.** (a) $b \to \sim m$; $b \vee m$; $m \to b$ (b) FTTT (c) The butler did it and the maid did it. (d) TTF (e) Neither did it; TF. (f) The butler did it.
72. (a) $\{1, 2, 3, 4, 5, 6, 8\}$, $\{2, 4\}$ (b) $\{7\}$, $\{1, 2, 3, 4, 5, 7\}$, $\{1, 2, 3, 4, 5, 7\}$
(c) P', Q', $P \cup Q$, $P \cap Q$, $P' \cup Q$, U, $\emptyset$

Section 2.5 (page 92)

1. Deductive; Premises: I must go to class today. Every time I go, I need to take notes. Conclusion: I will have to take notes today. **2.** Deductive; Premises: Textbooks cost too much. This book is a textbook. Conclusion: It costs too much.

3. Inductive; Premise: The last four presidents of the United States have been men. Conclusion: Every president has been a man. **4.** Deductive; Premises: I had 12 apples. I gave 5 away at the Crafts Fair. Conclusion: I have 7 left. **5.** Deductive; Premises: All the merchants on this street raised the price of raisins. Ms. Carter is a merchant. Conclusion: She raised the price of raisins. **6.** Deductive; Premise: Roosters do not lay eggs. Conclusion: My pet rooster Roger will not lay an egg. **7.** Deductive; Premises: Prudent people never buy $25,000 cars. Cheryl Bradkin is prudent. Conclusion: Cheryl would never buy a $25,000 car. **8.** Inductive; Premise: This year's winner of the flower show has a greenhouse. Conclusion: A greenhouse is necessary if you want to win. **9.** 20 **10.** 37 **11.** 512 **12.** 567 **13.** 84 **14.** 47 **15.** 6/7 **16.** 21/23 **17.** 49 **18.** 216 **19.** 1 **20.** 1 **21.** 126 **22.** 86 **23.** 660 **24.** 486 **25.** 2410 **26.** 2423 **27.** $2 + 4 + 8 + 16 + 32 = 64 - 2$; $62 = 62$ **28.** $3 + 6 + 9 + 12 + 15 = 15(6)/2$; $45 = 45$ **29.** $3 + 9 + 27 + 81 + 243 = 3(243 - 1)/2$; $363 = 363$ **30.** $5(6) + 5(36) + 5(216) + 5(1296) + 5(7776) = 6(7776 - 1)$; $46,650 = 46,650$ **31.** $\frac{1}{1\cdot 2} + \frac{1}{2\cdot 3} + \frac{1}{3\cdot 4} + \frac{1}{4\cdot 5} + \frac{1}{5\cdot 6} = \frac{5}{6}$; $\frac{5}{6} = \frac{5}{6}$ **32.** $\frac{1}{2} + \frac{1}{4} + \frac{1}{8} + \frac{1}{16} + \frac{1}{32} = 1 - \frac{1}{32}$; $\frac{31}{32} = \frac{31}{32}$ **33.** $21 + 23 + 25 + 27 + 29 = 125 = 5^3$; $125 = 125$ **34.** $21^2 - 15^2 = 6^3$; $216 = 216$ **35.** $8(1) + 1 = 9 = 3^2$; $8(3) + 1 = 25 = 5^2$; $8(6) + 1 = 49 = 7^2$; $8(10) + 1 = 81 = 9^2$ **36.** (a) 30, 42, 56, 72, 90, 110 (b) The second row of differences gives the constant difference 2. (c) $2 = 2(1)$; $6 = 2(3)$; $12 = 2(6)$; $20 = 2(10)$; $30 = 2(15)$; $42 = 2(21)$; $56 = 2(28)$; $72 = 2(36)$; $90 = 2(45)$; $110 = 2(55)$

37.

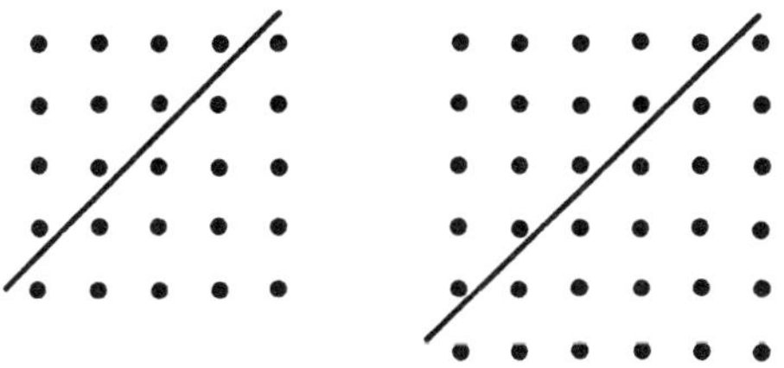

38. $1 = 1$; $6 = 1 + 5$; $15 = 1 + 5 + 9$; $28 = 1 + 5 + 9 + 13$; $45 = 1 + 5 + 9 + 13 + 17$ **39.** Triangular: 28, 36; square: 36, 49, 64; pentagonal: 35, 51, 70, 92; hexagonal: 28, 45, 66, 91, 120; heptagonal: 18, 34, 55, 81, 112, 148; octagonal: 8, 21, 40, 65, 96, 133, 176

40. The pattern is 1, 0, 0, 1, 0, 0, 1, 0, 0, ...

42. $3(T_{n-1}) + n = [3(n - 1)(n)/2] + n = (3n^2 - 3n + 2n)/2 = (3n^2 - n)/2 = n(3n - 1)/2 = P_n$

43. 1275 **44.** 124,750 **45.** 2500 **46.** 10,000 **47.** 20,100 **48.** 2550

49. 1, 3, 6, 10, 15 (This is the sequence of triangular numbers.)

50. (a) Seventh row: 1, 6, 15, 20, 15, 6, 1; eighth row: 1, 7, 21, 35, 35, 21, 7, 1; ninth row: 1, 8, 28, 56, 70, 56, 28, 8, 1; tenth row: 1, 9, 36, 84, 126, 126, 84, 36, 9, 1 (b) On the third diagonal (c) Values whose digits correspond to the entries of the first five rows of Pascal's triangle (d) 1, 2, 4, 8, 16, 32, 64, 128, 256, 512; the sum of the entries on the eleventh row is 2(512) = 1024. (e) i. 1 ii. 1, 1 iii. 1, 2, 1 iv. 1, 3, 3, 1 (f) 21

An Extension Mathematical Induction (page 98)

1. First, show true for n = 1.

$$1 = 1(1 + 1)/2$$

$$1 = 1$$

Second, show that if true for k, then also true for k + 1.

$$1 + 2 + 3 + \ldots + k = k(k + 1)/2$$

$$1 + 2 + 3 + \ldots + k + (k + 1) = k(k + 1)/2 + (k + 1)$$

By algebraic manipulation, the right side is $\frac{(k + 1)[(k + 1) + 1]}{2}$.

Therefore, the statement is true for all counting numbers n.

2. First, show true for n = 1.

$$2(1) = 1(1 + 1)$$

$$2 = 2$$

Second, show that if true for k, then also true for k + 1.

$$2 + 4 + 6 + \ldots + 2k = k(k + 1)$$

$$2 + 4 + 6 + \ldots + 2k + 2(k + 1) = k(k + 1) + 2(k + 1)$$

By algebraic manipulation, the right side is $(k + 1)[(k + 1) + 1]$.

Therefore, the statement is true for all counting numbers n.

3. First, show true for n = 1.

$$\frac{1}{1\cdot 2} = \frac{1}{1+1}$$
$$\frac{1}{2} = \frac{1}{2}$$

Second, show that if true for k, then also true for k + 1.

$$\frac{1}{1\cdot 2} + \frac{1}{2\cdot 3} + \ldots + \frac{1}{k(k+1)} = \frac{k}{k+1}$$
$$\frac{1}{1\cdot 2} + \frac{1}{2\cdot 3} + \ldots + \frac{1}{k(k+1)} + \frac{1}{(k+1)[(k+1)+1]} = \frac{k}{k+1} + \frac{1}{(k+1)(k+2)}$$

By algebraic manipulation, the right side is $\frac{k+1}{(k+1)+1}$.

Therefore, the statement is true for all counting numbers n.

4. First, show true for n = 1.

$$1(1+1) = \frac{1(1+1)(1+2)}{3}$$
$$2 = 2$$

Second, show that if true for k, then also true for k + 1.

$$1\cdot 2 + 2\cdot 3 + 3\cdot 4 + \ldots + k(k+1) = \frac{k(k+1)(k+2)}{3}$$
$$1\cdot 2 + 2\cdot 3 + 3\cdot 4 + \ldots + k(k+1) + (k+1)(k+2) = \frac{k(k+1)(k+2)}{3} + (k+1)(k+2)$$

By algebraic manipulation, the right side is $\frac{(k+1)[(k+1)+1][(k+1)+2]}{3}$.

Therefore, the statement is true for all counting numbers n.

Section 2.6 (page 101)

1. Valid **2.** Valid **3.** Not valid **4.** Not valid **5.** Valid

6. Not valid **7.** Valid **8.** Valid **9.** Not valid **10.** Not valid

11. Not valid **12.** Not valid **13.** Not valid **14.** Not valid

15. Not valid **16.** Not valid **17.** Valid **18.** Invalid **19.** Valid

20. Invalid **21.** Invalid **22.** Invalid **23.** Valid **24.** Valid

25. Invalid **26.** Valid **27.** Not valid **28.** Not valid **29.** Not valid

30. Not valid **31.** Valid **32.** Valid **35.** It takes 7 1/2 min. (Boil them at the same time.) **36.** There will be 1 (big) haystack. **37.** None; there is no dirt in a hole. **38.** One is not a nickel, but the other is. The two coins are a half dollar and a nickel. **39.** The two children row across. One stays on the opposite

bank and the other returns. One soldier rows across, and the child on the opposite bank then rows back. The two children row across. One stays and the other returns. Now another soldier rows across. This process continues until all the soldiers are across. **40.** The person takes the goat across and returns alone. On the second trip, the person takes the wolf across and returns with the goat. On the third trip, the goat is left on the first side while the person takes the cabbage across. Then the person returns alone and brings the goat back across. **41.** For three weighings, first balance four against four. Of the lighter four, balance two against the other two. Finally, of the lighter two, balance them one against the other. To find the bad coin in two weighings, divide the eight coins into groups of 3, 3, 2. Weigh the groups of three against each other on the scale. If the groups weigh the same, the fake is in the two left out and can be found in one additional weighing. If the two groups of three do not weigh the same, pick the lighter group. Choose any two of the coins and weigh them. If one of these is lighter, it is the fake; if they weigh the same, then the third coin is the fake one. **42.** The positions of the women are, from left to right, Johnson, Andersen, and Thompson. **43.** There are 12 in a dozen. **44.** He will reach the top after 28 days. After 27 days, the kangaroo is 27 ft above the bottom of the well. On the 28th day, the kangaroo jumps up 3 ft and hops out. **45.** Choose the half a trunk full of dimes; a dime is a much smaller coin than a nickel. **46.** The pound of feathers weighs more. There are 16 oz in a pound of feathers and only 12 oz in a pound of gold.
47. You can subtract 2 from 21 once; then you are subtracting 2 from 19.
48. The tank was half full at 59 min.

Section 2.7 (page 109)

1. Invalid **2.** Valid **3.** Valid **4.** Invalid **5.** Valid **6.** Invalid
7. Invalid **8.** Invalid **9.** Valid **10.** Invalid **11.** Valid
12. Invalid **13.** Valid **14.** Valid **15.** Invalid **16.** Invalid
17. Valid **18.** Invalid **19.** Invalid **20.** Valid **21.** Valid **22.** Valid

23. Invalid **24.** Invalid **25.** Invalid **26.** Invalid **27.** Valid
28. Valid **29.** Valid **30.** Valid **31.** The final column is TTTT.
32. He stays. **33.** I'll take a trip. **34.** Sue takes chemistry. **35.** If it is my poultry, then it is a duck. **36.** If he is your son, then he cannot do logic.
37. If it is a guinea pig, then it is hopelessly ignorant of music.
38. If the person is a teetotaler, then the person is not a pawnbroker.
39. If it is a teachable kitten, then it does not have green eyes.
40. If it is an opium-eater, then it has no self-command. **41.** If I can read it, then I have not filed it. **42.** If it is written on blue paper, then it is filed.
43. (a) $p \to \sim s$ (b) $r \to s$ (c) $q \to p$ (d) None of my poultry are officers.
44. (a) $r \to p$ (b) $\sim r \to \sim q$ (c) $s \to \sim p$ (d) Your sons are not fit to serve on a jury. **45.** (a) $s \to r$ (b) $p \to q$ (c) $q \to \sim r$ (d) Guinea pigs don't appreciate Beethoven. **46.** (a) $r \to \sim s$ (b) $u \to t$ (c) $\sim r \to p$ (d) $\sim u \to \sim q$ (e) $t \to s$ (f) All pawnbrokers are honest. **47.** (a) $p \to s$ (b) $\sim r \to \sim u$ (c) $t \to p$ (d) $s \to \sim q$ (e) $\sim t \to \sim r$ (f) Kittens with green eyes are not willing to play with a gorilla. **48.** (a) $p \to q$ (b) $\sim u \to \sim s$ (c) $t \to \sim r$ (d) $q \to s$ (e) $v \to p$ (f) $\sim r \to \sim u$ (g) Opium-eaters do not wear white kid gloves. **49.** (a) $r \to w$ (b) $\sim u \to \sim t$ (c) $v \to \sim s$ (d) $x \to r$ (e) $\sim q \to t$ (f) $y \to p$ (g) $w \to s$ (h) $\sim x \to \sim q$ (i) $p \to \sim u$ (j) I can't read any of Brown's letters.

50. If a nail was wanted, then the shoe was lost.

If a shoe was wanted, then the horse was lost.

If a horse was wanted, then the rider was lost.

If a rider was wanted, then the battle was lost.

If the battle was wanted, then the war was lost.

Therefore, if a nail was wanted, then the war was lost.

The argument is valid by repeated application of reasoning by transitivity.

Section 2.8 (page 115)

1. Ambiguity **2.** Ambiguity **3.** False cause **4.** Non sequitur **5.** Composition **6.** Non sequitur **7.** Ambiguity **8.** Non sequitur **9.** Composition **10.** Composition **11.** Emotion **12.** Emotion **13.** Experts **14.** False cause **15.** Ambiguity **16.** Non sequitur **17.** False cause **18.** Composition **19.** Non sequitur **20.** Experts **21.** Experts **22.** Composition **23.** False cause **24.** False cause **25.** Complex question **26.** Non sequitur **27.** Composition **28.** Composition

Chapter 2 Test (page 117)

1. Statement **2.** Not a statement **3.** Statement **4.** She passes algebra and she does not pass history. **5.** If she does not pass algebra, then she passes history. **6.** Some cluckers are not chickens. **7.** No spiders eat their mates. **8.** True **9.** True **10.** True **11.** TTTF **12.** TTTT **13.** TTTT **14.** If he would work, then he would pass mathematics. **15.** If Snoopy flies a kite, then Lucy is not around. **16.** If you own a bird, then you have yesterday's newspaper. **17.** If you are unemployed, then you can get food stamps. **18.** If I need mustard, then I'll buy a sandwich. **19.** If it's not after 7 P.M., then I drink coffee. **20.** If Tom's going, then Sandra's going. **21.** Converse: $(q \vee r) \rightarrow \sim p$; contrapositive: $\sim(q \vee r) \rightarrow p$ **22.** Inductive **23.** Deductive **24.** 44 **25.** 1 **26.** Invalid **27.** Valid **28.** Valid **29.** Invalid **30.** Valid

CHAPTER 3

Section 3.1 (page 124)

1. Simple grouping; 36 **2.** Positional; 5 **3.** Positional; 14 **4.** Multiplicative grouping; 7 **5.** Simple grouping; 627 **6.** Simple grouping; 643 **7.** Multiplicative grouping; 23 **8.** Positional; 52 **9.** Simple grouping; 781 **10.** Positional; 75 **11.** Multiplicative grouping; 80 **12.** Multiplicative grouping; 260 **13.** Simple grouping; 100 **14.** Positional; 500 **15.** Positional; 390 **16.** Multiplicative grouping; 1252 **17.** Simple grouping; 1375 **18.** Simple grouping; 779 **19.** Multiplicative grouping; 2375 **20.** Simple grouping; 3138 **21.** Positional; 586 **22.** Simple grouping; 1355 **23.** Positional; 4867 **24.** Multiplicative grouping; 12,611

25. ΛIII, ⊙Λ(∴)I, ⊙(∴)

26. ΛIIII, ⊙Λ(∷)I, ⊙(∷)

27. ΛΛIIII, (··)Λ(∷)I, (··)(∷)

28. ΛΛΛΛII, (∷)Λ(··)I, (∷)(··)

29. NΛΛII, ⊙N(··)Λ(··)I, ⊙(··)(··)

30. NΛΛΛI, ⊙N(∴)Λ⊙I, ⊙(∴)⊙

31. NΛΛΛΛII, ⊙N(∷)Λ(··)I, ⊙(∷)(··)

32. NNII, (··)N(··)I, (··)○(··)

33. NNNI, (∴)N⊙I, (∴)○⊙

34. NNNΛΛ, (∴)N(··)Λ, (∴)(··)○

35. M, ⊙M, ⊙○○○

36. MM, (··)M, (··)○○○

37. MMNNΛΛΛ, (··)M(··)N(∷)Λ, (··)(··)(∷)○

38. MMNNNNΛΛΛII, (··)M(∷)N(∷)Λ(··)I, (··)(∷)(∷)(··)

39. WW, (··)W, (··)○○○○

40. W, ⊙W, ⊙○○○○

Section 3.2 (page 132)

1. 23,201 **2.** 4546 **3.** 3,400,026 **4.** 500,681 **5.** 82,653 **6.** 476,545 **7.** 7,170,668 **8.** 4,040,436 **9.** 99∩∩∩∩
99∩∩∩∩ **10.** IIII **11.** 𓆼𓆼

12. ∩∩ **13.** 𓆼𓆼𓆼, 𓆼||||| **14.** 𓂭𓂭𓂭𓂭, 𓂭𓆼𓆼

15. 𓆼𓆼𓍢𓍢𓍢∩∩∩∩|||||||| **16.** 𓆼 **17.** 𓆼𓆼𓆼𓆼𓆼𓆼𓆼∩∩∩∩∩∩

18. 𓆼𓆼𓆼𓆼𓆼𓆼𓆼𓆼𓆼|||| **19.** 𓁨𓁨𓁨𓁨𓁨𓆐𓆐𓆐𓆐𓆐𓆐𓆐𓆐𓂭𓂭𓆼𓆼𓆼𓆼

20. 𓁨𓁨𓁨𓁨𓆐𓆐𓂭𓂭𓂭𓂭𓂭𓂭𓆼 **21.** 23 **22.** 42 **23.** 86 **24.** 68

25. 2450 **26.** 976 **27.** 2001 **28.** 3479 **29.** 21,000 **30.** 23,000

31. 14,000,000 **32.** 22,000,000 **33.** XII **34.** XXXVII **35.** XLVII

36. LVIII **37.** CDLXXIV **38.** CCLXXXVIII **39.** DCCLIX **40.** CMLXXXIII

41. MDCCXXVIII **42.** MMMCCIX **43.** $\overline{\overline{\overline{\text{XII}}}}$ **44.** $\overline{\overline{\overline{\text{XXXVIII}}}}$ **45.** 394 **46.** 815

47. 11,232 **48.** 8420 **49.** 21 **50.** 13 **51.** 37 **52.** 28 **53.** 275

54. 136 **55.** 68 **56.** 216 **57.** 357 **58.** 946 **59.** 722 **60.** 1081

61. 533,000 shekels **62.** 622,500 shekels **63.** 22 **64.** 32 **65.** 1282

66. 872 **67.** 2601 **68.** 3331 **69.** 80,474 **70.** 9,072,343 **71.** 6,480,723

72. 135 **73.** 872 **74.** 9876 **75.** 4036 **76.** 5010 **77.** 3000

78. 200 **79.** 1111 **80.** 三十九 **81.** 五十一 **82.** 九十二 **83.** 一百六

84. 四百十二 **85.** 三百 **86.** 二千七百六十九 **87.** 九千零十 **88.** 七千零二

89. ‹‹▼ **90.** ‹‹‹▼▼ **91.** ▼▼▼▼ ‹‹‹▼▼▼ ‹‹ **92.** ▼▼▼ ▼▼▼ ‹‹‹ ‹‹ ▼▼

93. ‹‹▼▼▼▼▼▼ ‹▼▼▼▼ **94.** ‹‹‹▼▼ ‹‹▼▼ ‹‹ ‹‹ **95.** ▼ ‹‹▼▼▼ ▼▼▼ ‹‹‹

96. ▼▼ ‹ ‹‹ ‹‹▼▼ **97.** ‹▼▼ ▼▼▼▼▼ **98.** ‹‹▼▼▼ ▼▼ ▼▼▼

Section 3.3 (page 145)

1. $(5 \times 10^1) + (9 \times 10^0)$ **2.** $(7 \times 10^1) + (4 \times 10^0)$ **3.** $(4 \times 10^2) + (2 \times 10^1) + (6 \times 10^0)$ **4.** $(5 \times 10^2) + (4 \times 10^1) + (6 \times 10^0)$ **5.** $(1 \times 10^3) + (9 \times 10^2) + (8 \times 10^1) + (4 \times 10^0)$ **6.** $(3 \times 10^3) + (7 \times 10^2) + (1 \times 10^1) + (2 \times 10^0)$

7. $(2 \times 10^4) + (9 \times 10^3) + (8 \times 10^2) + (4 \times 10^1) + (6 \times 10^0)$

8. $(3 \times 10^4) + (0 \times 10^3) + (8 \times 10^2) + (9 \times 10^1) + (7 \times 10^0)$

9. $(2 \times 10^6) + (5 \times 10^5) + (0 \times 10^4) + (8 \times 10^3) + (9 \times 10^2) + (0 \times 10^1) + (1 \times 10^0)$

10. $(7 \times 10^6) + (6 \times 10^5) + (0 \times 10^4) + (3 \times 10^3) + (4 \times 10^2) + (9 \times 10^1) + (0 \times 10^0)$

11. $(4 \times 10^3) + (7 \times 10^2) + (1 \times 10^1) + (2 \times 10^0)$ **12.** $(9 \times 10^3) + (8 \times 10^2) + (1 \times 10^1) + (7 \times 10^0)$ **13.** $(7 \times 10^6) + (0 \times 10^5) + (0 \times 10^4) + (2 \times 10^3) + (0 \times 10^2) + (0 \times 10^1) + (7 \times 10^0)$ **14.** $(1 \times 10^7) + (2 \times 10^6) + (5 \times 10^5) + (0 \times 10^4) + (7 \times 10^3) + (0 \times 10^2) + (8 \times 10^1) + (0 \times 10^0)$ **15.** 98 **16.** 72

17. 600 **18.** 489 **19.** 7805 **20.** 2130 **21.** 57,843 **22.** 20,150

23. 8,020,305 **24.** 90,300,120 **25.** 77 **26.** 78 **27.** 979 **28.** 983

29. 55 **30.** 12 **31.** 222 **32.** 322 **33.** 166 **34.** 118 **35.** 825

36. 931 **37.** 6910 **38.** 11,583 **39.** 4 **40.** 28 **41.** 107 **42.** 217

43. 108 **44.** 221 **45.** 14 **46.** 22 **47.** 208 **48.** 512 **49.** 2992

50. 3705 **51.** 28,742 **52.** 32,985 **53.** 60,082

54. 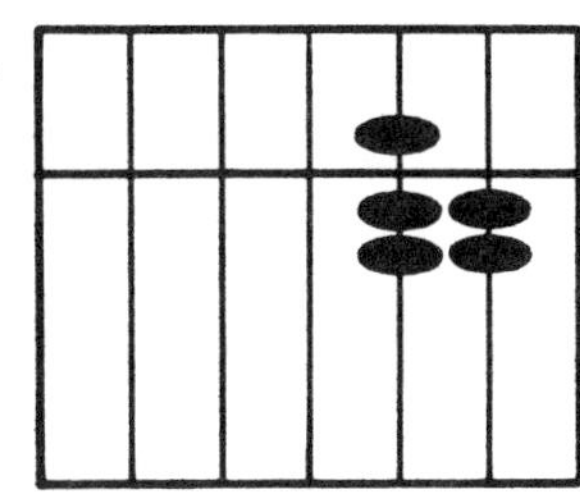 **55.** 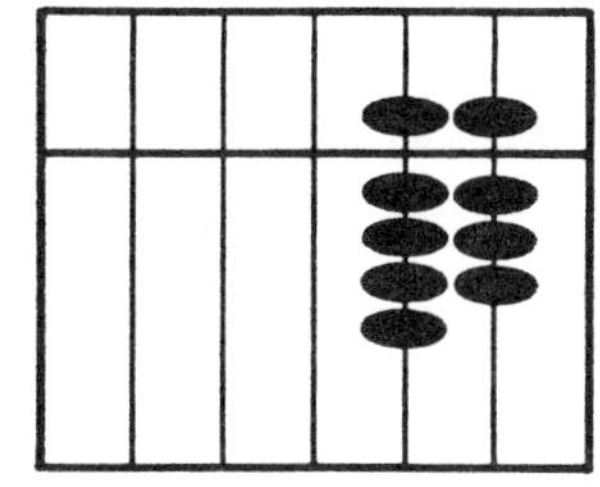 **56.** 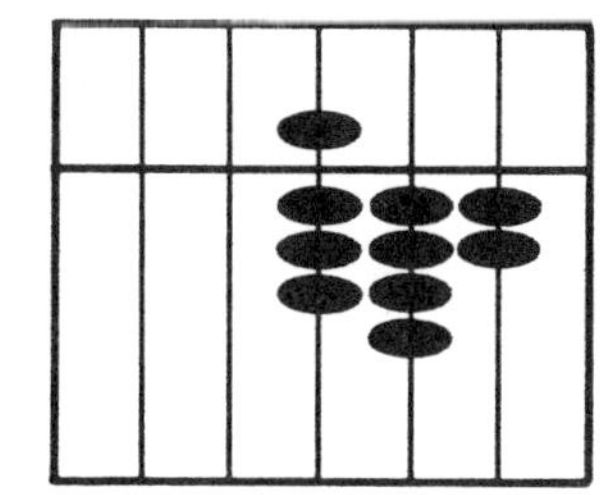

57. 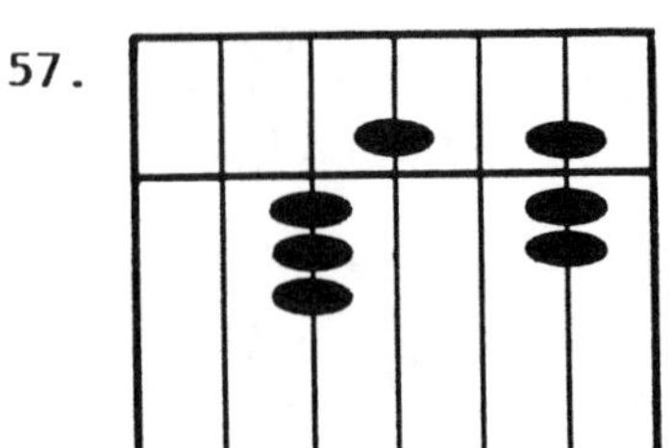

58. 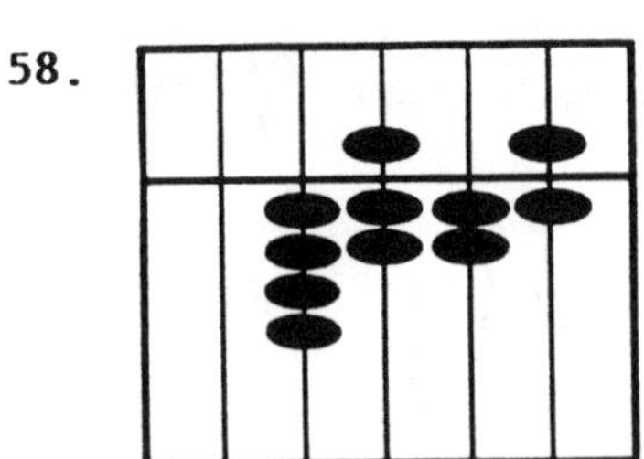

59. 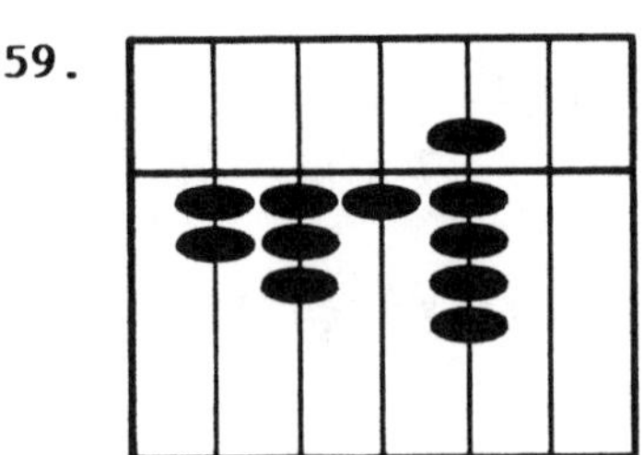

60.

61. 78 **62.** 428 **63.** 13,515 **64.** 11,912

65. 3600 **66.** 4371 **67.** 16,761 **68.** 48,734

69. 358,292 **70.** 283,968 **71.** 210 **72.** 576

73. 1600 **74.** 34,944 **75.** 447,212

76. 3,050,168 **77.** 648 **78.** 832 **79.** 805

80. 3564 **81.** 8814 **82.** 8643

Section 3.4 (page 155)

1. 39 **2.** 46 **3.** 58 **4.** 53 **5.** 84 **6.** 239 **7.** 302 **8.** 469

9. 2525 **10.** 3231 **11.** 19,796 **12.** 24,409 **13.** 52_{eight} **14.** 71_{eight}

15. 121_{eight} **16.** 134_{eight} **17.** 222_{eight} **18.** 610_{eight} **19.** 1733_{eight}

20. 1353_{eight} **21.** $11{,}434_{eight}$ **22.** $17{,}322_{eight}$ **23.** $26{,}444_{eight}$

24. $41{,}130_{eight}$ **25.** 23 **26.** 17 **27.** 44 **28.** 39 **29.** 43 **30.** 69

31. 124 **32.** 47 **33.** 113 **34.** 73 **35.** 153 **36.** 93 **37.** 476

38. 1384 **39.** 239 **40.** 2333 **41.** 214_{five} **42.** 140_{seven} **43.** 666_{seven}

44. 2044_{five} **45.** 3001_{four} **46.** 1113_{eight} **47.** 3434_{seven} **48.** 292_{twelve}

49. 2644_{twelve} **50.** 999_{eleven} **51.** $1T42_{eleven}$ **52.** $13{,}472_{eight}$

53. $22E8_{twelve}$ **54.** $3ET5_{twelve}$ **55.** $4TT1_{eleven}$ **56.** $5T89_{eleven}$

57. $2T88_{twelve}$ **58.** $11{,}610_{eight}$ **59.** $20{,}402_{seven}$ **60.** $1{,}032{,}020_{four}$

61. 9 **62.** 28 **63.** 115 **64.** 95 **65.** 63 **66.** 127 **67.** 694

68. 1262 **69.** 1011_{two} **70.** 10001_{two} **71.** 10101_{two} **72.** 11110_{two}

73. 101111_{two} **74.** 1011100_{two} **75.** 100011110_{two} **76.** 101011001_{two}

77. 315_{eight} **78.** 255_{eight} **79.** 567_{eight} **80.** 1567_{eight}

81. 100111010_{two} **82.** 101100011_{two} **83.** 1010110111_{two} **84.** 111001100010_{two}

85. 110_{four} **86.** 32_{twelve} **87.** 214_{seven} **88.** 631_{seven} **89.** 2021_{eight}

90. $11{,}041_{five}$ **91.** 1727_{eight} **92.** $221{,}130_{four}$ **93.** 166_{twelve} **94.** 1171_{eight}

95. A number appears in a given column only when its binary representation contains the digit 1 in the place value listed at the top of the column. For example, $26 = 11010_{two} = 1(16) + 1(8) + 1(2) = 16 + 8 + 2$. **96.** Every counting number is a unique sum of binary place values. Once it is known which columns of the table contain a given number, that number is found by adding up the appropriate place values from the tops of those columns.

97.

A	B	C	D	E	F
1	2	4	8	16	32
3	3	5	9	17	33
5	6	6	10	18	34
7	7	7	11	19	35
9	10	12	12	20	36
11	11	13	13	21	37
13	14	14	14	22	38
15	15	15	15	23	39
17	18	20	24	24	40
19	19	21	25	25	41
21	22	22	26	26	42
23	23	23	27	27	43
25	26	28	28	28	44
27	27	29	29	29	45
29	30	30	30	30	46
31	31	31	31	31	47
33	34	36	40	48	48
35	35	37	41	49	49
37	38	38	42	50	50
39	39	39	43	51	51
41	42	44	44	52	52
43	43	45	45	53	53
45	46	46	46	54	54
47	47	47	47	55	55
49	50	52	56	56	56
51	51	53	57	57	57
53	54	54	58	58	58
55	55	55	59	59	59
57	58	60	60	60	60
59	59	61	61	61	61
61	62	62	62	62	62
63	63	63	63	63	63

98. 64

99. 500,000

100. 3,000,000

An Extension The Hexadecimal System (page 159)

1. 1011010_{two} **2.** 10110110_{two} **3.** 11101111_{two} **4.** 11011011_{two}

5. 10001111001_{two} **6.** 100000000111_{two} **7.** 11100110100101_{two}

8. 101001001101010_{two} **9.** $37_{sixteen}$ **10.** $36_{sixteen}$ **11.** $16E_{sixteen}$

12. $5DC_{sixteen}$ **13.** $177D8_{sixteen}$ **14.** $36EF8_{sixteen}$ **15.** 1000100_{two}

16. 1001011_{two} **17.** 1010010_{two} **18.** 1010100_{two} **19.** HELP **20.** CHUCK

Section 3.5 (page 165)

1. 43_{five} **2.** 40_{five} **3.** 1000_{five} **4.** 203_{five} **5.** 1112_{five}

6. 1000_{five} **7.** 411_{five} **8.** 31_{five} **9.** 314_{five} **10.** 334_{five}

11. 1323_{five} **12.** 1311_{five} **13.** 1423_{five} **14.** 1121_{five} **15.** $21,104_{five}$

16. $220,233_{five}$ **17.** 2011_{five} **18.** $43,131_{five}$ **19.** 2333_{five}

20. $320,043_{five}$ **21.** 41_{five} **22.** 34_{five} **23.** 342_{five} **24.** $242,424_{five}$

25. Row 2: 10, 11; row 3: 10, 12; row 4: 10, 12; row 5: 10, 12; row 6: 6, 10, 11, 12, 13, 14, 15 **26.** Row 3: 12, 15, 24; row 4: 15, 26; row 5: 13, 26; row 6: 15, 24, 33, 42

27. 110_{seven} **28.** 136_{seven} **29.** 1156_{seven} **30.** 1422_{seven} **31.** 204_{seven}

32. 304_{seven} **33.** 4352_{seven} **34.** 2655_{seven} **35.** 354_{seven} **36.** 222_{seven}

37. $20,343_{seven}$ **38.** $33,242_{seven}$ **39.** 1100_{three} **40.** 241_{nine} **41.** 42_{six}

42. 23_{four} **43.** 3048_{twelve} **44.** 5108_{eleven} **45.** 12_{four} **46.** 362_{eight}

47. 122_{seven} **48.** 2110_{four} **49.** $E43_{twelve}$ **50.** $1FE_{sixteen}$

51. $1,220,222_{three}$ **52.** $2,526,336_{eight}$ **53.** 473_{nine} **54.** $34,012_{six}$

55. 3010_{four} **56.** 258_{eleven} **57.** $E804_{twelve}$ **58.** $A9_{sixteen}$

59. The numeral must end in 0. **60.** 400, 230, 4030 **61.** 50, 240, 5230

62. 60, 240, 250, 1970

63.

+	0	1
0	0	1
1	1	10

64. 100_{two} **65.** 10111_{two} **66.** 1000100_{two}

67. 10100101_{two} **68.** 110_{two} **69.** 1000_{two}

70. 10000_{two} **71.** 11011_{two} **72.** 11110_{two} **73.** 1011_{two} **74.** 111001_{two}

75. 100001111_{two}

76.

x	0	1
0	0	0
1	0	1

77. 100_{two} **78.** 110_{two} **79.** 1010_{two} **80.** 1110_{two}

81. 1010101_{two} **82.** 1010100_{two} **83.** 1001010010_{two} **84.** 110000001_{two}

85. 1001_{two} **86.** 1101_{two} **87.** 11000_{two} **88.** 11100_{two}

Chapter 3 Test (page 169)

1. Simple grouping; 17 **2.** Multiplicative grouping; 119 **3.** Positional; 1391

4. Egyptian; 3555 **5.** Roman; 67 **6.** Babylonian; 21 **7.** Babylonian; 40,333

8. $(2 \times 10^1) + (8 \times 10^0)$ **9.** $(4 \times 10^3) + (6 \times 10^2) + (9 \times 10^1) + (0 \times 10^0)$

10. 6574 **11.** 317 **12.** 111 **13.** 490 **14.** 55 **15.** 1202_{four}

16. 5542_{eight} **17.** 1529_{twelve} **18.** 838_{nine} **19.** 11110010_{two} **20.** 764_{eight}

21. 2446_{eight} **22.** 2622_{eight} **23.** 10010_{two} **24.** $34,658_{twelve}$

25. 1101_{two}

CHAPTER 4

Section 4.1 (page 177)

1. 101, 103, 107, 109, 113, 127, 131, 137, 139, 149, 151, 157, 163, 167, 173, 179, 181, 191, 193, 197, 199 **2.** 15 **3.** 10 **4.** 10 **5.** 11 **6.** They actually get less numerous. **7.** 2 and 3 **8.** No, because one would have to be even, and the only even prime is 2. **9.** No, because one of the three will be divisible by 3.

10. There are an infinite number of possibilities, for example, 8, 9, 10.

11. 1, 2, 3, 4, 6, 12 **12.** 1, 2, 3, 6, 9, 18 **13.** 1, 2, 4, 5, 10, 20

14. 1, 2, 4, 7, 14, 28 **15.** 1, 2, 4, 13, 26, 52 **16.** 1, 3, 7, 9, 21, 63

17. 1, 2, 3, 4, 5, 6, 8, 10, 12, 15, 20, 24, 30, 40, 60, 120 **18.** 1, 2, 4, 43, 86, 172 **19.** 1, 2, 5, 10, 17, 25, 34, 50, 85, 170, 425, 850 **20.** 1, 2, 3, 4, 6, 9, 12, 18, 27, 36, 54, 81, 108, 162, 243, 324, 486, 972 **21.** 1, 2, 7, 11, 14, 22, 77, 154

22. 1, 179 **23.** Yes **24.** Yes **25.** Yes **26.** Yes **27.** No **28.** No

29. Yes **30.** Yes **31.** No **32.** No **33.** No **34.** No **35.** $3 \cdot 5$

36. $3 \cdot 7$ **37.** $2^2 \cdot 3^2$ **38.** $2 \cdot 3^3$ **39.** $2^4 \cdot 3 \cdot 5$ **40.** $2^2 \cdot 3 \cdot 5^2$ **41.** $2^3 \cdot 3^2 \cdot 5$

42. $5^2 \cdot 17$ **43.** $3 \cdot 13 \cdot 17$ **44.** $3 \cdot 5 \cdot 59$ **45.** $2^8 \cdot 5$ **46.** $3^2 \cdot 5^2 \cdot 7$

47. $2 \cdot 5^2 \cdot 37$ **48.** $2^2 \cdot 3^2 \cdot 71$ **49.** $3^2 \cdot 5 \cdot 131$ **50.** $3^2 \cdot 829$ **51.** 90

52. 600 **53.** 7350 **54.** 2310 **55.** 5544 **56.** 2925 **57.** 315

58. 3168 **59.** 14,287 **60.** After several steps, the result is 7. **61.** Yes

62. Yes **63.** Yes **64.** $8 + 9 + 9 + 9 = 35$ **65.** $4 + 3 + 6 = 13$

66. $35 - 13 = 22$ **67.** Yes **68.** Yes **69.** Yes **70.** No

71. 0, 2, 4, 6, 8 **72.** 1, 4, 7 **73.** 0, 4, 8 **74.** 0, 5 **75.** 0, 6

76. 0, 8 **77.** 6 **78.** Any digit **79.** 3 **80.** 3 **81.** 9 **82.** 12

83. 9 **84.** 8 **85.** 12 **86.** 30

Section 4.2 (page 182)

1. $496 = 1 + 2 + 4 + 8 + 16 + 31 + 62 + 124 + 248$ **2.** $8128 = 1 + 2 + 4 + 8 + 16 + 32 + 64 + 127 + 254 + 508 + 1016 + 2032 + 4064$ **3.** 33,550,336 **4.** $2^{216,090}(2^{216,091} - 1)$

5. Abundant **6.** Abundant **7.** Deficient **8.** Deficient

9. 12, 18, 20, 24, 30, 36, 40, 42, 48, 54, 56, 60, 66, 70, 72, 78, 80, 84, 88, 90, 96

10. 1 + 3 + 5 + 7 + 9 + 15 + 21 + 27 + 35 + 45 + 63 + 105 + 135 + 189 + 315 = 975; since 975 > 945, 945 is abundant. **11.** The only proper divisor of a prime number is 1, so the sum of the proper divisors of any prime number is 1. Since 1 is less than the prime, the prime must be deficient. **12.** The sum of the proper divisors of 1184 is 1 + 2 + 4 + 8 + 16 + 32 + 37 + 74 + 148 + 296 + 592 = 1210. The sum of the proper divisors of 1210 is 1 + 2 + 5 + 10 + 11 + 22 + 55 + 110 + 121 + 242 + 605 = 1184. By definition, 1184 and 1210 are amicable. **13.** (a) Yes. The sum of all the divisors of a perfect number will be twice the number. (b) 3(120) = 360 = 1 + 2 + 3 + 4 + 5 + 6 + 8 + 10 + 12 + 15 + 20 + 24 + 30 + 40 + 60 + 120 (c) No. For example, 120 possesses this property but it is not perfect. **14.** The sum of *all* the divisors of 672 is 1 + 2 + 3 + 4 + 6 + 7 + 8 + 12 + 14 + 16 + 21 + 24 + 28 + 32 + 42 + 48 + 56 + 84 + 96 + 112 + 168 + 224 + 336 + 672 = 2016. Since 3(672) = 2016, 672 is triply perfect. **15.** Composite; M = 30,031 = 59•509 **16.** No. Mathematicians require formal proofs of statements before they can be accepted as true. **17.** For n = 41, the expression is equal to 41^2, which is not prime. **18.** No. 1763 is composite, since 1763 = 41•43. More than one answer may be possible in Exercises 19-24. **19.** 5 + 7 **20.** 7 + 13 **21.** 11 + 13 **22.** 13 + 17 **23.** 23 + 23 **24.** 5 + 47 **25.** 17 and 19 **26.** 41 and 43 **27.** 59 and 61; 71 and 73 **28.** None **29.** 101 and 103 **30.** 107 and 109

Section 4.3 (page 187)

1. 10 **2.** 10 **3.** 60 **4.** 120 **5.** 168 **6.** 11 **7.** 38 **8.** 65 **9.** 10 **10.** 2 **11.** 12 **12.** 7 **13.** 6 **14.** 28 **15.** 144 **16.** 60 **17.** 96 **18.** 120 **19.** 140 **20.** 672 **21.** 96 **22.** 210 **23.** 884 **24.** 1140 **25.** 144 **26.** 840 **27.** 216 **28.** 180 **29.** 48 **30.** 90 **31.** 45 **32.** 120 **33.** 2880 **34.** 1680 **35.** 60 **36.** 56 **37.** 315

38. 60 **39.** 540 **40.** 1440 **41.** 5 **42.** 12 **43.** 24 **44.** 12 **45.** 30 **46.** 70 **47.** 350 **48.** 180 **49.** 360 **50.** 1260 **51.** 2400 **52.** 1680 **53.** $4m^3$; $24m^4$ **54.** $5y^8$; $150y^{10}$ **55.** $2a^3b$; $1800a^5b^2$ **56.** $18x^3z^4$; $108x^9z^6$ **57.** $5(a - 2)^2$; $300(a - 2)^5$ **58.** $48(m + 5)^3$; $288(m + 5)^6$ **59.** False **60.** True (It may be 1, but that is fine.) **61.** True **62.** True **63.** True **64.** True **65.** True **66.** True

Section 4.4 (page 195)

1. 11, 17, 23, 29, 35; arithmetic **2.** 9, 21, 33, 45, 57; arithmetic **3.** -4, -1, 2, 5, 8; arithmetic **4.** -7, -2, 3, 8, 13; arithmetic **5.** -2, -8, -14, -20, -26; arithmetic **6.** -1, -12, -23, -34, -45; arithmetic **7.** 2, 4, 8, 16, 32; geometric **8.** 3, 9, 27, 81, 243; geometric **9.** -2, 4, -8, 16, -32; geometric **10.** -3, 9, -27, 81, -243; geometric **11.** 6, 12, 24, 48, 96; geometric **12.** -8, -16, -32, -64, -128; geometric **13.** 2/3, 3/4, 4/5, 5/6, 6/7; neither **14.** 1, 4/3, 3/2, 8/5, 5/3; neither **15.** 1/2, 1/3, 1/4, 1/5, 1/6; neither **16.** 1/9, 1/10, 1/11, 1/12, 1/13; neither **17.** Arithmetic; 8 **18.** Arithmetic; 6 **19.** Arithmetic; 3 **20.** Arithmetic; 11 **21.** Geometric; 3 **22.** Geometric; 2 **23.** Neither **24.** Neither **25.** Arithmetic; -3 **26.** Arithmetic; -6 **27.** Arithmetic; 3 **28.** Arithmetic; 4 **29.** Geometric; -2 **30.** Geometric; -2 **31.** Neither **32.** Neither **33.** 70 **34.** 69 **35.** 65 **36.** 83 **37.** 7 **38.** 17 **39.** -65 **40.** -90 **41.** 78 **42.** 50 **43.** -65 **44.** -123 **45.** 234 **46.** 264 **47.** 636 **48.** 600 **49.** 1716 **50.** 1302 **51.** 690 **52.** 540 **53.** -48 **54.** -174 **55.** -558 **56.** -312 **57.** 500,500 **58.** 50,005,000 **59.** 1458; 2184 **60.** 224; 441 **61.** 2; 126 **62.** 3; 1092 **63.** -384; -252 **64.** -1; 2604 **65.** -64/27; 266/27 **66.** -60.75; -33.25 **67.** -729/512; 1443/512 **68.** .0512; -3.5568 **69.** 4/81; -133/648 **70.** -15/512; 315/512

71. (a) 120 (b) 55 (c) 65 (d) Player A; player B (e) 56; 64; player B

72. (a) 28¢ (b) 17¢ (c) $8.95 (d) $239.98 **73.** (a) $10,000, $10,800, $11,600, $12,400, $13,200 (b) $800 (c) $17,200 **74.** (a) 2043 sq in (b) 8192 sq in (c) 32,768 sq in (d) 262,144 sq in **75.** (a) 729/4096 or about 18% (b) 6561/65,536 or about 10% **76.** (a) 36 letters after these two mailings (b) 216 **77.** (a) 1296 (b) 46,656 (c) 1,679,616 (d) 362,797,056 **78.** (a) 1/32 (b) 1/8 (c) 1/2 (d) 2 (e) 64 (f) 2048 (g) 2,097,152 in or about 33 mi **79.** Choose the doubling method. The total wages earned for the month using this method would be $21,474,836.47. **80.** (a) 3x/16 (counting the original triangle as the first) (b) 93x/16 (counting the original triangle as the first)

Section 4.5 (page 202)

1. 987 **2.** 1597 **3.** 2584 **4.** 4181 **5.** 6765 **6.** 10,946 **7.** 75,025 **8.** 514,229 **9.** 24,157,817 **10.** 165,580,141 **11.** 1, 1, 2, 3, 5, 8 **12.** 13 **13.** 21 **14.** 34 **15.** 55 **16.** Yes **17.** Each sum is itself a Fibonacci number. **18.** Each sum is 1 less than a Fibonacci number. **19.** (a) 441 - 64 = 377; 377 = 377 (b) 1 - 2 + 5 - 13 + 34 - 89 = -64; -64 = -64 **20.** (a) 170 - 169 = 1 (b) 169 - 165 = 4 (c) 178 - 169 = 9 We are obtaining the squares of the terms of the Fibonacci sequence. For this pattern to continue, the next difference should be 25. Since 169 - 144 = 25, the pattern does continue. **21.** The decimal expression begins .011235. Beginning with the hundredths place we obtain the first five terms of the Fibonacci sequence. **22.** The quotients approach the golden ratio. **23.** The sum of the ten numbers is 55x + 88y = 11(5x + 8y). The seventh number in the list is 5x + 8y. **24.** The next two diagonal sums are 8 and 13 (the next two terms of the Fibonacci sequence). **25.** The ratio of length to width is approximately the golden ratio. **26.** (a) 199, 322, 521, 843, 1364 (b) Each sum is 2 less than a Lucas number. (c) Each sum is 1 less than a Lucas number. (d) The difference is always 5. (e) 8 + 21 = 29 **27.** There will be 8 spirals in one direction and 13 spirals in the other. 8 and 13 are consecutive Fibonacci numbers.

An Extension Magic Squares (page 206)

1. 807 **2.** 807 **3.** 807 **4.** 807 **5.** 807

6. The magic number is 34. The verification of the additional property is as follows:

$16^2 + 3^2 + 2^2 + 13^2 + 9^2 + 6^2 + 7^2 + 12^2 = 5^2 + 10^2 + 11^2 + 8^2 + 4^2 + 15^2 + 14^2 + 1^2 =$

748.

7.

30	39	48	1	10	19	28
38	47	7	9	18	27	29
46	6	8	17	26	35	37
5	14	16	25	34	36	45
13	15	24	33	42	44	4
21	23	32	41	43	3	12
22	31	40	49	2	11	20

8. 2056 **9.** 130 **10.** 1092 **11.** 514 **12.** 514

13. (a) 6 (b) 17 (c) 16 (d) 6 (e) 7 (f) 13 (g) 14 (h) 20

14. (a) 21 (b) 24 (c) 22 (d) 14 (e) 1 (f) 12 (g) 20 (h) 23

15.

16	2	3	13
5	11	10	8
9	7	6	12
4	14	15	1

The second and third columns are interchanged.

16. 369

17.

39	48	57	10	19	28	37
47	56	16	18	27	36	38
55	15	17	26	35	44	46
14	23	25	34	43	45	54
22	24	33	42	51	53	13
30	32	41	50	52	12	21
31	40	49	58	11	20	29

The magic sum is 238.

18. First row: 24; second row: 29; third row: 34; fourth row: 36, 39

Chapter 4 Test (page 210)

1. Not a prime **2.** Not a prime **3.** $2^2 \cdot 3 \cdot 5$ **4.** $5^2 \cdot 13$ **5.** No **6.** Yes

7. Yes **8.** Yes **9.** Yes **10.** Yes **11.** No **12.** No **13.** 5

14. 80 **15.** 12 **16.** 144 **17.** 180 **18.** 4, 10, 16, 22, 28

19. 3, 8, 15, 24, 35 **20.** 6, 4, 2, 0, -2 **21.** 3, 12, 48, 192, 768

22. 6, -12, 24, -48, 96 **23.** 129 **24.** 125,250 **25.** 1, 1, 2, 3, 5, 8, 13, 21

26. $1 + 1 + 2 + 3 + 5 + 8 = 21 - 1$; $20 = 20$

CHAPTER 5

Section 5.1 (page 218)

1. Commutative **2.** Commutative **3.** Associative **4.** Commutative **5.** Closure **6.** Identity **7.** Identity **8.** Identity **9.** Identity **10.** Associative **11.** Distributive **12.** Distributive **13.** False **14.** True **15.** True **16.** False **17.** False **18.** False **19.** False **20.** True **21.** False **22.** True **23.** True **24.** False **25.** Identity: no; commutative: no, no; associative: no; closure: no, no **26.** There would be no identity for addition. **27.** Closed **28.** Closed **29.** Not closed; $2 - 4$ **30.** Not closed; $2 \div 4$ **31.** Not closed; $1 + 3$ **32.** Not closed; $1 - 3$ **33.** Closed **34.** Closed **35.** Closed **36.** Closed **37.** Closed **38.** Not closed; $8 \div 10$ **39.** Associative, commutative, associative, associative, distributive, identity and associative, distributive **40.** Distributive, associative, distributive **41.** $5 + 5 + 5 + 5 + 5 + 5$ **42.** $2 + 2 + 2$ **43.** $4 + 4 + 4 + 4 + 4 + 4 + 4 + 4$

An Extension Defining Whole Number Operations Using Sets (page 221)

1. Let $A = \{a, b, c\}$ and let $B = \{d, e, f, g\}$. $A \cap B = \emptyset$ and $A \cup B = \{a, b, c, d, e, f, g\}$. $n(A) = 3$ and $n(B) = 4$, so $3 + 4 = n(A \cup B) = 7$. **2.** Let $A = \{a, b, c\}$ and let $B = \{d, e, f, g\}$. $n(A) = 3$ and $n(B) = 4$. $A \times B = \{(a, d), (a, e), (a, f), (a, g), (b, d), (b, e), (b, f), (b, g), (c, d), (c, e), (c, f), (c, g)\}$; $n(A \times B) = 12$, so $3 \cdot 4 = 12$. **3.** 4 **4.** 2 **5.** $\{m, n, o, p, q\}$ **6.** 5 **7.** No **8.** If $A \cap B \neq \emptyset$, then the cardinal number of $A \cup B$ will be less than $n(A) + n(B)$. **9.** $\geq$ **10.** $7 = 3 + 4$ **11.** $5 = 5 + 0$ **12.** $16 = 2 \times 8$ **13.** $26 = 26 \times 1$ **14.** Definition of the whole number 0; definition of the whole number a and multiplication property for equations; set theory definition of multiplication; Cartesian product of any set and the null set is the null set; definition of the whole number 0 **15.** Let $A = \{a, b, c\}$ and let $B =$

$\{d, e, f, g, h\}$. $n(A) = 3$ and $n(B) = 5$. $\{d, e, f\}$ is a proper subset of B which is equivalent to A. Therefore, $3 < 5$. **16.** If $n(A) = a$ and $n(B) = b$, $a \le b$ if and only if A is equivalent to a subset of B. (Just omit the word "proper.")

Section 5.2 (page 231)

1. True **2.** True **3.** True **4.** False **5.** False **6.** True **7.** True **8.** False (0 is neither.) **9.** True **10.** True

11. −4 0 2 3 5 **12.** −6 −3 0 1 2 **13.** −2 −1 0 1 2

14. −5 −4 −3 −2 −1 0 **15.** −3 −2 −1 0 **16.** 0 4 5 6

17. −4 −3 −2 −1 0 **18.** −6 −5 −4 −3 0 **19.** $<$ **20.** $<$ **21.** $<$

22. $<$ **23.** $>$ **24.** $>$ **25.** $>$ **26.** $>$ **27.** $<$ **28.** $<$ **29.** $>$

30. $>$ **31.** 5 **32.** 3 **33.** 2 **34.** 6 **35.** −14 **36.** −27 **37.** −23

38. −13 **39.** 1 **40.** −33 **41.** 4 **42.** −1 **43.** −11 **44.** −11

45. −26 **46.** −47 **47.** 10 **48.** 15 **49.** 19 **50.** 38 **51.** 6

52. 6 **53.** −13 **54.** −16 **55.** −12 **56.** −15 **57.** 18 **58.** 42

59. −36 **60.** −108 **61.** 150 **62.** 480 **63.** −5 **64.** −10 **65.** 2

66. 5 **67.** 3 **68.** 6 **69.** −2 **70.** −10 **71.** −36 **72.** −56

73. 12 **74.** 60 **75.** 18 **76.** 36 **77.** 40 **78.** 35 **79.** 4

80. −3 **81.** −11 **82.** −9 **83.** −5 **84.** −7 **85.** 9 **86.** 4

87. 56 **88.** 95 **89.** 35 **90.** 28 **91.** 5 **92.** 1 **93.** 1 **94.** 3

95. −2 **96.** −1 **97.** 5 **98.** 3 **99.** 17 **100.** 56 **101.** 6

102. 9 **103.** −32 **104.** −99 **105.** 2 **106.** 0 **107.** −32 **108.** −21

109. Let 2k and 2m represent two even integers. (k and m are integers.) Then $2k + 2m = 2(k + m)$ by the distributive property. $k + m$ is an integer since the integers are closed for addition; therefore, the sum is even. **110.** Let $2k + 1$ and $2m + 1$ represent two odd integers. (k and m are integers.) Then $(2k + 1) + (2m + 1) = 2k + 2m + 2 =$

2(k + m + 1). k + m + 1 is an integer since the integers are closed for addition; therefore, the sum is even. **111.** Let 2k + 1 and 2m represent odd and even integers, respectively. (k and m are integers.) Then (2k + 1)•2m = 4km + 2m = 2(2km + m). 2km + m is an integer by the closure properties; therefore, the product is even.
112. Let 2k + 1 and 2m + 1 represent two odd integers. (k and m are integers.) Then (2k + 1)(2m + 1) = 4km + 2k + 2m + 1 = 2(2km + k + m) + 1. 2km + k + m is an integer since the integers are closed for multiplication and addition; therefore, the product is odd.
113. 30 in, 26 in **114.** 32 mi, 30 mi **115.** 50%, 44% **116.** 65%, 57%

Section 5.3 (page 240)

1. 1/2 **2.** 8/9 **3.** 3/11 **4.** 3/13 **5.** 43/48 **6.** 41/90 **7.** 37/45 **8.** 91/120 **9.** 2423/2880 **10.** 1493/1680 **11.** 7/30 **12.** 23/56 **13.** 97/315 **14.** 41/60 **15.** 463/540 **16.** 43/288 **17.** 27/20 or 1 7/20 **18.** 3/28 **19.** 1/5 **20.** 2/3 **21.** 3 **22.** 1 **23.** 3/10 **24.** 3/2 or 1 1/2 **25.** 1/9 **26.** 1/4 **27.** 3/20 **28.** 16 **29.** 5/12 **30.** −1/6 **31.** 1/2 **32.** 3/2 or 1 1/2 **33.** 7/40 **34.** 7/2 or 3 1/2 **35.** 23/60 **36.** 45/64 **37.** 8/87 **38.** −5/6 **39.** −15/16 **40.** −3/20 **41.** 13/24 **42.** 197/380 **43.** 11/21 **44.** 23/22 or 1 1/22 **45.** −1 **46.** −9 **47.** −17/288 **48.** −1/75 **49.** 13/3 **50.** 31/8 **51.** 29/10 **52.** 62/11 **53.** 3 3/5 **54.** 6 3/4 **55.** 6 1/3 **56.** 4 5/6 **57.** 6 1/8 **58.** 6 1/2 **59.** 16 19/30 **60.** 15 11/36 **61.** 3 11/15 **62.** 1 2/3 **63.** 4 3/8 **64.** 17 7/8 **65.** 8 5/32 **66.** 17 5/12 **67.** 2 1/2 **68.** 5/12 **69.** > **70.** > **71.** > **72.** > **73.** < **74.** < **75.** = **76.** = **77.** < **78.** > **79.** > **80.** < **81.** 11/15, 23/30 **82.** 14/15, 23/24 **83.** 7/9, 4/5, 6/7 **84.** 6/11, 3/5, 5/8 **85.** 3/10, 1/3, 3/8, 3/7 **86.** 5/6, 6/7, 9/10, 10/11 **87.** 5/12, 1/2, 8/15, 4/7 **88.** 2/3, 12/17, 11/15, 3/4 **89.** 5/8 **90.** 3/8 **91.** 19/30 **92.** 29/48 **93.** 1/5 **94.** 13/15 **95.** 1/4 **96.** 11/72 **97.** 41/18 or 2 5/18 **98.** 4/3 or 1 1/3 **99.** −5/8

100. -3/4 **101.** 1/4 **102.** -7/6 or -1 1/6 **103.** 110/153 **104.** 323/330

105. 8/15 **106.** 7/14 or 1/2 **107.** 3/3 or 1 **108.** 11/6 or 1 5/6

109. 5/2 or 2 1/2 **110.** 21/2 or 10 1/2 **111.** Monday: 1, 3/2, 1/4, 1/2, 1/4, 3/2, 1, 3/2, 1, 3/2, 1/8; Thursday: 4, 6, 1, 2, 1, 6, 4, 6, 4, 6, 1/2

112. Monday: 2/3, 1/6, 1/4, 1/6, 6, 1, 1/6, 1/4, 1/2; Thursday: 2 2/3 or 8/3, 2/3, 1, 2/3, 24, 4, 2/3, 1, 2 **113.** 3 **114.** 5/3 or 1 2/3 **115.** 3/7

116. 11/3 or 3 2/3 **117.** -103/89 or -1 14/89 **118.** 38/9 or 4 2/9 **121.** >

122. > **123.** > **124.** > **125.** < **126.** < **127.** = **128.** =

Section 5.4 (page 251)

1. $.\overline{4}$ **2.** $.\overline{58}$ **3.** $.\overline{92}$ **4.** $.\overline{65}$ **5.** $.\overline{469}$ **6.** $.\overline{810}$ **7.** $.9134\overline{5}$

8. $.217\overline{6}$ **9.** $.083\overline{25}$ **10.** $.749\overline{13}$ **11.** $6.09\overline{90}$ **12.** $5.86\overline{68}$ **13.** .75

14. .875 **15.** .1875 **16.** .28125 **17.** $.41\overline{6}$ **18.** $.91\overline{6}$ **19.** $.\overline{27}$

20. $.\overline{81}$ **21.** $.\overline{285714}$ **22.** $.7\overline{3}$ **23.** $.1\overline{3}$ **24.** $.4\overline{6}$ **25.** 2/5

26. 9/10 **27.** 17/20 **28.** 9/25 **29.** 21/200 **30.** 467/500 **31.** 499/625

32. 1397/2000 **33.** 8/9 **34.** 1/9 **35.** 6/11 **36.** 4/11 **37.** 41/333

38. 172/333 **39.** 4 92/99 **40.** 6 13/99 **41.** 13/30 **42.** 4/15 **43.** 2

44. 31/10 or 3 1/10 **45.** Rational **46.** Rational **47.** Irrational

48. Irrational **49.** Rational **50.** Irrational **51.** Rational **52.** Rational

53. Rational **54.** Rational **55.** Rational **56.** Rational **57.** One answer: .5438914769... **58.** One answer: 1.802713695... **59.** One answer: .9152057432...

60. One answer: 2.84793271489937... **61.** One answer: rational .915, irrational .9134726137... **62.** One answer: rational $.03\overline{4}$, irrational .032169412738...

63. One answer: rational .17, irrational .170385241153... **64.** One answer: rational $.7988\overline{3}$, irrational .79906347125... **65.** One answer: .0875917632 **66.** One answer: .7685 **67.** Repeating **68.** Repeating **69.** Terminating **70.** Terminating

71. Terminating **72.** Terminating **73.** True **74.** False **75.** False

76. True **77.** True **78.** False **79.** False **80.** True **81.** False

82. True **83.** Yes, yes, yes, no, yes **84.** No, no, yes, no, yes

85. No, yes, yes, yes, yes **86.** No, no, yes, no **87.** No, no, no, no, yes

88. No, no, no, yes, yes **89.** Yes, no, yes **90.** No, no, yes, no, yes

91. No, no, no, yes **92.** No, no, no, yes, yes **93.** No, no, no, no

94. No, no, no, no **95.** $\subseteq$ **96.** $\subseteq$ **97.** $\cup$ **98.** $\cup$ **99.** $\cap$

100. $\cap$ **101.** $\cup$ **102.** $\subseteq$ **103.** $\subseteq$ or = **104.** $\subseteq$ or = **105.** $\cup$ or $\cap$

106. $\cap$ or $\cup$ **107.** (a) $.\overline{3}$ (b) $.\overline{6}$ (c) $.\overline{9}$ **108.** 3(1/3) = 3(.33333...);
1 = .99999...

Section 5.5 (page 260)

1. 13.5 **2.** 20.8 **3.** 38.9 **4.** 55.4 **5.** 24.7 **6.** 39.22

7. 1.3674 **8.** 3.97389 **9.** 37.251 **10.** 31.943 **11.** 109.76 **12.** 483.22

13. 29.1 **14.** 25.8 **15.** 24.2 **16.** 23.4 **17.** 28 **18.** 47

19. 315.2 **20.** 1193.6 **21.** $91,150.00 **22.** $185.11 **23.** $173.49

24. (a) $11,042.49 (b) $8997.26 (c) $3901.35 **25.** $8.35 **26.** $428.08

27. 28.4 mpg **28.** 1,600,000,000 gal **29.** $23,285.10 **30.** $17,641.86

31. (a) 78.4 (b) 78.41 **32.** (a) 3689.5 (b) 3689.54 **33.** (a) .1
(b) .08 **34.** (a) .1 (b) .07 **35.** (a) 12.7 (b) 12.69

36. (a) 43.9 (b) 43.90 **37.** (a) 58.5 (b) 58.48 **38.** (a) 112.5
(b) 112.46 **39.** 42% **40.** 87% **41.** 36.5% **42.** 79.2% **43.** .8%

44. .93% **45.** 210% **46.** 890% **47.** .46 **48.** .92 **49.** .08 **50.** .03

51. 1.59 **52.** 2.74 **53.** .005 **54.** .0008 **55.** 166.88 **56.** 282.68

57. 26.768 **58.** 174.468 **59.** 120.54 **60.** 173.85 **61.** $1238.70

62. $410.67 **63.** 42.48 **64.** 106 **65.** 114 **66.** 875 **67.** 65%

68. 27% **69.** $1612 **70.** $9060 **71.** 1650 cars **72.** $181.83

73. 5135 students **74.** 25% **75.** (a) .7 million metric tons (b) 65 million grams

76. Approximately 1.45% **77.** $11.90 **78.** $14,500 **79.** $79,787

80. 2,100,000 vehicles **81.** $255 **82.** $68 **83.** $935 **84.** $35.70

85. 66 2/3% **86.** 46.3% **87.** 32.4% **88.** 25% **89.** 15.6% **90.** 50%

91. \$4.50 **92.** \$5.70 **93.** \$.75 **94.** \$1.20 **95.** \$43.05 **96.** \$46.65

97. No. 160 min = 160/60 hr = $2.\overline{6}$ hr **98.** 1.5 hr

Section 5.6 (page 268)

1. 3.606 **2.** 6.481 **3.** 5.568 **4.** 7.348 **5.** 8.832 **6.** 9.592

7. 11.402 **8.** 15.166 **9.** 21.679 **10.** 24.290 **11.** 29.155 **12.** 30.496

13. Yes, yes **14.** No, yes, yes **15.** No, no, yes, no, yes **16.** Yes, no, yes

17. No, yes **18.** No, yes, no **19.** No, no, yes, yes **20.** No, no, yes, yes

21. No, no, no, no **22.** No, no, no, no **23.** 1.732 **24.** 2.828 **25.** 3.464

26. 3.873 **27.** 7.071 **28.** 8.367 **29.** 7.810 **30.** 9.220 **31.** $4\sqrt{2}$

32. $5\sqrt{2}$ **33.** $3\sqrt{3}$ **34.** $5\sqrt{3}$ **35.** $10\sqrt{2}$ **36.** $12\sqrt{2}$ **37.** $10\sqrt{10}$

38. $50\sqrt{2}$ **39.** $24\sqrt{5}$ **40.** $16\sqrt{6}$ **41.** $2\sqrt{2}$ **42.** $3\sqrt{3}$ **43.** $13\sqrt{3}$

44. $-34\sqrt{3}$ **45.** $10\sqrt{2}$ **46.** $-7\sqrt{2}$ **47.** $3\sqrt{2}/2$ **48.** $5\sqrt{6}/6$ **49.** $9\sqrt{7}/7$

50. $11\sqrt{3}/3$ **51.** $-3\sqrt{3}$ **52.** $10\sqrt{2}$ **53.** $4\sqrt{3}$ **54.** $-2\sqrt{2}$ **55.** $2\sqrt[3]{2}$

56. $3\sqrt[3]{2}$ **57.** $2\sqrt[3]{3}$ **58.** $3\sqrt[3]{3}$ **59.** $2\sqrt[3]{5}$ **60.** $5\sqrt[3]{2}$ **61.** $4\sqrt[3]{2}$ **62.** $3\sqrt[3]{5}$

63. No. These are only common rational approximations for π. **64.** The result is 3.1415929, which agrees with the first seven digits. **65.** The result is 3.1415927, which agrees with the first eight digits. **66.** (a) 3.1415926 (b) 3.141592653589 (c) 3.14159265358979 **67.** One example is "Gee, I have a buddy." **68.** 482.8 cm^2

69. 18.8 m^2 **70.** 33.5 m^3 **71.** 452.2 m^2 **72.** 1934.2 cm^2 **73.** 502.4 cm^3

74. (a) 1.618 (b) -.618 (c) 1 (d) -1 **75.** (a) $2/(1 + \sqrt{5})$ (b) $(1 - \sqrt{5})/-2$ (c) The result, .618034, is the negative of the number found there.

An Extension Complex Numbers (page 272)

1. Complex **2.** Complex **3.** Real, complex **4.** Real, complex

5. Imaginary, complex **6.** Imaginary, complex **7.** Real, complex

8. Real, complex **9.** Imaginary, complex **10.** Imaginary, complex

11. Real, complex **12.** Real, complex

Chapter 5 Test (page 275)

1. Commutative **2.** Associative **3.** Identity **4.** Inverse **5.** Inverse

6. Distributive **7.** Commutative **8.** Identity **9.** Closure **10.** Associative

11. (a) Closed (b) Not closed; for example, 1 + 3 = 4 and 4 is not in the set.

12. 0 **13.** −1 **14.** 36 **15.** 12 **16.** 11/16 **17.** 57/160 **18.** −2/5

19. 3/2 or 1 1/2 **20.** > **21.** = **22.** .45 **23.** $.41\overline{6}$ **24.** 18/25

25. 58/99 **26.** Rational **27.** Irrational **28.** 14.68 **29.** 8.275

30. 38.7 **31.** 24.3 **32.** (a) 9.04 (b) 9.045 **33.** 413.84 **34.** 101.5

35. 1.25% **36.** $15.\overline{6}$% **37.** $5\sqrt{6}$ **38.** $13\sqrt{7}/7$ **39.** $-32\sqrt{2}$

40. Yes, yes, yes **41.** No, yes, no, yes **42.** No, yes, no, yes

43. No, no, yes, yes **44.** No, yes, no, yes **45.** Yes, yes **46.** Yes, yes, yes

47. No, no, yes, yes **48.** No, no, no, yes

CHAPTER 6

Section 6.1 (page 283)

1. 8 **2.** 9 **3.** 8 **4.** 0 **5.** 3 **6.** 2 **7.** 4 **8.** 1 **9.** 1 **10.** 0 **11.** 2 **12.** 4 **13.** Row 2: 0, 6, 10; row 3: 9, 0, 9; row 4: 0, 4, 0, 8, 0; row 5: 1, 9, 2, 7; row 6: 6, 0, 0; row 7: 4, 11, 6, 8, 3, 5; row 8: 8, 4, 0, 0; row 9: 6, 3, 9, 3, 9, 6, 3; row 10: 6, 4, 0, 10, 8, 6, 4; row 11: 10, 9, 8, 7, 6, 5, 4, 3, 2 **14.** 5 **15.** 2 **16.** 10 **17.** 9 **18.** 11 **19.** 11 **20.** 5 **21.** 5 **22.** 3 **23.** 11 **24.** 3 **25.** 1 **26.** 1 **27.** 0 **28.** 0 **29.** 5 **30.** Row 1: 0; row 2: 0; row 3: 0, 1, 2; row 4: 0, 1, 2; row 5: 0, 2, 4; row 6: 0, 2, 4 **31.** Yes **32.** Yes **33.** Yes **34.** Yes **35.** Yes **36.** 5 **37.** 1 **38.** 3 **39.** 3 **40.** 4 **41.** 1 **42.** 1 **43.** 5

44.

×	0	1	2	3	4	5	6
0	0	0	0	0	0	0	0
1	0	1	2	3	4	5	6
2	0	2	4	6	1	3	5
3	0	3	6	2	5	1	4
4	0	4	1	5	2	6	3
5	0	5	3	1	6	4	2
6	0	6	5	4	3	2	1

45. Yes **46.** Yes **47.** Yes **48.** Yes **49.** Yes **50.** 1 **51.** 4 **52.** 5 **53.** 2 **54.** 3 **55.** 6 **56.** 1500 **57.** 1900 **58.** 1000 **59.** 1500 **60.** 1600 **61.** Yes

62. No; there is no inverse for 2. **63.** Yes **64.** No; there is no inverse for 3. **65.** Yes **66.** Prime

Section 6.2 (page 289)

1. False **2.** True **3.** True **4.** False **5.** True **6.** False **7.** False **8.** True **9.** True **10.** True **11.** True **12.** True **13.** 5 **14.** 3 **15.** 1 **16.** 4 **17.** 4 **18.** 0 **19.** 0 **20.** 0 **21.** 4 **22.** 0 **23.** 0 **24.** 1 **25.** 0 **26.** 10 **27.** 2 **28.** 7 **29.** 3 **30.** 6 **31.** 7 **32.** 3 **33.** (a) Row 1: 2, 0; row 2: 0, 1 (b) All properties satisfied (c) 0 is its own inverse; 1 and 2 are inverses.

34. (a) Row 1: 2, 3, 0; row 2: 3, 0, 1; row 3: 0, 1, 2 (b) All properties satisfied

(c) 0 is its own inverse, as is 2; 1 and 3 are inverses. **35.** (a) Row 1: 0; row 2: 0, 1; row 3: 4, 0, 1, 2; row 4: 0, 1, 2, 3 (b) All properties satisfied (c) 0 is its own inverse; 2 and 3 are inverses, as are 1 and 4. **36.** (a) Row 1: 0; row 2: 0, 1; row 3: 4, 5, 6, 0, 1, 2; row 4: 5, 6, 0, 1, 2, 3; row 5: 6, 0, 1, 2, 3, 4 (b) All properties satisfied (c) 0 is its own inverse; 1 and 6 are inverses, as are 2 and 5 and 3 and 4. **37.** (a) 1 (b) All properties satisfied (c) 1 is its own inverse.
38. (a) 1 (b) All properties satisfied (c) 1 is its own inverse, as is 2.
39. (a) Row 2: 0, 2; row 3: 2, 1 (b) No inverse property (c) 1 is its own inverse, as is 3; no inverse for 2. **40.** (a) Row 2: 1, 3; row 3: 1, 2; row 4: 3, 2, 1 (b) All properties satisfied (c) 1 is its own inverse, as is 4; 2 and 3 are inverses.
41. (a) Row 2: 1, 3, 5; row 3: 2, 1; row 4: 1, 5, 2, 6, 3; row 5: 3, 1, 4; row 6: 5, 3, 2 (b) All properties satisfied (c) 1 is its own inverse, as is 6; 2 and 4 are inverses, as are 3 and 5. **42.** (a) Row 2: 1, 3, 7; row 3: 3, 0; row 4: 3, 2, 1; row 5: 6, 7, 4; row 7: 3, 1, 6, 4; row 8: 6, 5, 2 (b) No inverse property (c) 1 is its own inverse, as is 8; 2 and 5 are inverses, as are 4 and 7; there is no inverse for 3 or 6.
43. Prime **44.** {4, 9, 14, 19, 24, 29, ...} **45.** {7, 16, 25, 34, 43, 52, ...}
46. {2, 6, 10, 14, 18, 22, ...} **47.** {3, 10, 17, 24, 31, 38, ...}
48. {5, 10, 15, 20, 25, 30, ...} **49.** {6, 16, 26, 36, 46, 56, ...}
50. {3, 14, 25, 36, 47, 58, ...} **51.** {2, 9, 16, 23, 30, 37, ...}
52. {1, 9, 17, 25, 33, 41, ...} **53.** {5, 12, 19, 26, 33, 40, ...} **54.** No answers
55. {2, 5, 8, 11, 14, 17, ...} **56.** {2, 6, 10, 14, 18, 22, ...}
57. No answers **58.** No answers **59.** Identity **60.** Identity
61. {4, 9, 14, 19, 24, 29, ...} **62.** {7, 19, 31, 43, 55, 67, ...}
63. {10, 28, 46, 64, 82, 100, ...} **64.** {2, 6, 10, 14, 18, 22, ...}
65. 100,000 **66.** 33,421 + k(100,000), where k is a nonnegative integer **67.** 2
68. 2, 3, 4 **69.** 2, 4, 6 **70.** 3, 6 **71.** 2, 4, 5, 6, 8
72. 2, 3, 4, 6, 8, 9, 10 **73.** None **74.** None **75.** None **76.** Prime

77. Monday **78.** Tuesday **79.** Wednesday **80.** Friday **81.** September, December **82.** March, November **83.** September, December **84.** October

85. (c) 6
(d) 9, 9
(e) 1, 1
(f) 4, 4
(g) 7, 7
(h) 10, 10
(i) 2, 2
(j) 5, 5
(k) 8, 8

(l)

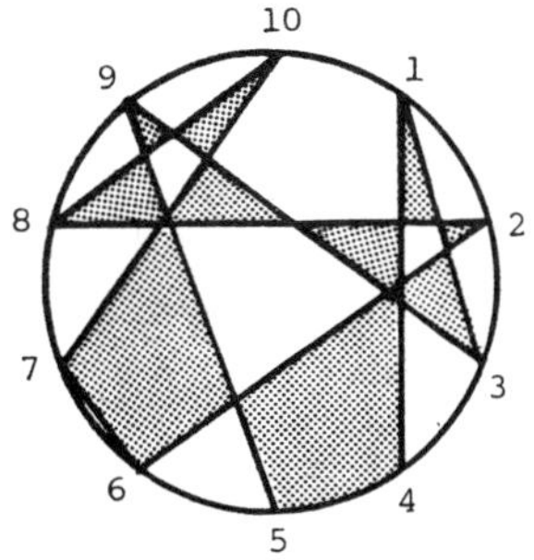

86. Incorrect **87.** Correct **88.** Incorrect **89.** Incorrect **90.** 7 **91.** 0 **92.** 4 **93.** 4 **94.** 6

Section 6.3 (page 297)

1. All properties; 1 is its own inverse, as is 4; 2 and 3 are inverses.
2. All properties; 1 is its own inverse, as is 2. **3.** Commutative, associative, and identity properties **4.** All properties except inverse; there is no inverse for 2, 4, or 6. **5.** All properties; 1, 3, 5, and 7 are their own inverses.
6. All properties except inverse; there is no inverse for 5. **7.** Commutative, closure **8.** All properties; B and A are inverses; F is its own inverse.
9. All properties; J and U are inverses; A and T are their own inverses.
10. All properties; s and r are inverses; t is its own inverse, as is u.
11. Closure, associative, identity, inverse; m, q, r, and s are their own inverses; n and p are inverses. **12.** Commutative property does not hold (for example, $q \text{ A } u \neq u \text{ A } q$); s and q are inverses; each other element is its own inverse. **13.** a **14.** b **15.** c **16.** a **17.** c **18.** a **19.** a **20.** b

21. Row b: d; row c: d, b; row d: b, c **22.** All **23.** Associative, commutative, identity (U), closure **24.** Associative, commutative, identity (Ø), closure

25.

	a	b	c	d
a	a	b	c	d
b	b	a	d	c
c	c	d	a	b
d	d	c	b	a

Section 6.4 (page 302)

1. Yes **2.** No **3.** No **4.** No **5.** No **6.** No **7.** 468 **8.** 438 **9.** 285 **10.** 413 **11.** 380 **12.** 792 **13.** 875 **14.** 2322 **15.** 1496 **16.** 2870 **17.** 79,992 **18.** 699,993 **19.** 16p **20.** 16r **21.** 14z **22.** 18k **23.** 6p **24.** 13r **25.** 2a **26.** 2y **27.** 11r **28.** 8m **29.** 10k **30.** 31b **31.** −6a **32.** −10x **33.** 5k + 2r can't be further simplified. **34.** 9z + 4y can't be further simplified. **35.** 4p + 7r **36.** 2k **37.** 0 **38.** −5y **39.** 5p **40.** 20z **41.** −16y **42.** 3k **43.** 5(3m + 2k) **44.** 10(2p + 7y) **45.** 6b(2a + 5p) **46.** 4m(n − 2p) **47.** 2b(30ac − 6c + 5a) **48.** 7p(5mq − 8m + 4) **49.** Can't be factored **50.** Can't be factored **51.** $6(p^2 + 3q^2)$ **52.** $15(r^2 + 2t^2)$ **53.** $20(5y^3 - 3y^2 + 6z^2)$ **54.** $18(4m^2 + 3m^3 - 6n^2)$ **55.** Each side simplifies to e. **56.** Each side simplifies to a. **57.** Each side simplifies to d. **58.** Each side simplifies to c.

59.

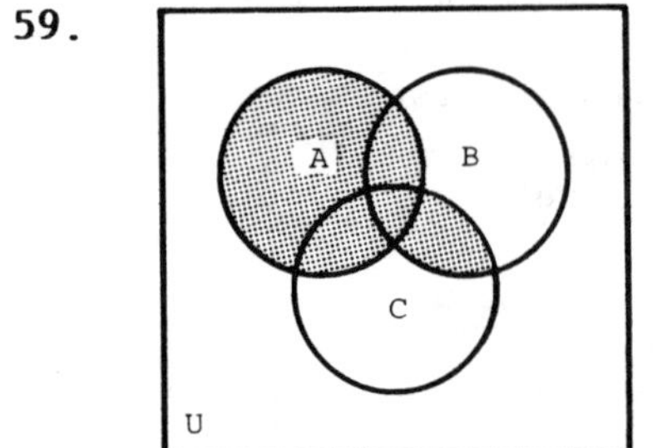

A ∪ (B ∩ C) = (A ∪ B) ∩ (A ∪ C)

60.

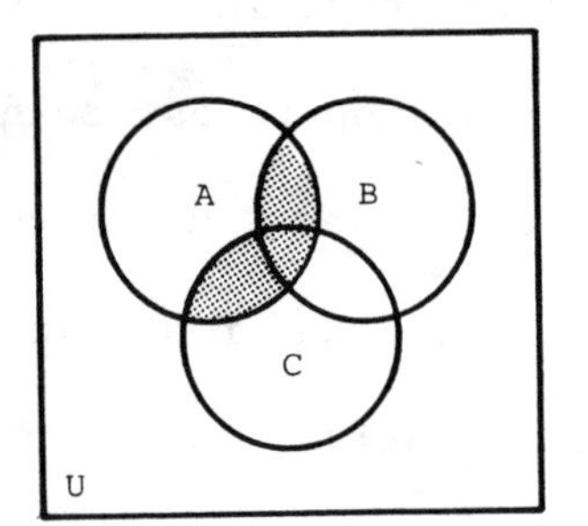

A ∩ (B ∪ C) = (A ∩ B) ∪ (A ∩ C)

61. TTTTTFFF for each final column **62.** TTTFFFFF for each final column

Section 6.5 (page 309)

1. No; closure **2.** No; identity, inverse **3.** No; inverse **4.** No; identity, inverse, associative **5.** Yes **6.** Yes **7.** No; associative, identity, inverse **8.** No; closure, identity, inverse **9.** No; closure $(1 + 1 = 2)$ **10.** No; inverse **11.** Yes **12.** Yes **13.** No; closure **14.** Yes **15.** Multiples of 2, of 3, of 4, of 5, of 6, for example **16.** P **17.** S **18.** P **19.** R **20.** S **21.** V **22.** Q **29.** N **30.** Q **31.** R **32.** S **33.** T **34.** V **35.** Yes **36.** Yes **37.** Yes **38.** Yes **39.** Yes **40.** All **41.** No **42.** Yes **43.** No **44.** Yes **45.** No **46.** Prime **47.** 2 **48.** 4 **49.** 3 **50.** 1 **51.** 2 **52.** $3^1 = 3$, $3^2 = 4$, $3^3 = 2$, $3^4 = 1$, $3^5 = 3$; a generator **53.** $4^1 = 4$, $4^2 = 1$, $4^3 = 4$, $4^4 = 1$; not a generator **54.** No **55.** Yes, 3 is a generator. **56.** No **57.** No **58.** Yes **59.** Yes **60.** No

Chapter 6 Test (page 312)

1. 5 **2.** 7 **3.** 9 **4.** 8 **5.** 0 **6.** 3 **7.** 4 **8.** 5 **9.** 2 **10.** 5 **11.** False **12.** False **13.** True **14.** 3 **15.** 3 **16.** 0

17.

+	0	1	2	3	4	5	6	7
0	0	1	2	3	4	5	6	7
1	1	2	3	4	5	6	7	0
2	2	3	4	5	6	7	0	1
3	3	4	5	6	7	0	1	2
4	4	5	6	7	0	1	2	3
5	5	6	7	0	1	2	3	4
6	6	7	0	1	2	3	4	5
7	7	0	1	2	3	4	5	6

18.

×	0	1	2	3	4	5	6
0	0	0	0	0	0	0	0
1	0	1	2	3	4	5	6
2	0	2	4	6	1	3	5
3	0	3	6	2	5	1	4
4	0	4	1	5	2	6	3
5	0	5	3	1	6	4	2
6	0	6	5	4	3	2	1

19. $\{7, 16, 25, 34, 43, 52, 61, \ldots\}$ **20.** $\{2, 5, 8, 11, 14, 17, 20, 23, \ldots\}$ **21.** $\{3, 8, 13, 18, 23, 28, 33, \ldots\}$ **22.** $\{17\}$ **23.** b **24.** e **25.** c **26.** Yes **27.** Yes **28.** No **29.** Yes; c **30.** Yes, each element is its own inverse. **31.** 616 **32.** 5x **33.** $4(4k - 3z)$ **34.** Yes **35.** No

CHAPTER 7

Section 7.1 (page 322)

1. 4 **2.** 7 **3.** 15 **4.** 16 **5.** 15 **6.** 15 **7.** 2 **8.** 7

9. −3 **10.** −4 **11.** 4 **12.** 20 **13.** 7 **14.** 5 **15.** 5 **16.** 12

17. −2 **18.** 10 **19.** 4 **20.** −3 **21.** −5 **22.** −3 **23.** −5/2

24. 3/2 **25.** 1 **26.** −4 **27.** −2 **28.** 5 **29.** 0 **30.** 0 **31.** 18p

32. 16z **33.** −4k **34.** −3y **35.** −9y + 15 **36.** 2m + 7 **37.** −2z + 2

38. 5k − 3 **39.** 6y − 4 **40.** 5m − 22 **41.** 10y + 18 **42.** −26k + 67

43. −2k − 2 **44.** −3r + 5 **45.** 7 **46.** 19 **47.** −2 **48.** −1 **49.** 18

50. −10 **51.** −3 **52.** 2 **53.** 8 **54.** 2 **55.** −5 **56.** −6 **57.** 0

58. 3 **59.** No solution **60.** No solution **61.** All real numbers

62. All real numbers **63.** 1.4 **64.** 2.3 **65.** 9/2 **66.** 4/7 **67.** 0

68. No solution **69.** All real numbers **70.** All real numbers

Section 7.2 (page 327)

1. 4 + x or x + 4 **2.** x + (−6) or −6 + x **3.** −1 + x or x + (−1)

4. x + 12 or 12 + x **5.** x + (−18) or −18 + x **6.** x + 12 or 12 + x **7.** x − 5

8. x − 6 **9.** x − 9 **10.** x − 16 **11.** 9x **12.** 2x **13.** 3x

14. (3/5)x **15.** x/6 **16.** −9/x **17.** x/(−4) **18.** 7/x

19. 8(x + 3) **20.** x + 2x (or 3x) **21.** 3(x/2) **22.** 8x − 8

23. −7(x − 2) **24.** (1/2)x + (x + 9) or (3/2)x + 9 **25.** 3x − 2 = 22; 8

26. 6 + 4x = 42; 9 **27.** 4(x + 3) = 36; 6 **28.** 5(x + 8) = 60; 4

29. 2x + x = 90; 30 **30.** −2(x + 8) = −8; −4 **31.** x − 6 = 7x; −1

32. 2x − 4 = x − 4; 0 **33.** 5x + 2x = 10; 10/7 **34.** 11x − 7x = 9; 9/4

35. x + (x + 6) = 44; 19 **36.** x + (x + 30) = 516; 243 **37.** x + (x + 42) = 138; 48

38. x + (x + 25) = 173; 74 **39.** x + (x + 12) = 84; 36 **40.** x + (x + 17) = 165; 74

41. 24 cm **42.** Length = 14 cm, width = 2 cm **43.** 5m **44.** 17 cm

45. 30 cm **46.** Length = 18 units, width = 10 units **47.** 16 m, 18 m, 21 m

48. 30 cm, 40 cm, 50 cm **49.** 10% **50.** 13.3% **51.** $67.50 **52.** $10.51 **53.** EER = B/W **54.** 9.6 **55.** 2 hr **56.** 3 hr **57.** 2 1/2 hr **58.** 40 mph, 60 mph **59.** 7.5 gal **60.** 4 liters **61.** 17.5 quarts of 25% acid, 7.5 quarts of 35% acid **62.** 3 1/3 gal **63.** 30 liters **64.** 12 liters **65.** 100 **66.** 10 **67.** 86 **68.** 98

Section 7.3 (page 337)

1. 3/2 **2.** 5/9 **3.** 36/55 **4.** 3/2 **5.** 2/5 **6.** 15/4 **7.** 5/8 **8.** 5/9 **9.** 1/10 **10.** 16/5 **11.** 8/5 **12.** 7/12 **13.** 1/6 **14.** 16/1 or 16 **15.** 4/15 **16.** 3/10 **17.** 8-oz size **18.** 20-count size **19.** 13-oz size **20.** 32-oz size **21.** 40-oz size **22.** 32-oz size **23.** True **24.** True **25.** True **26.** True **27.** False **28.** False **29.** True **30.** True **31.** False **32.** True **33.** True **34.** False **35.** 21 **36.** 2 **37.** 40 **38.** 16 **39.** 5 **40.** 27 **41.** 16 **42.** 32 **43.** 7/2 or 3 1/2 **44.** 15/2 or 7 1/2 **45.** 8/3 or 2.667 (rounded) **46.** 8 1/3 or 8.333 (rounded) **47.** 27/8 or 3.375 **48.** 1 5/9 or 1.556 (rounded) **49.** 15/2 or 7 1/2 **50.** -3/2 or -1 1/2 **51.** 7/15 **52.** 25/19 or 1 6/19 **53.** -31 **54.** 87/4 or 21 3/4 **55.** $\frac{6}{5} = \frac{15}{x}$; $x = \frac{25}{2}$ or $12\frac{1}{2}$ **56.** $\frac{10}{m} = \frac{25}{10}$; $m = 4$ **57.** $\frac{42}{a} = \frac{30}{75}$; $a = 105$ **58.** $\frac{25}{20} = \frac{z}{50}$; $z = \frac{125}{2}$ or $62\frac{1}{2}$ **59.** $\frac{k}{8} = \frac{4}{6}$; $k = \frac{16}{3}$ or $5\frac{1}{3}$ **60.** $\frac{100}{40} = \frac{r}{3}$; $r = \frac{15}{2}$ or $7\frac{1}{2}$ **61.** 20 oz **62.** 9 tanks **63.** 2 1/2 bars **64.** 50 min **65.** 9 lb **66.** $5.50 **67.** 9 in **68.** $96 **69.** 7 lb **70.** 1080 mi **71.** $150 **72.** $412.50 **73.** $30 **74.** $22.32 **75.** 22.4 yd **76.** 3 3/4 cups **77.** 42 **78.** 160 **79.** 3π **80.** 25/4 **81.** 1/3 **82.** 7 **83.** 153.86 sq cm **84.** 780 mi **85.** 24,000 watts **86.** 2.5 ohms **87.** 3062.5 lb per sq in **88.** 284 4/9 lb **89.** The surface area is quadrupled (multiplied by 4). **90.** The volume is multiplied by 64.

Section 7.4 (page 346)

1. $(m + 2)(m + 3)$ **2.** $(z + 10)(z + 1)$ **3.** $(y + 10)(y + 5)$ **4.** $(r + 4)(r + 5)$ **5.** $(p - 7)(p - 6)$ **6.** $(a - 10)(a - 4)$ **7.** $(k - 4)(k + 3)$ **8.** $(z - 5)(z + 3)$ **9.** $(x - 8)(x + 3)$ **10.** $(y - 7)(y + 3)$ **11.** $(p + 4)(p - 4)$ **12.** $(k + 10)(k - 10)$ **13.** 2, −5 **14.** 1, −6 **15.** 5/2, −3 **16.** 3/4, −5 **17.** 2/3, −7/2 **18.** 7/5, −1/3 **19.** 0, 7 **20.** 0, −5 **21.** 0, −9/2 **22.** 0, 11/4 **23.** −4, −1 **24.** 2, 1 **25.** 4, −3 **26.** 5, −1 **27.** 3, −1 **28.** 4, −1 **29.** 7 **30.** 4 **31.** 5, 2 **32.** −4, −3 **33.** 4, −4 **34.** 5, −5 **35.** $\sqrt{29}$, $-\sqrt{29}$ **36.** $\sqrt{53}$, $-\sqrt{53}$ **37.** 12, −8 **38.** 5, −7 **39.** 4, −3 **40.** 7/5, −3/5 **41.** $2 + \sqrt{11}$, $2 - \sqrt{11}$ **42.** $-3 + \sqrt{5}$, $-3 - \sqrt{5}$ **43.** $(3 + \sqrt{21})/2$, $(3 - \sqrt{21})/2$ **44.** $(2 + \sqrt{7})/3$, $(2 - \sqrt{7})/3$ **45.** $3i$, $-3i$ **46.** $7i$, $-7i$ **47.** $1 + i$, $1 - i$ **48.** $-3 + 4i$, $-3 - 4i$ **49.** $-2 + i\sqrt{3}$, $-2 - i\sqrt{3}$ **50.** $4 + i\sqrt{7}$, $4 - i\sqrt{7}$ **51.** $(3 + 4i)/2$, $(3 - 4i)/2$ **52.** $(2 + 5i)/5$, $(2 - 5i)/5$ **53.** 6, 1 **54.** 1, 4 **55.** $(5 + \sqrt{13})/6$, $(5 - \sqrt{13})/6$ **56.** $(7 + \sqrt{41})/4$, $(7 - \sqrt{41})/4$ **57.** $(-1 + \sqrt{5})/2$, $(-1 - \sqrt{5})/2$ **58.** $(1 + \sqrt{33})/4$, $(1 - \sqrt{33})/4$ **59.** 1, 5/2 **60.** $(-1 + \sqrt{73})/6$, $(-1 - \sqrt{73})/6$ **61.** 8/5, −8/5 **62.** 10/7, −10/7 **63.** 0, −1 **64.** 0, −2 **65.** .681, −.881 **66.** 1.816, .184 **67.** −.354, −5.646 **68.** 5.372, −.372 **69.** $1 + i$, $1 - i$ **70.** $3 + 2i$, $3 - 2i$ **71.** $(-1 + i\sqrt{11})/2$, $(-1 - i\sqrt{11})/2$ **72.** $(-1 + i\sqrt{19})/2$, $(-1 - i\sqrt{19})/2$ **73.** $(-3 + i\sqrt{31})/4$, $(-3 - i\sqrt{31})/4$ **74.** $(-1 + i\sqrt{47})/6$, $(-1 - i\sqrt{47})/6$ **75.** $(-2 + i)/3$, $(-2 - i)/3$ **76.** $(1 + 2i)/4$, $(1 - 2i)/4$ **77.** 5 m by 13 m **78.** 15/2 m by 8 m **79.** 7 in by 14 in **80.** 6 cm by 18 cm **81.** Base = 12 m, height = 6 m **82.** Base = 6 in, height = 8 in **83.** 5 ft by 13 ft **84.** 7 cm by 20 cm **85.** 5 m by 15 m **86.** 1 ft by 12 ft **87.** (a) In the negative direction, 40 in (b) 5 sec **88.** (a) After 1 sec (on the way up) and after 3 sec (on the way down) (b) 4 sec **89.** 54 mph **90.** 9 sec **91.** 5 cm, 12 cm, 13 cm **92.** 6, 8, 10 **93.** 24 m **94.** 8 in **95.** (a) \$54 (b) \$140 (c) 5/4 months (or 1 1/4 months) and 6 months **96.** 30 **97.** 50

98. (a) Write the expression on the right side as the sum of two fractions. (b) L/L = 1 (c) Substitute x for L/W and 1/x for W/L. (d) Multiply both sides by x. (e) Put the quadratic equation in standard form. (f) Quadratic; quadratic formula

99. $(1 + \sqrt{5})/2$ **100.** (a) Add −c on each side. (b) Multiply both sides by 4a. (c) Add b^2 on each side. (d) Factor the left side. (e) Substitute the result of part (d) into part (c). (f) Take the square root of each side. (g) Add −b on each side. (h) Divide each side by 2a.

Section 7.5 (page 355)

1.  0 4

2. 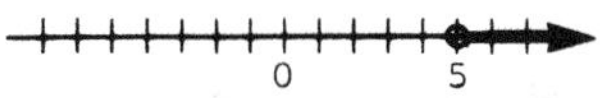 0 5

3. 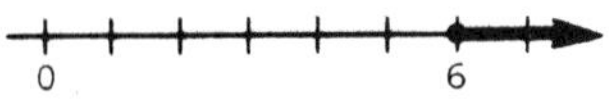 0 6

4. 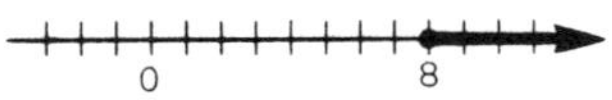 0 8

5.  -2 0

6. 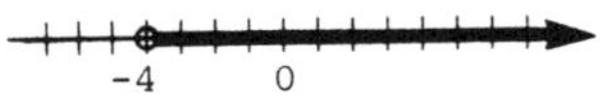 -4 0

7. 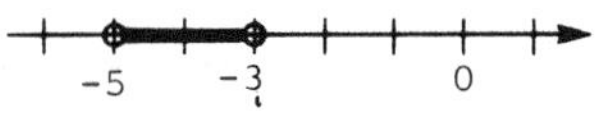 -5 -3 0

8. 0 3 5

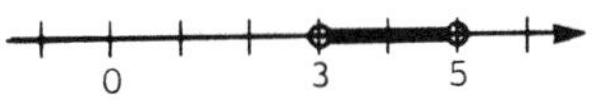

9. 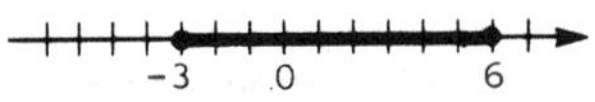 -3 0 6

10.  0 8 14

11.  0 1 6

12. 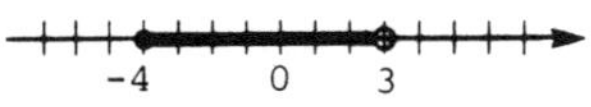 -4 0 3

13. $x \le -3$

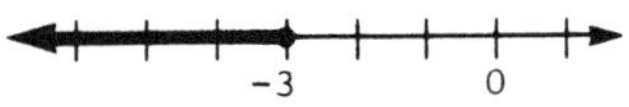

-3 0

14. $m > -8$

-8 0

15. $p > -6$

-6 0

16. $z \ge -8$

-8 0

17. $a > 0$

0

18. $k \le 0$

0

19. $x \le 4$

0 4

20. $y < 4$

0 4

21. $p \le -1$

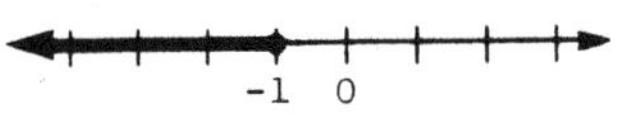

-1 0

22. $t \le 1$

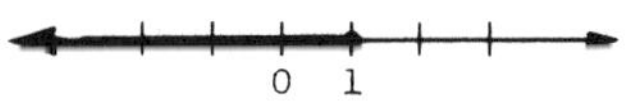

0 1

23. $k < 1$

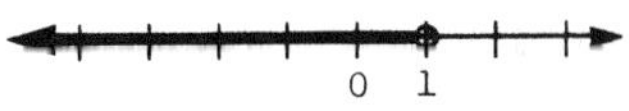

0 1

24. $a < -2$

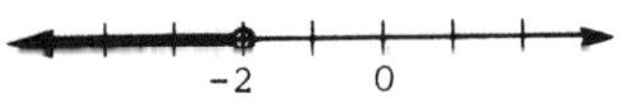

-2 0

25. $m > -1$

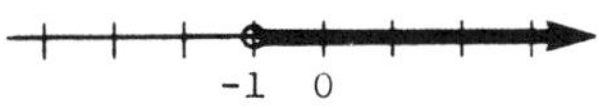

-1 0

26. $p \le 1/10$

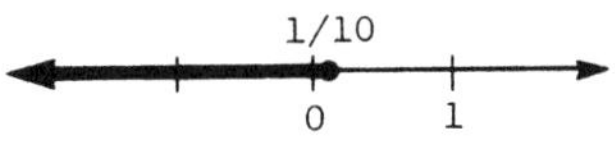

1/10

0 1

27. $y \le 1$

0 1

28. $r \geq 4$

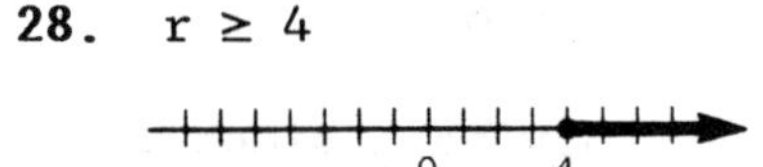

29. $p > 1/5$

30. $x > 1/3$

31. $-5 < y < 6$

32. $-9 < m < -4$

33. $7/3 \leq r \leq 4$

34. $-3/2 < p \leq 4$

35. $-11/2 \leq k \leq 7/2$

36. $-1 \leq y \leq 2$

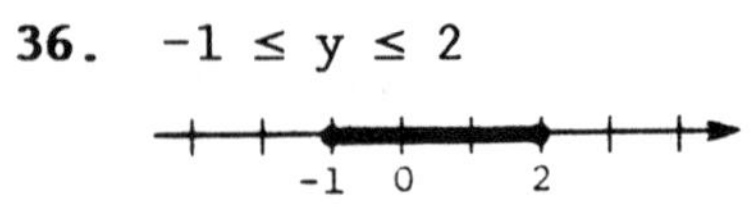

37. $p \geq -17/7$

38. $z \leq 50/9$

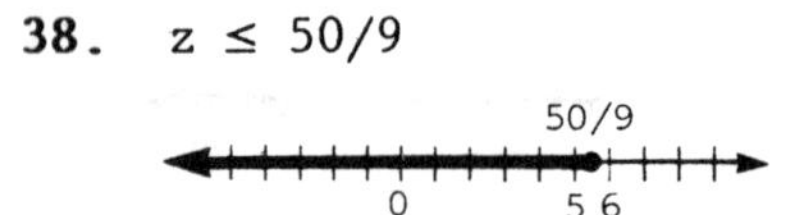

39. $k \geq .3$

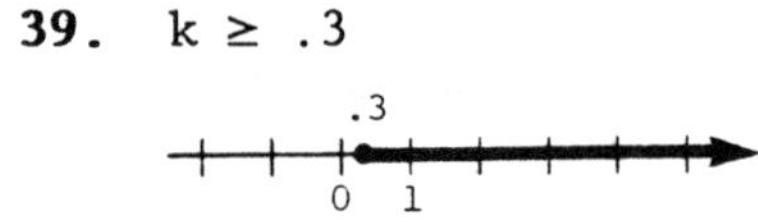

40. $m < -1.2$

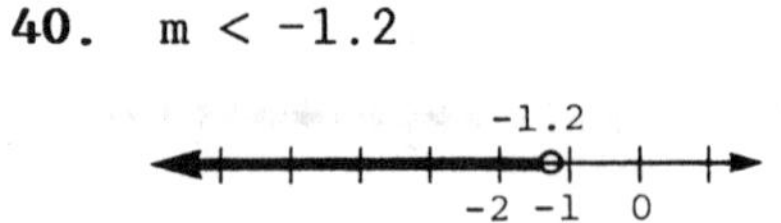

41. $z < 1.5$

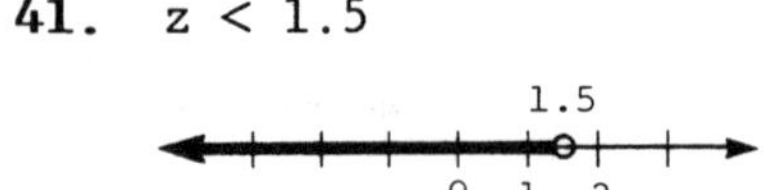

42. $k > .7$

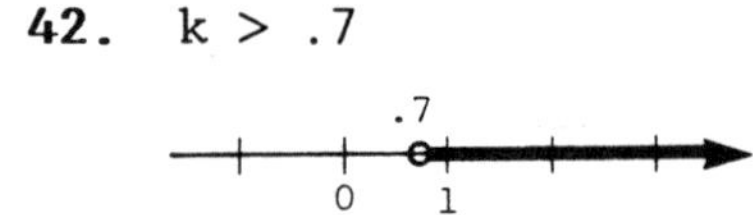

43. $m \leq .5$

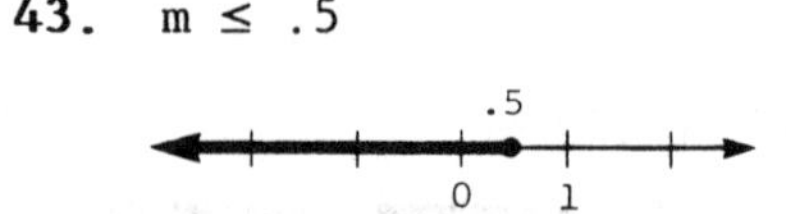

44. $a > 1.195$

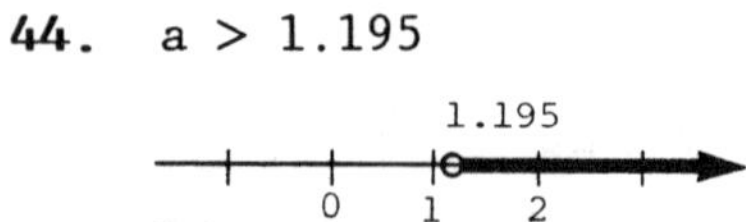

45. The number is between $-8/5$ and $6/5$. **46.** The number is between -8 and -2. **47.** The number is greater than or equal to 2. **48.** The number is at least 13. **49.** The number is at least 18. **50.** The number is no more than 8/7. **51.** 83 points **52.** 5 nickels **53.** 4 summers **54.** 4 green pills **55.** $x \geq 500$ **56.** $x \geq 15$ **57.** $x \geq 45$ **58.** $R < C$ for all positive x; the product will never break even. **59.** For positive values of x, C is always greater than R, so it is impossible to make a profit. **60.** Avis is better if $28(7) < 108 + .14x$, where x is the number of miles driven in a week. They must drive 629 mi for Avis to be a better deal. **61.** 50 mi **62.** Since $a > b$, $b - a < 0$. Multiplying both sides by $b - a$ in the first step also requires reversal of the direction of the inequality symbol.

Section 7.6 (page 361)

1. True **2.** True **3.** False **4.** True **5.** False **6.** True **7.** True

8. True **9.** True **10.** True **11.** False **12.** False

13.

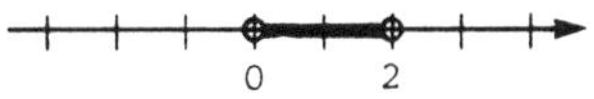

14.

15.

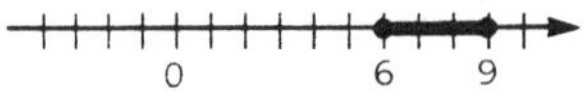

16.

17.

18.

19. No solution

20. No solution

21.

22.

23.

24.

25.

26.

27. All real numbers

28. All real numbers

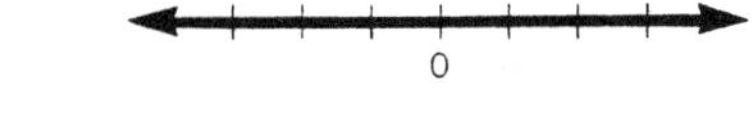

29. $2x > 8$ and $x + 6 < 14$

30. Let x = Norman's age; $x + (x + 5) < 23$.

31. $2x = 3$ and $x < 2$

32. $x + 2 < 14$ and $x - 4 > 5$

33. $8 \le x \le 12$

34. $x < 6$ or $x > 9$

35. 1, 3

36. 1, 5 **37.** −1/3, 1 **38.** 3/4, −7/4 **39.** 2/3, 8/3 **40.** 4/3, 10/3

41. −6, 14 **42.** 12, −16 **43.** 5/2, 7/2 **44.** 7/8, 1/8 **45.** −4/3, 2/9

46. 7, 1/5 **47.** −7/3, −1/7 **48.** 1, 0 **49.** −3/5, 11 **50.** 2/11, 6

51. $-3 \le x \le 3$

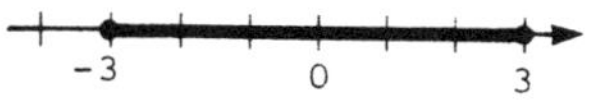

52. $-10 \le y \le 10$

53. $m < -1$ or $m > 1$

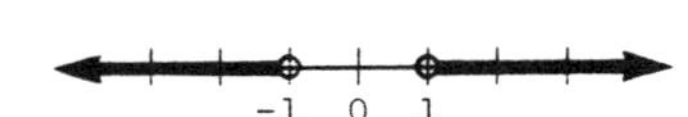

54. $z < -5$ or $z > 5$

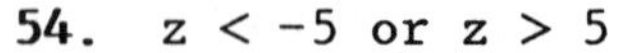

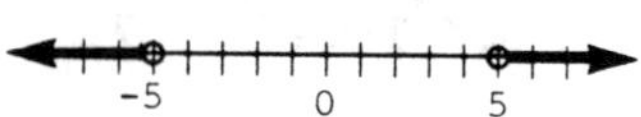

55. No solution

56. All real numbers

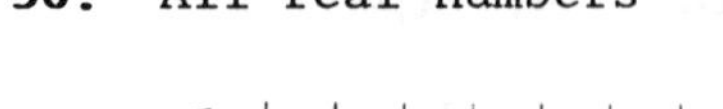

57. $-10 \le x \le 10$

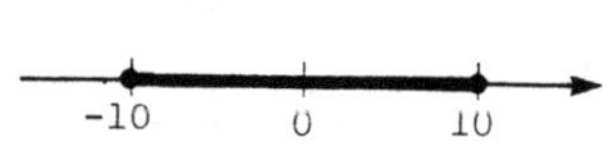

58. $-7 \le r \le 7$

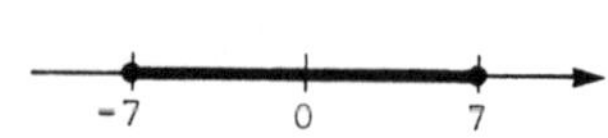

59. $-4 < x < -1$

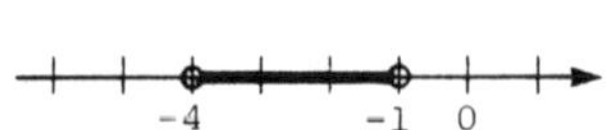

60. $-3/2 < x < 5/2$

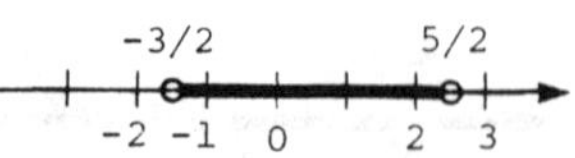

61. $m < -2/3$ or $m > 2$

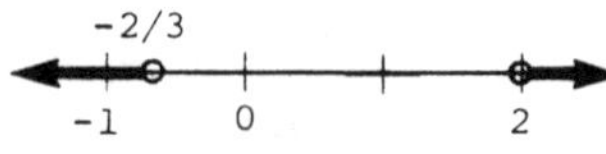

62. $x < -1$ or $x > 4$

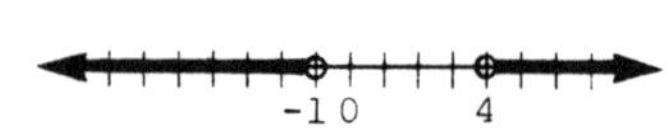

63. $z \le -8/3$ or $z \ge 2$

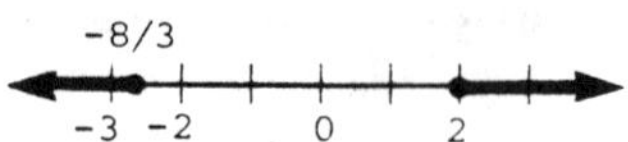

64. $b \le -3/2$ or $b \ge 1/4$

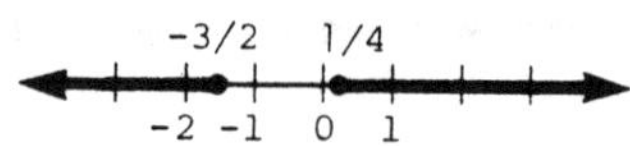

65. $-3/2 < x < 13/10$

66. $-11/3 < x < 7/3$

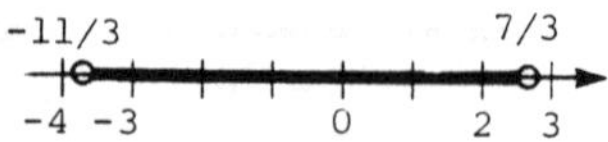

67. No solution

68. No solution

69. All real numbers

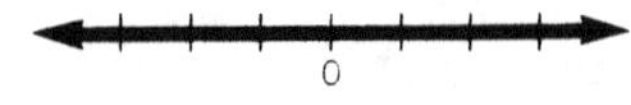

70. All real numbers

71. All real numbers except 5/3

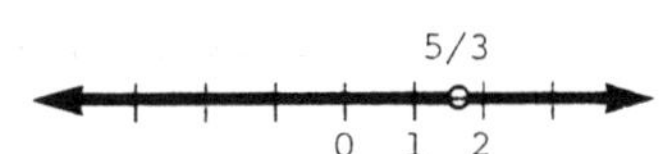

72. $z = -4/3$

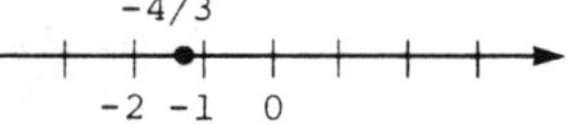

73. The number is between -6 and 6, inclusive. **74.** The number is less than or equal to -5 or greater than or equal to 5. **75.** The number is between $-7/4$ and $-5/4$, inclusive. **76.** The number is between $-3/2$ and $7/2$, inclusive. **77.** The number is less than or equal to -14 or greater than or equal to 10. **78.** The number is between $-13/3$ and -1, inclusive.

Chapter 7 Test (page 365)

1. 3 **2.** 3.6 **3.** All real numbers **4.** −5 **5.** \$100 **6.** 6 2/3 liters

7. 15 **8.** 16/9 or 1 7/9 **9.** 15/2 or 7 1/2 **10.** 84 oz **11.** \$28.50

12. 11/6 **13.** 567/25 **14.** $-7 + \sqrt{5}$, $-7 - \sqrt{5}$ **15.** 1/2, −5/3 **16.** 1, 3

17. 1/3, −1/2 **18.** 0, 7/5 **19.** 1.439, −.772 **20.** $(1 + 4i)/2$, $(1 - 4i)/2$

21. Length = 17 in, width = 3 in

22. $y \geq -8/9$

23. $z \leq 1$

24. $p \leq 2/5$

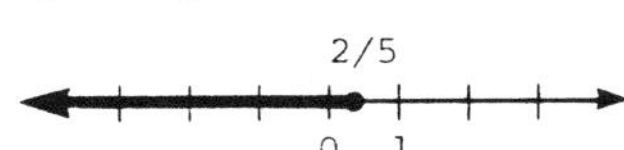

25. $-1 < z < 1$

26. 87 points

27.

28.

29. −1, 11 **30.** 4/3, −2/7 **31.** $-7/3 \leq p \leq -1$ **32.** $x < 1$ or $x > 6$

CHAPTER 8

Section 8.1 (page 376)

1.–12.

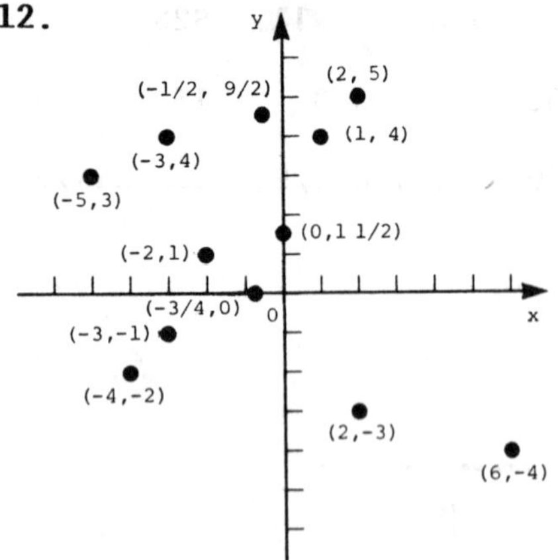

13. (2, 3) **14.** (-2, 5) **15.** (-4, 2)

16. (-5, 0) **17.** (-2, -2) **18.** (-4, -3)

19. (0, -5) **20.** (5, -4) **21.** (1, -2)

22. (4, 0)

23. (a) 50 (b) 60 (c) 80

(d)–(e)

Temperature
80
60
40
20
0
20 40 60 80 100 120 140 160
Number of chirps

(f) Missing numbers are 45, 55, 65, and 70.

(g) 40°F

24.

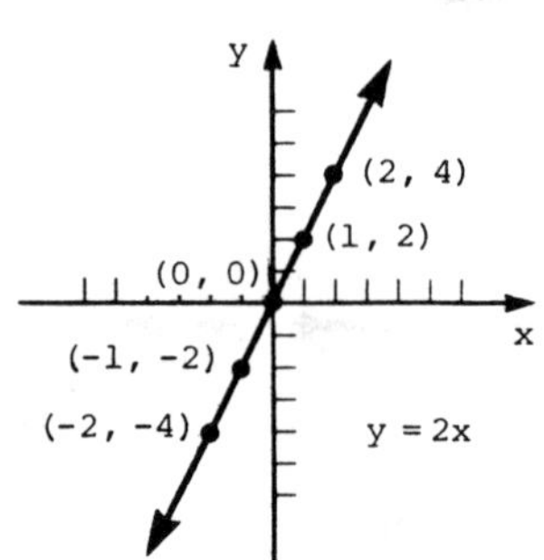

25.

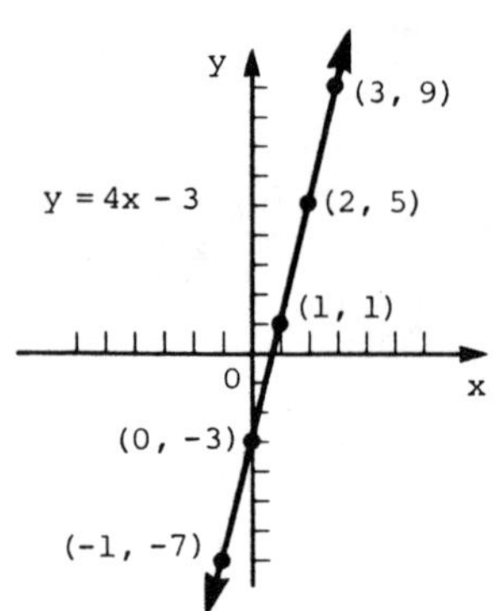

26.

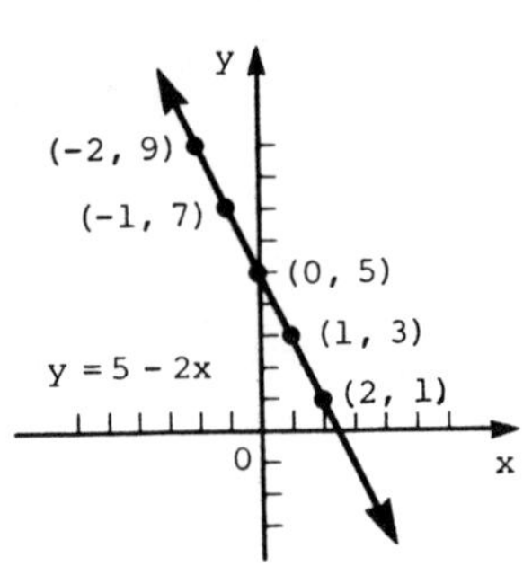

27.

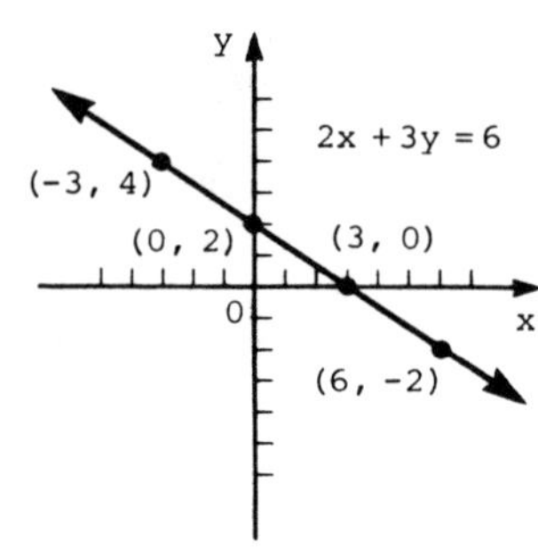

28.

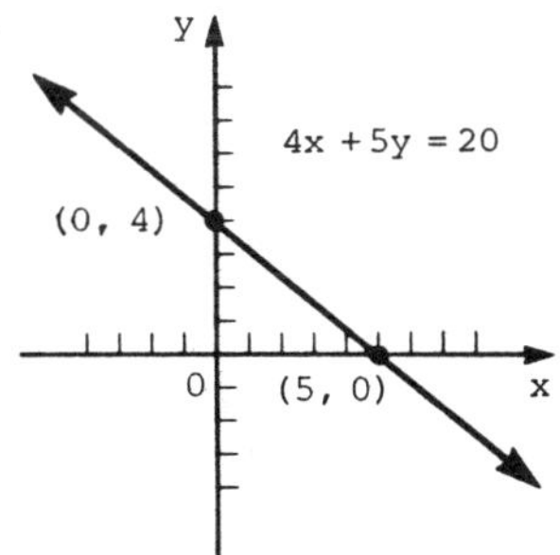

29.

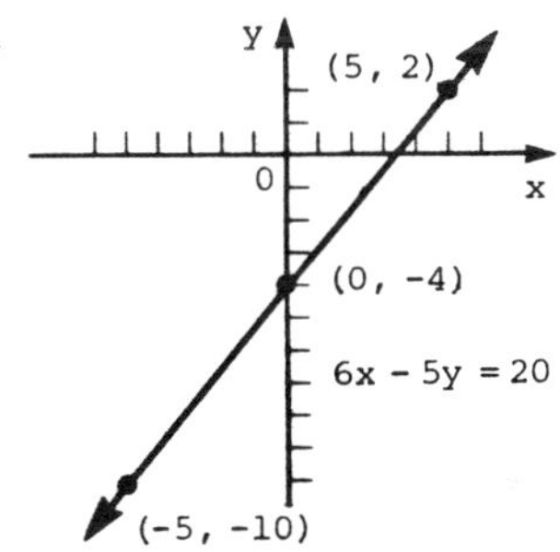

30.

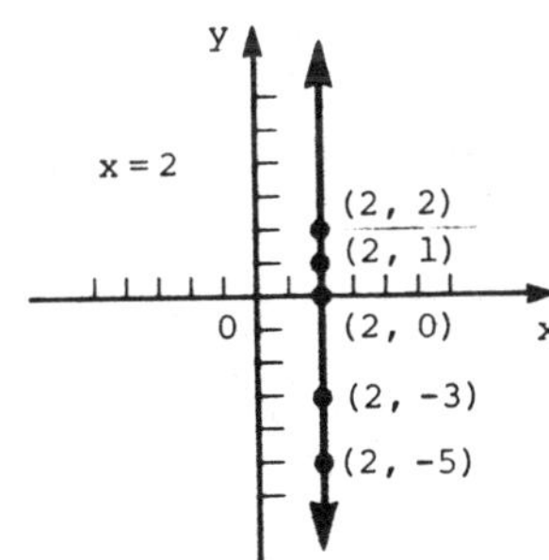

31.

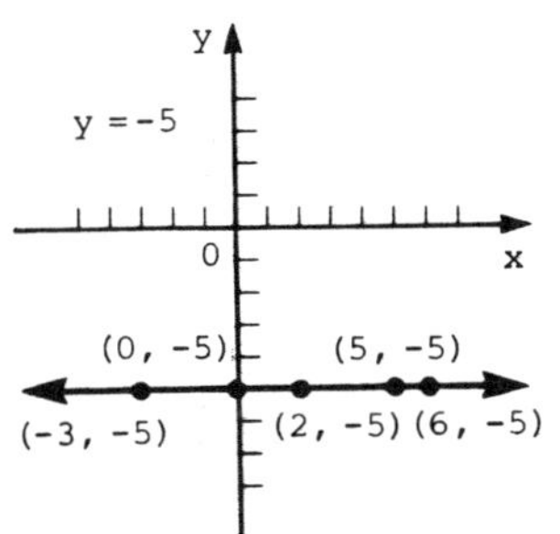

32.

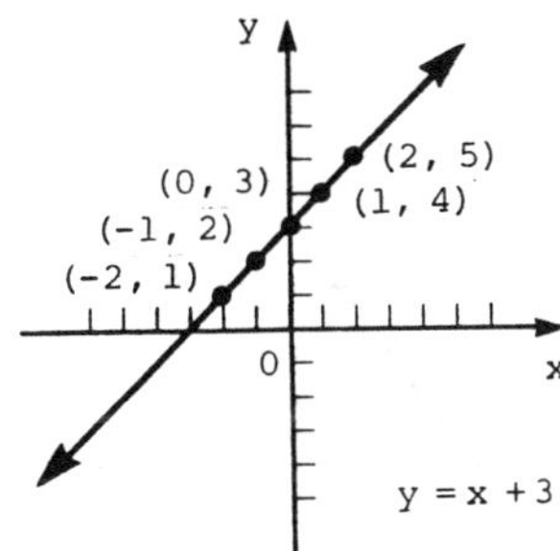

33.

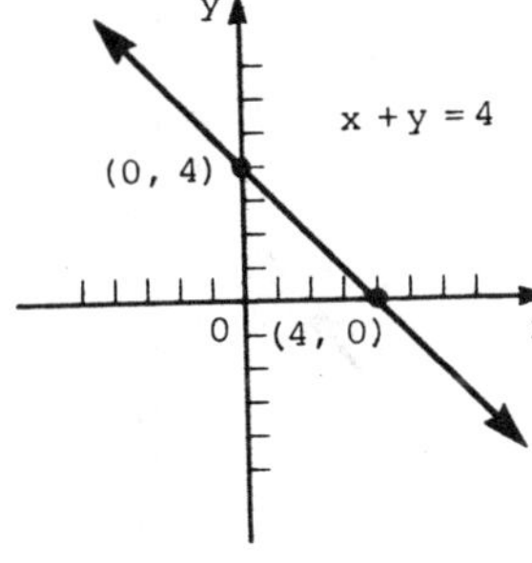

34.

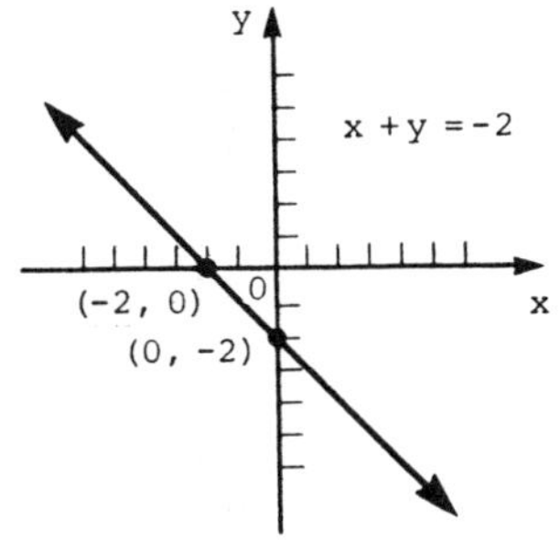

35.

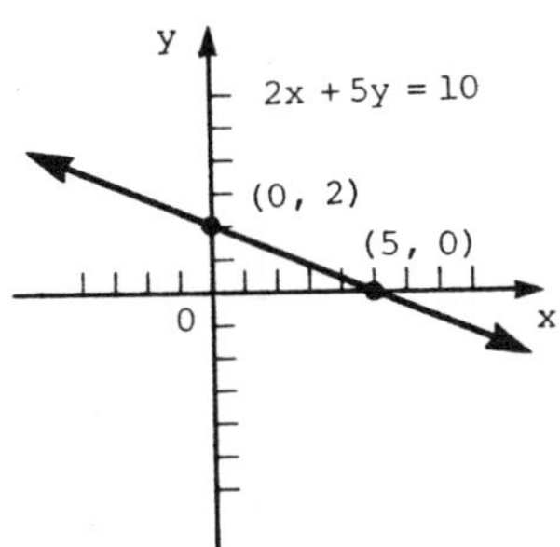

36.

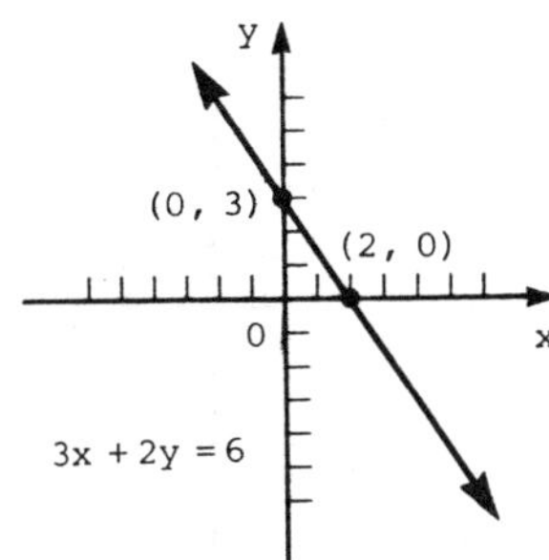

37.

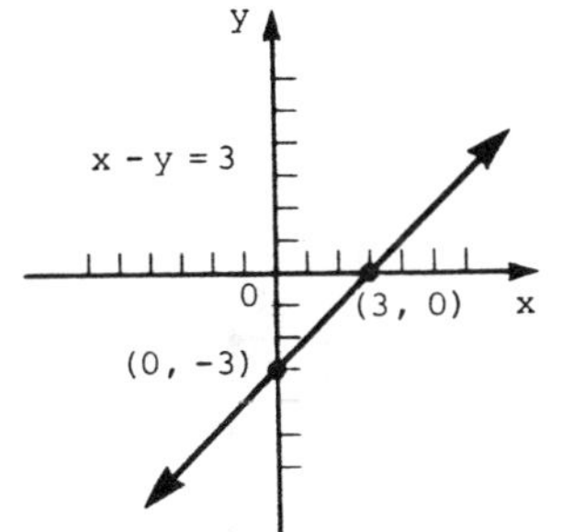

38.

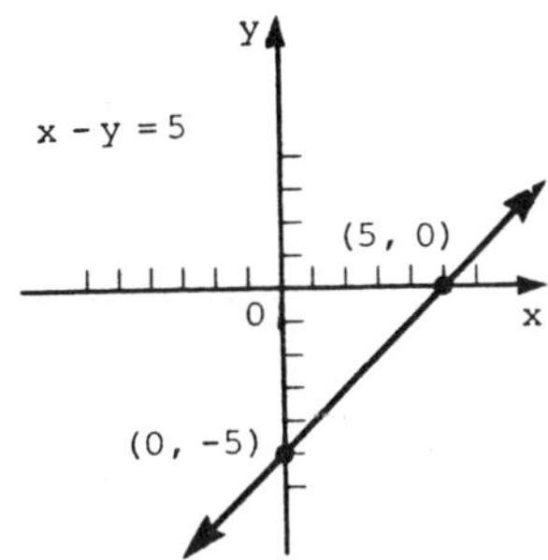

39.

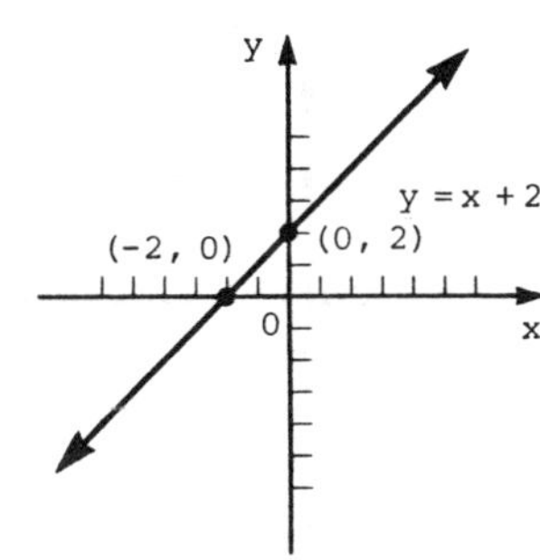

40.

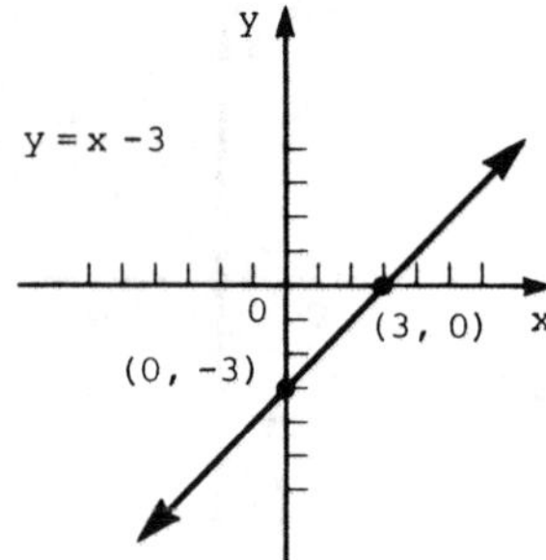

41.

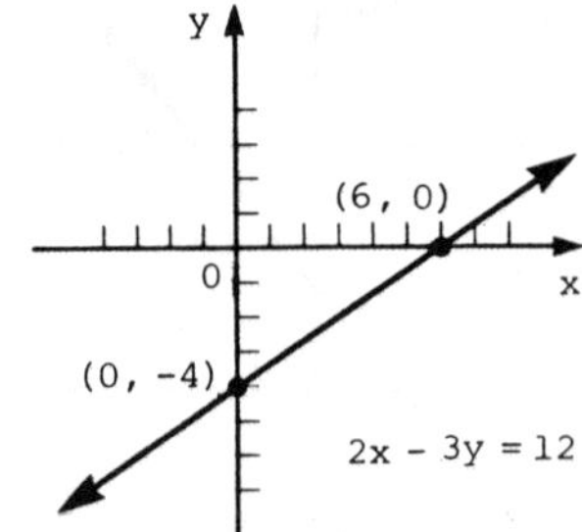

42.

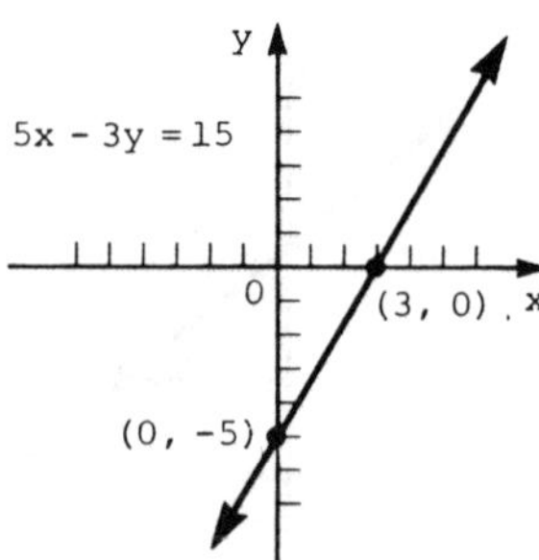

43.

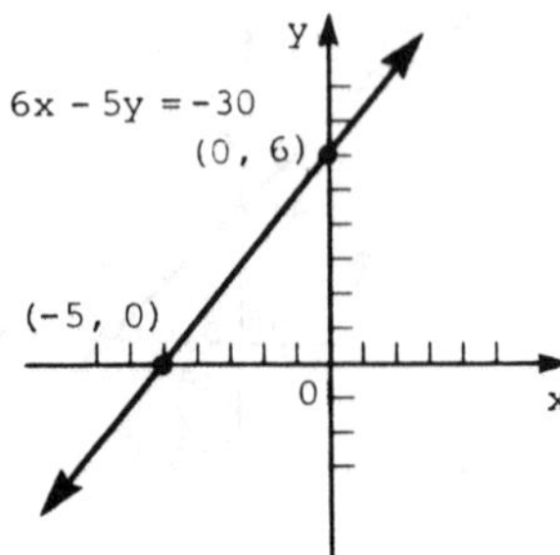

44.

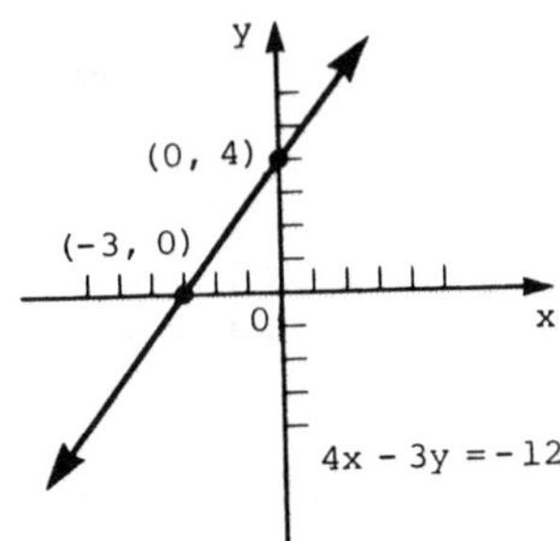

45.

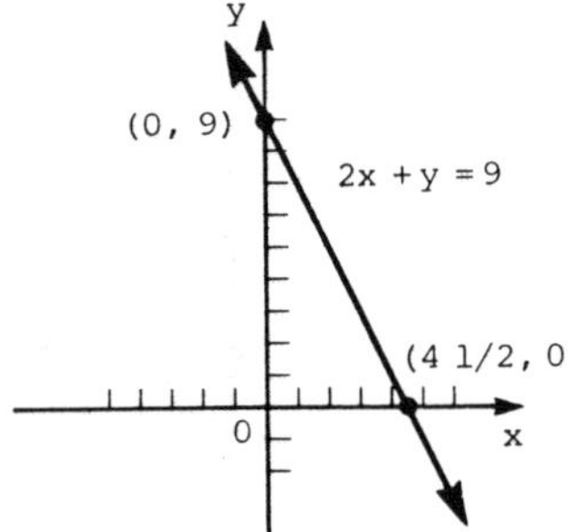

46.

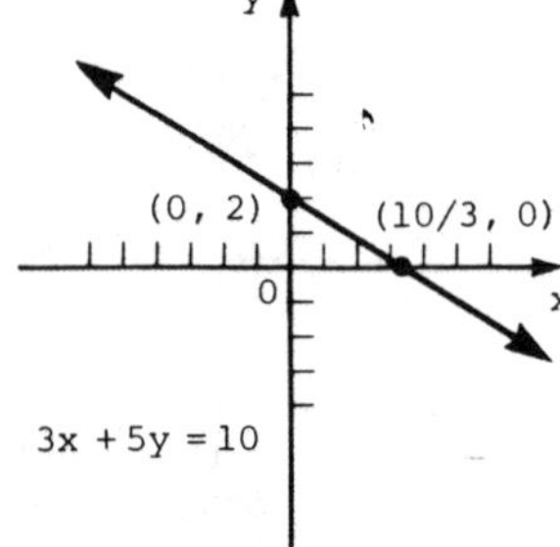

47.

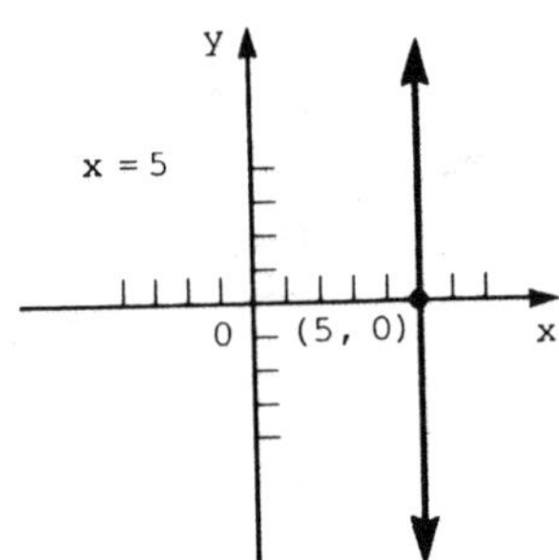

48.

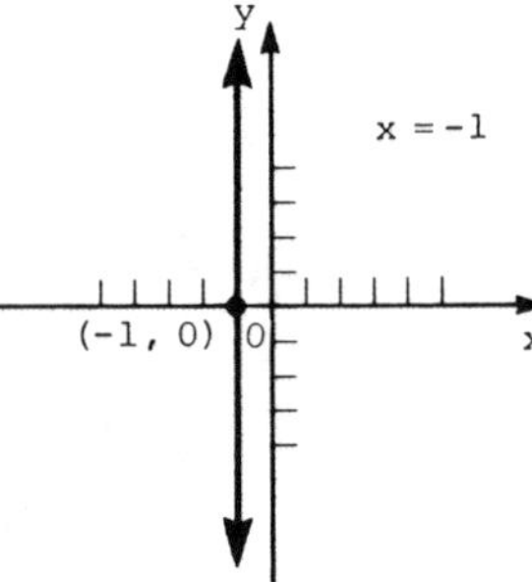

49.

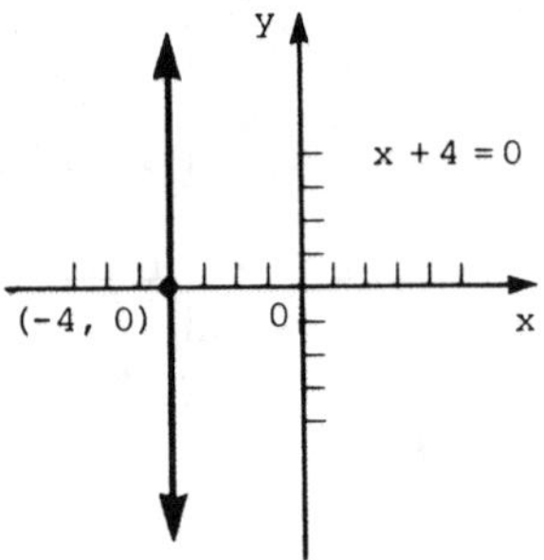

50.

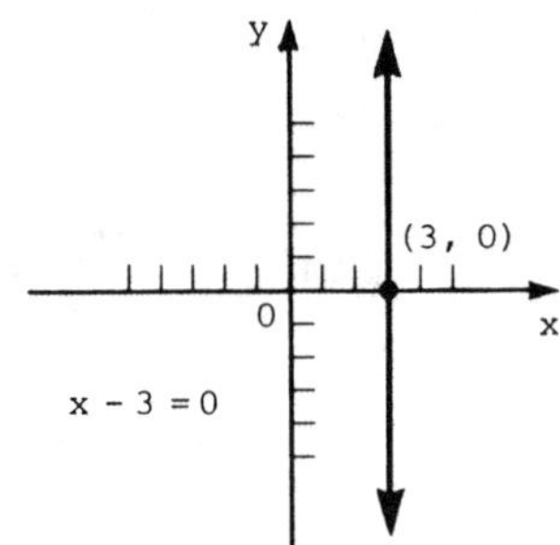

51.

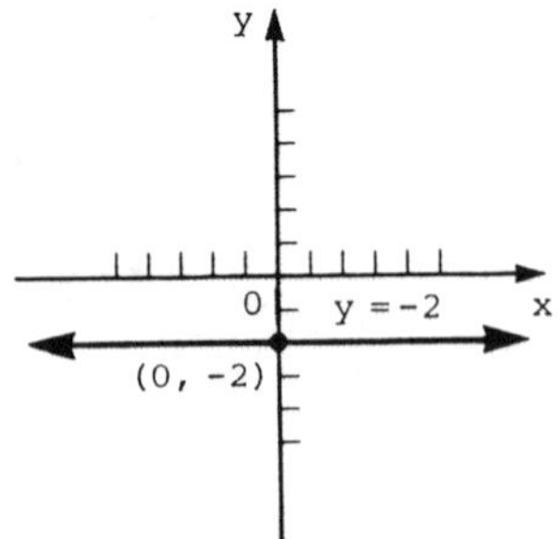

52.

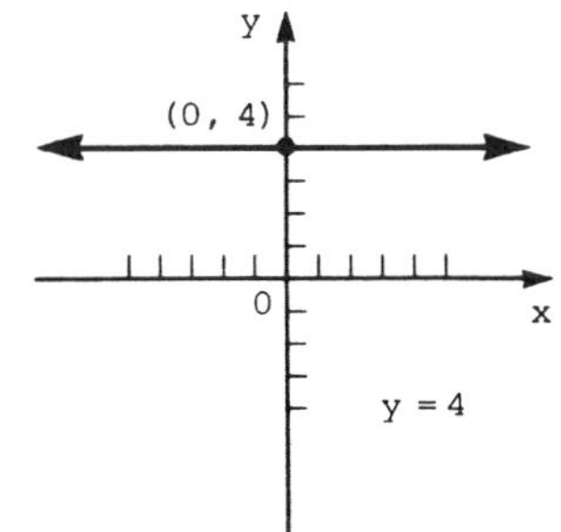

53.

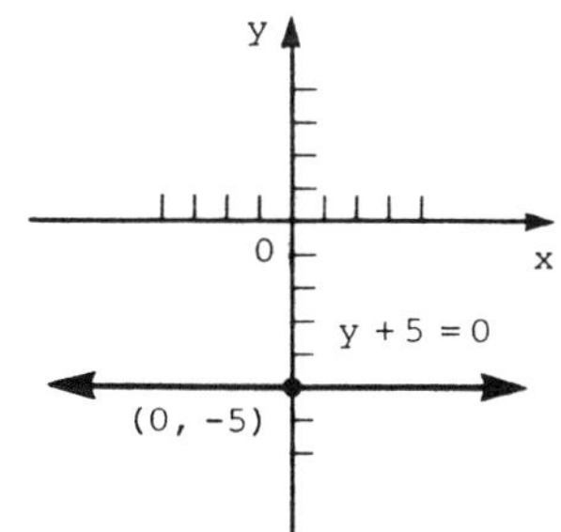

54.

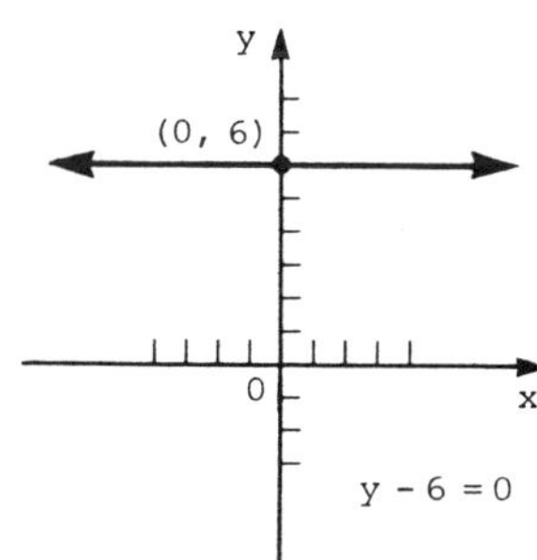

55.

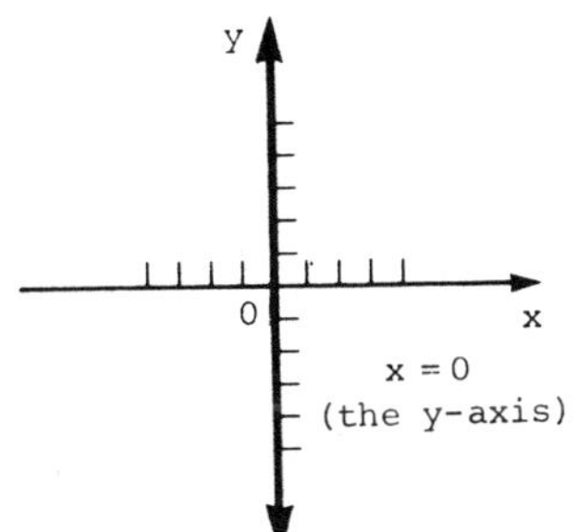

56.

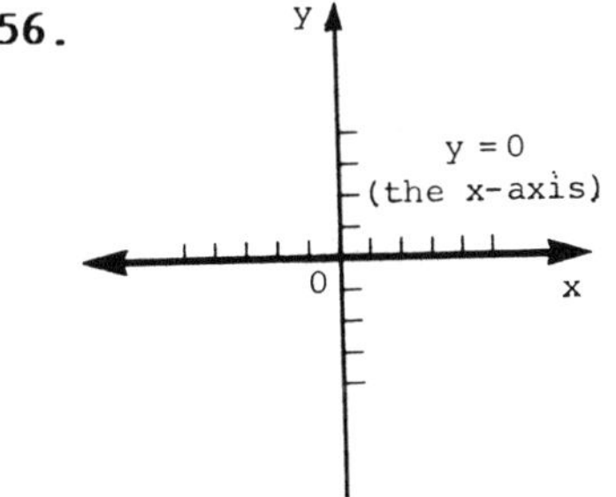

57.

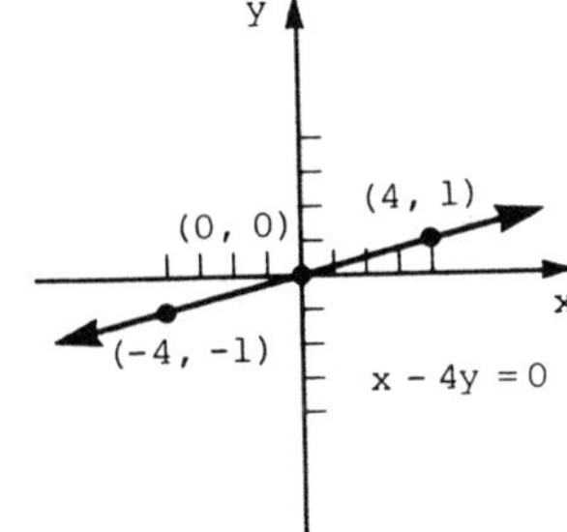

58.

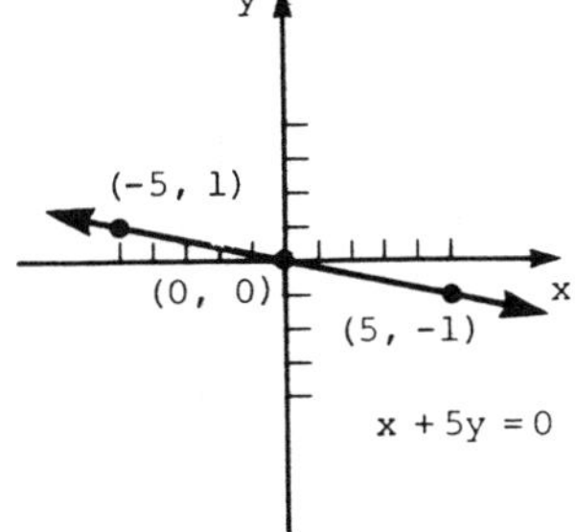

59.

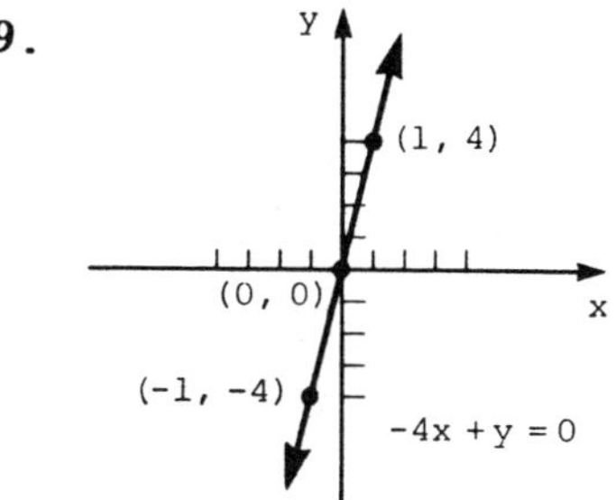

60.

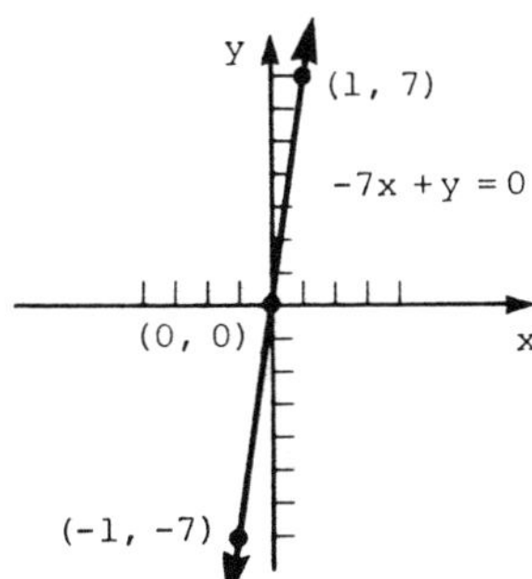

61.

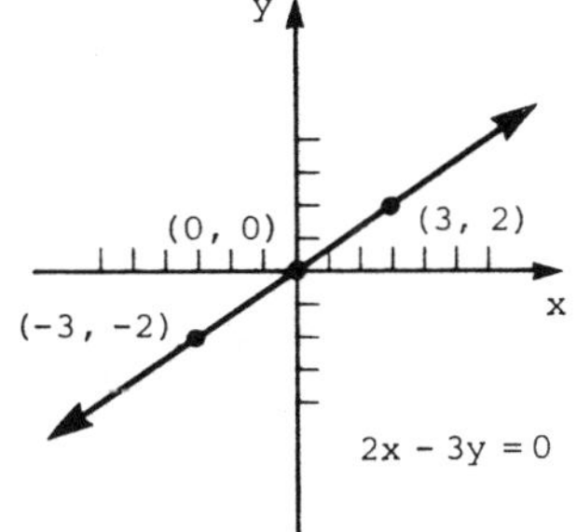

62.

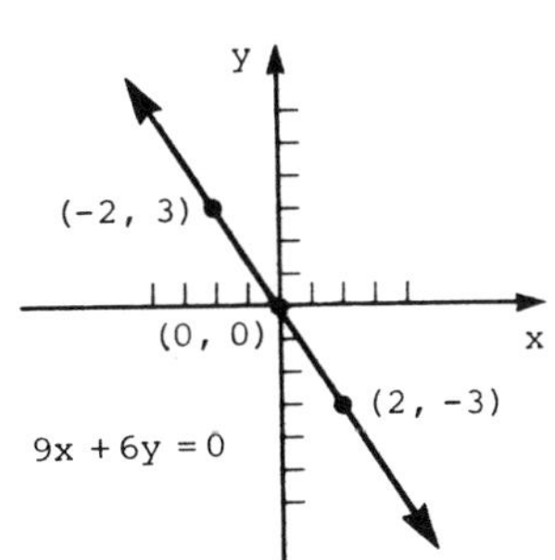

63.

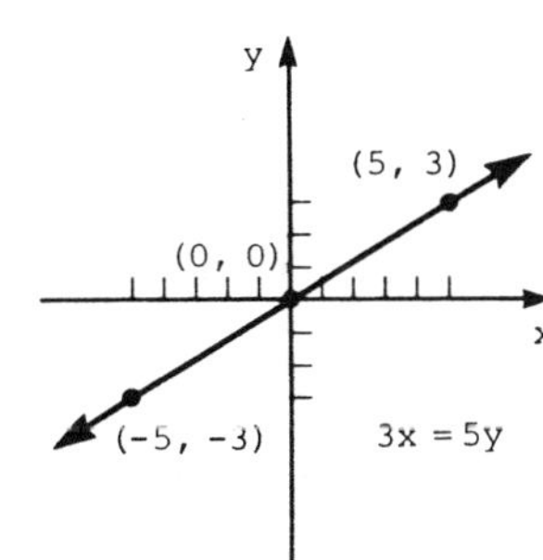

64.

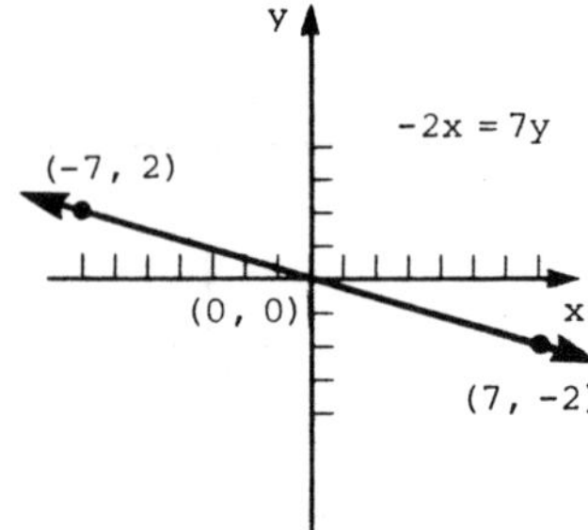

65. (a) (0, 0)
(b) (25, 2)
(c) (50, 6)
(d) (80, 24)
(e) (90, 49)
(f) (95, 88)
(g) (99, 215)
(h) (100, 325)

(i)

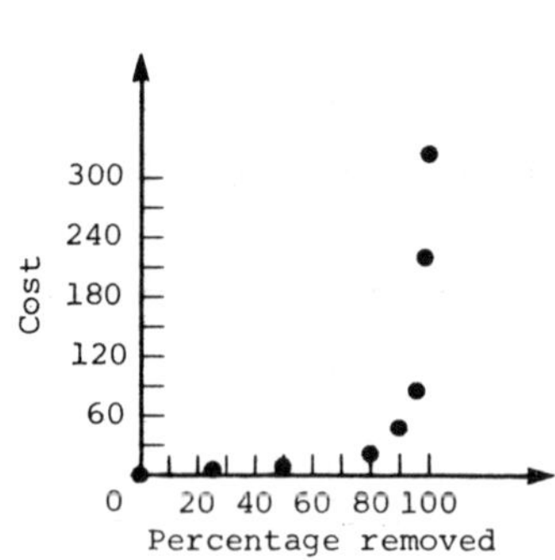

66.

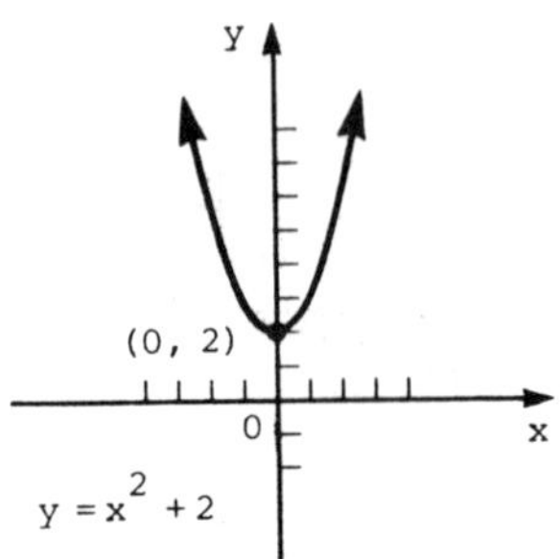

67.

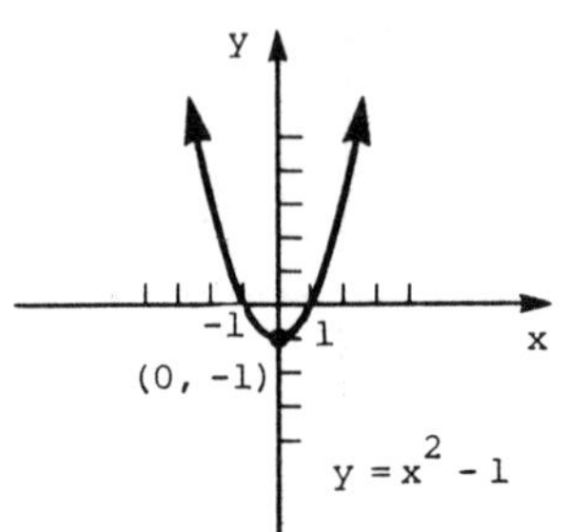

68.

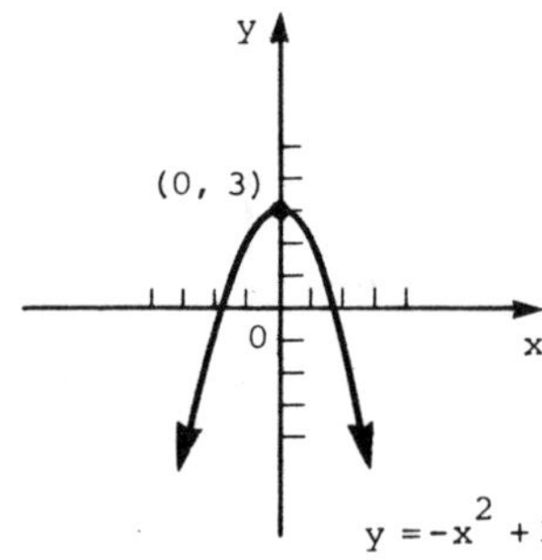

69.

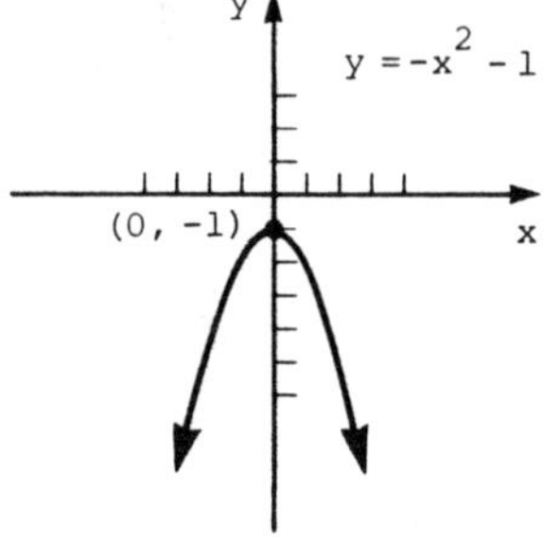

70.

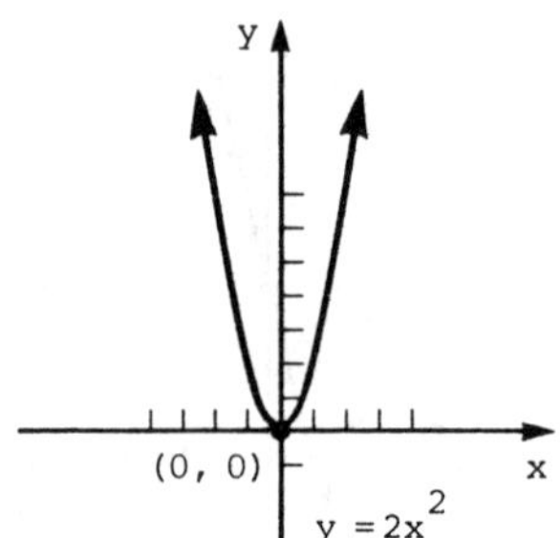

71.

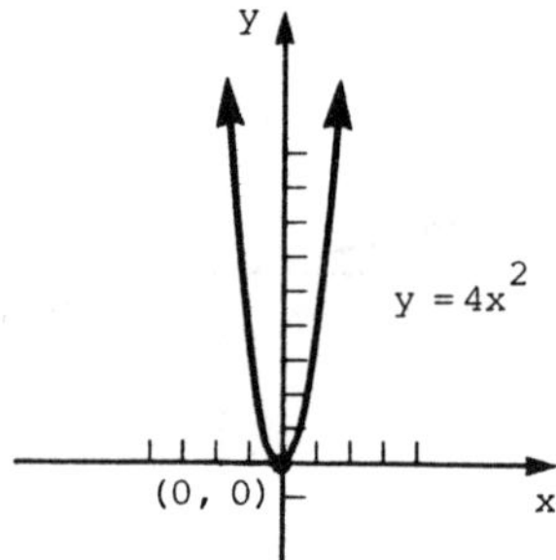

72.

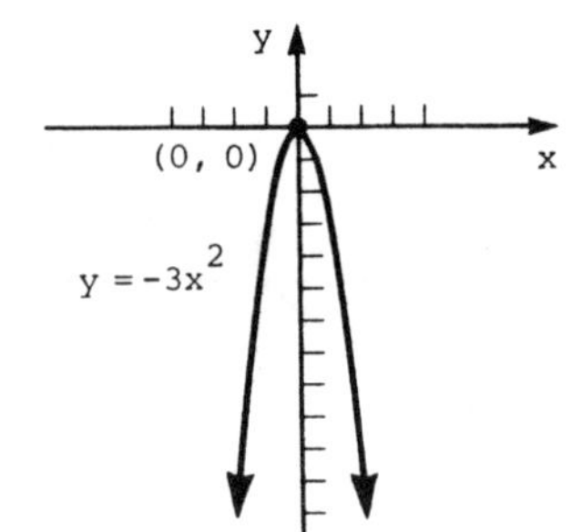

73.

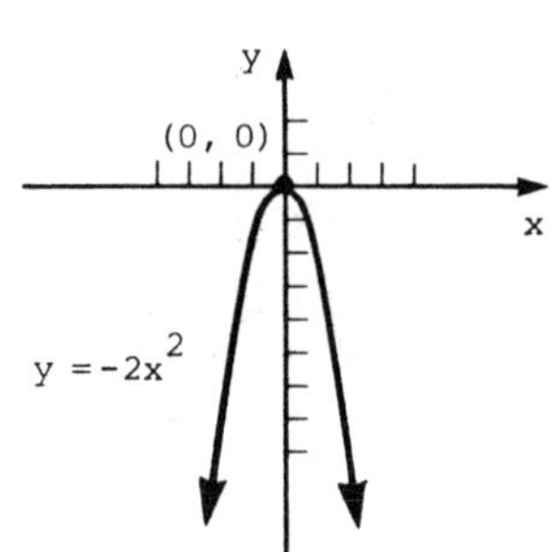

74.

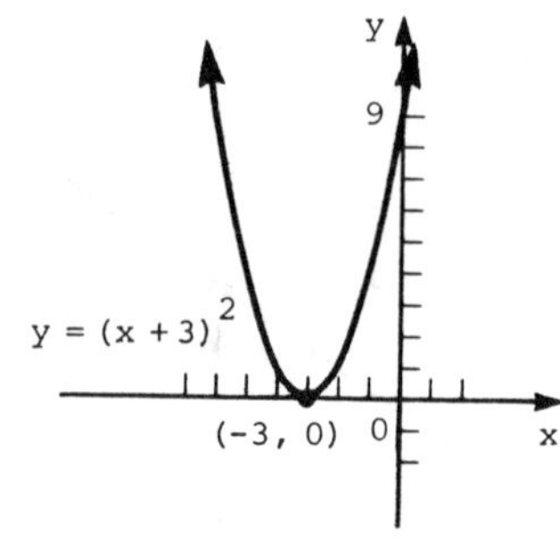

75.

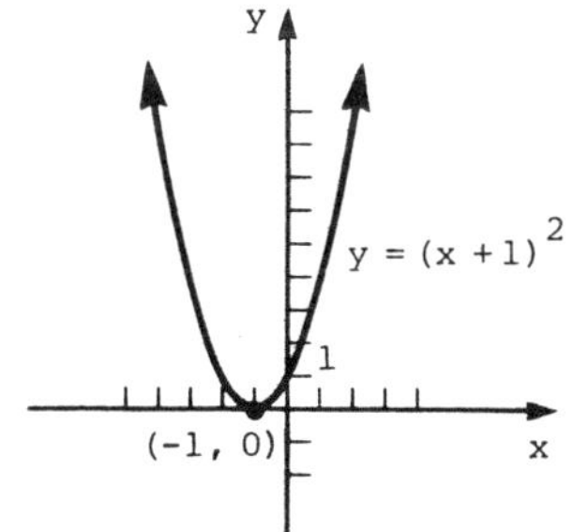

76.

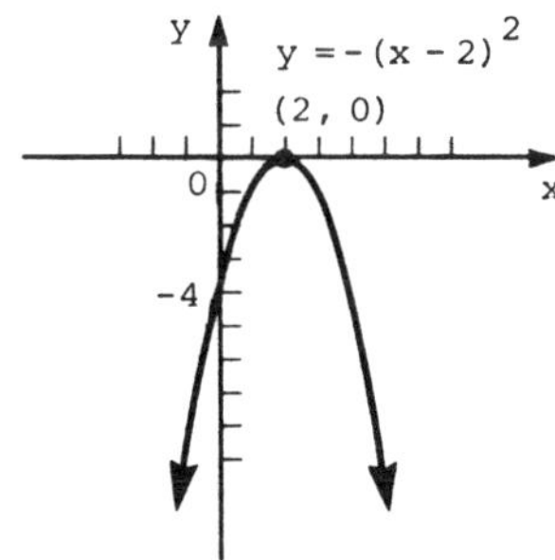

77.

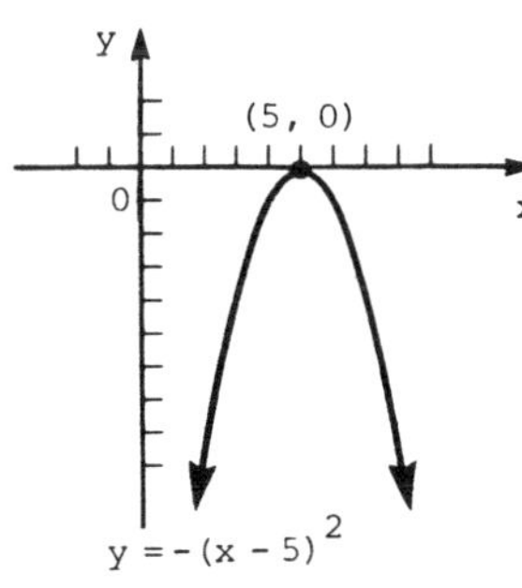

78.

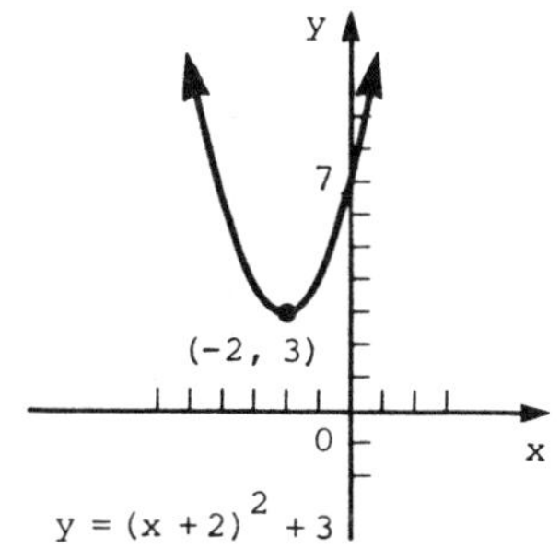

79.

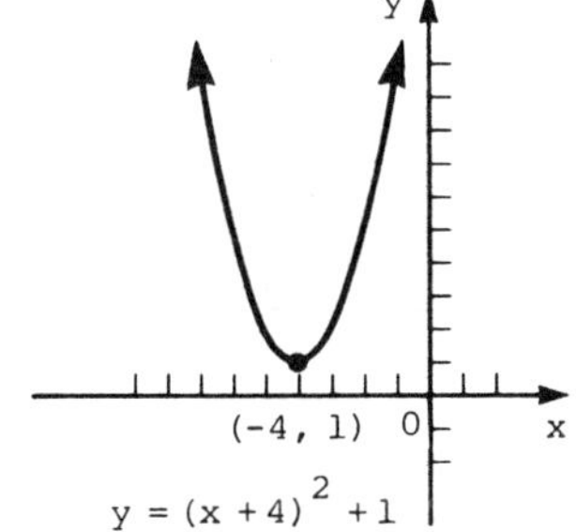

80.

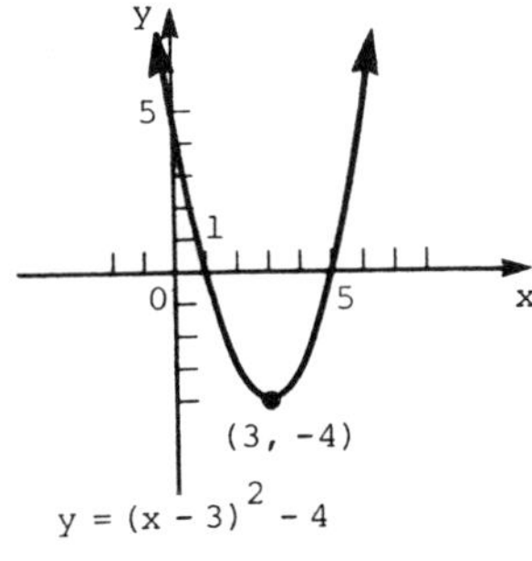

81.

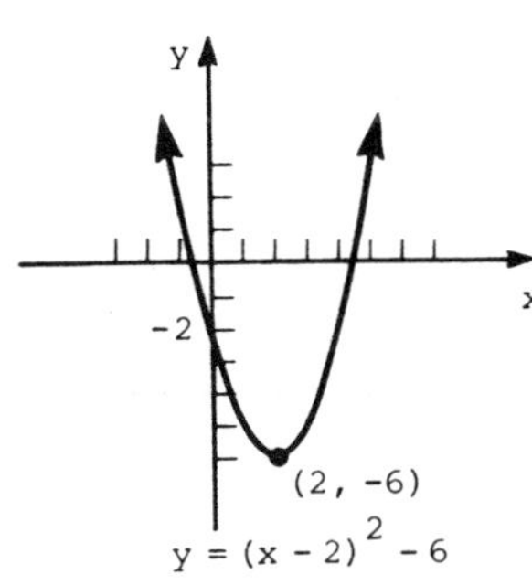

82.

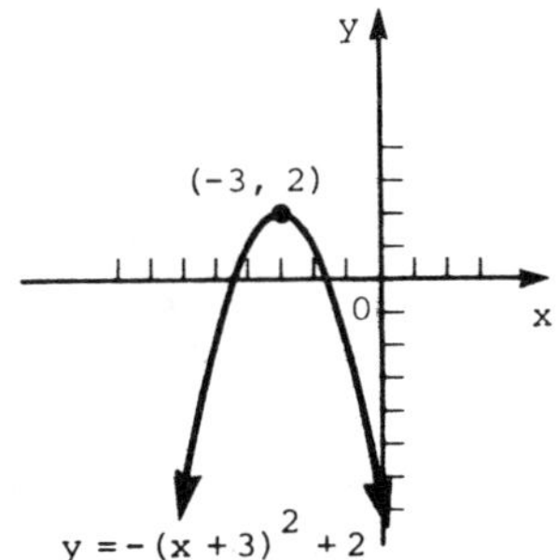

83.

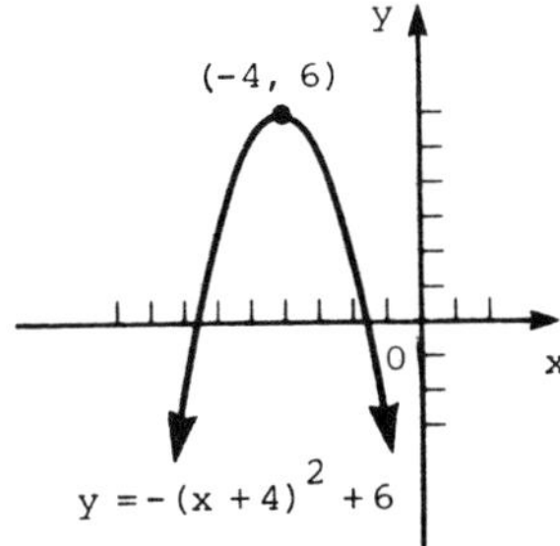

84. (a) \$208 (b) \$220 (c) \$248 (d) \$260 (e) \$300 (f) \$21,600

85. (a) $100 - x$ (b) $200 + 4x$ (c) $(100 - x)(200 + 4x) = 20{,}000 + 200x - 4x^2$

(d) (5, 20,900), (10, 21,600), (15, 22,100), (20, 22,400), (25, 22,500), (30, 22,400), (35, 22,100), (40, 21,600), (45, 20,900)

(e)

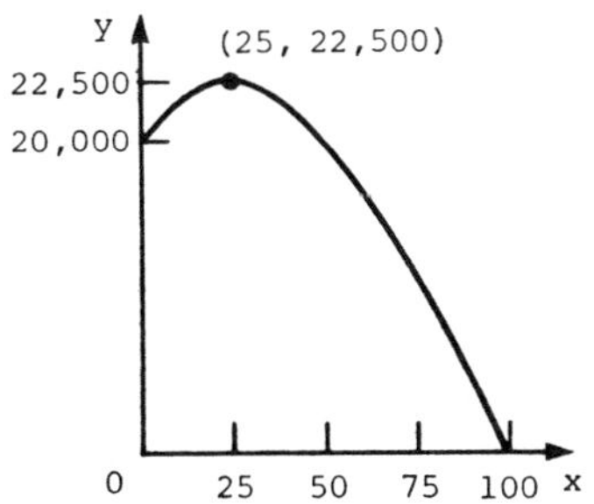

(f) \$22,500 (g) 25 tickets

(h) 75 tickets

Section 8.2 (page 387)

1. −1/2 **2.** 1 **3.** 3/10 **4.** −1 **5.** 0 **6.** No slope **7.** 7/6

8. −5/2 **9.** 9/2 **10.** 1/2 **11.** −5/8 **12.** 3/2 **13.** 0 **14.** No slope

15. No slope **16.** 0 **17.** 10/9 **18.** 110/117 **19.** 2 **20.** 5

21. −1 **22.** 1 **23.** −5 **24.** 9 **25.** −2 **26.** 4 **27.** 3/2

28. 3/2 **29.** −2/5 **30.** −9/7

31.

32.

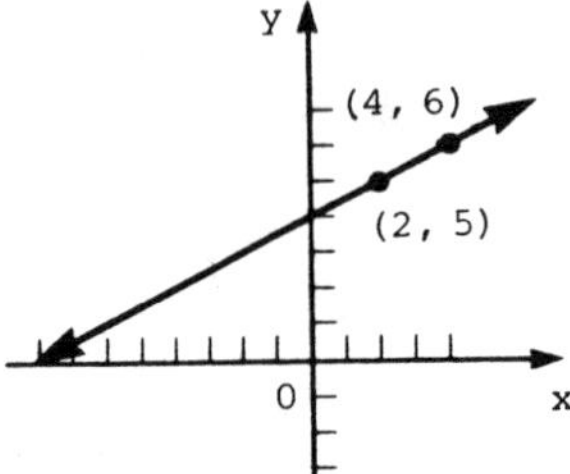

33.

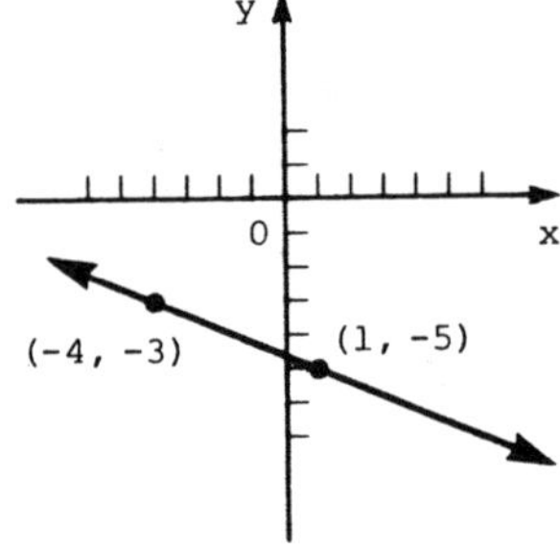

34.

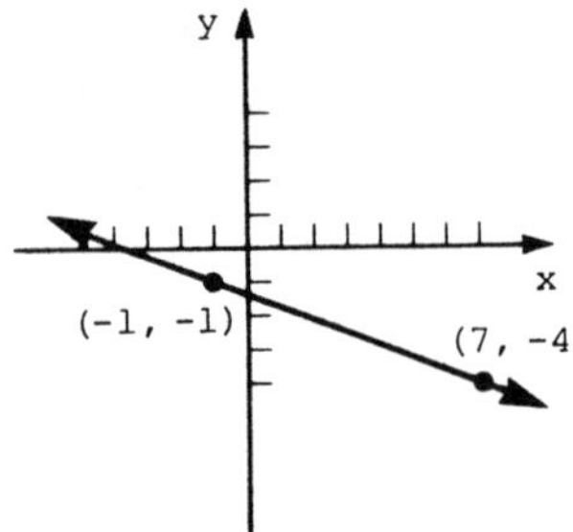

35.

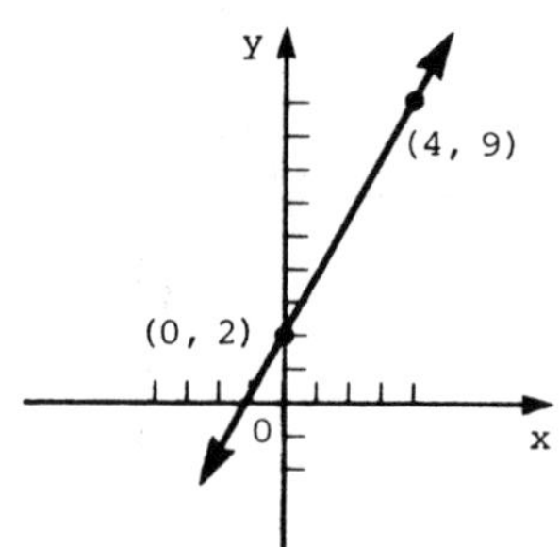

36.

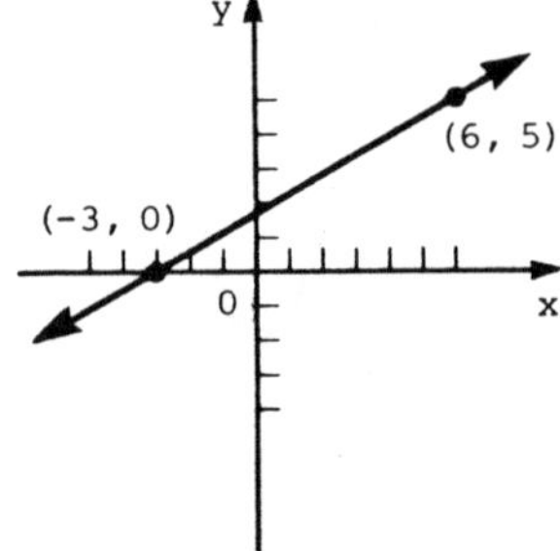

37.

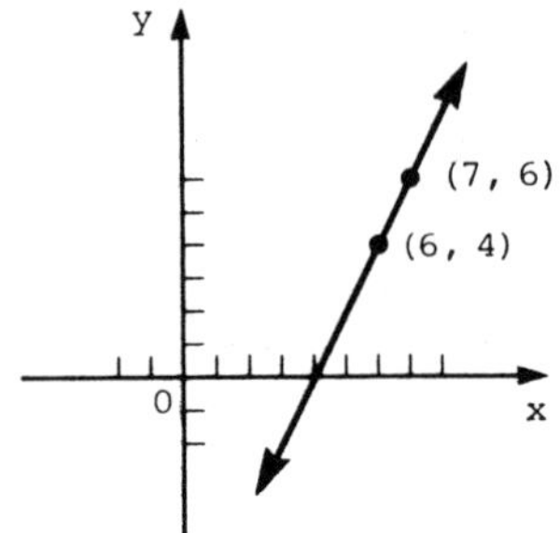

38.

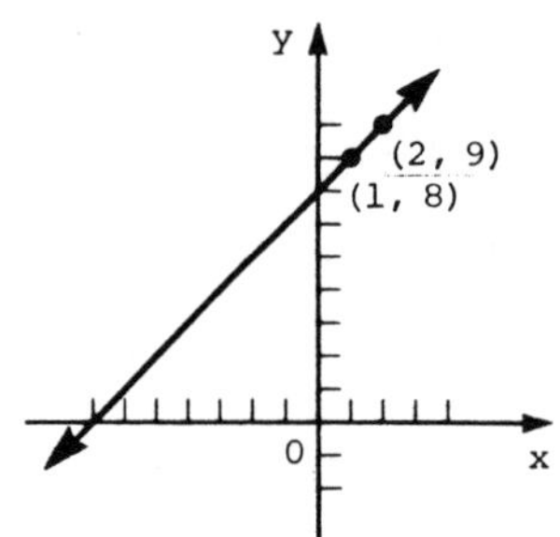

39.

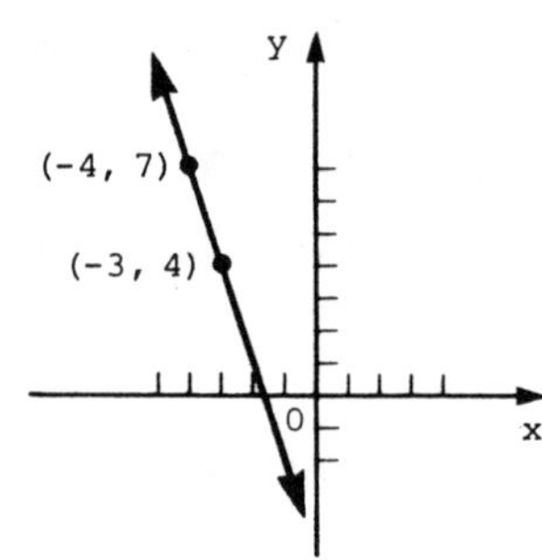

40. 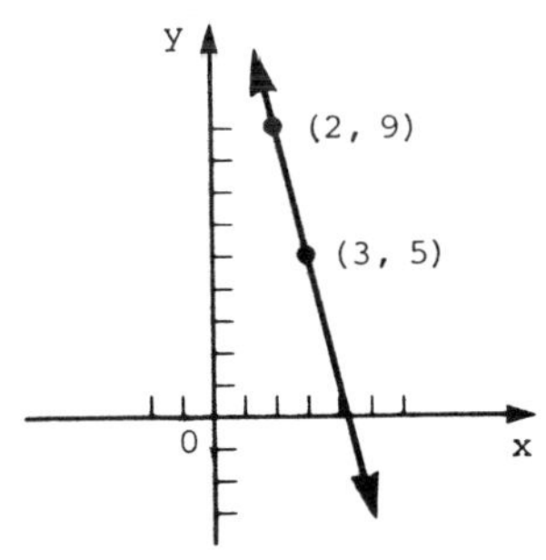

41. 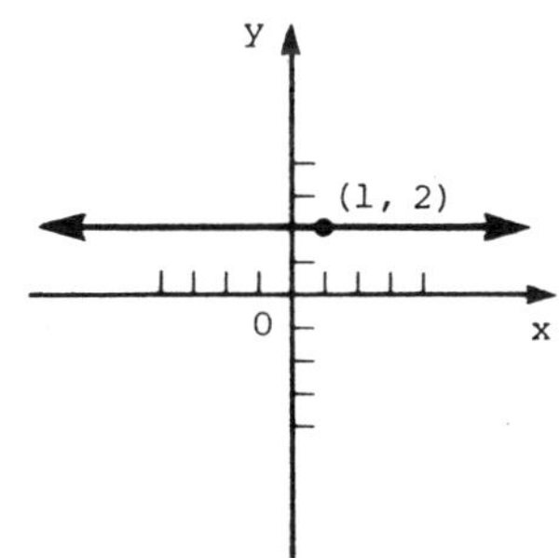

42. 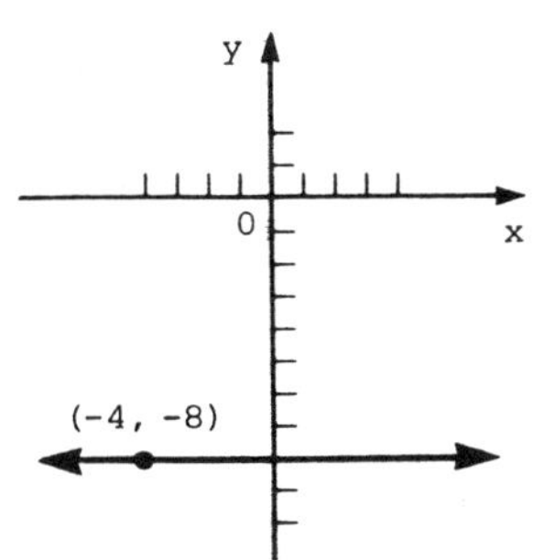

43. 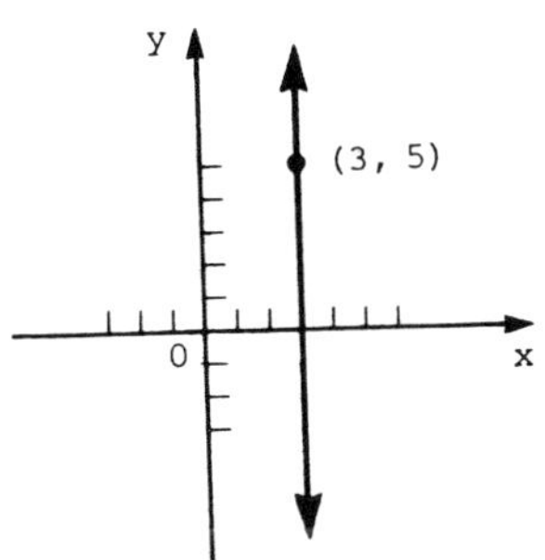

44. 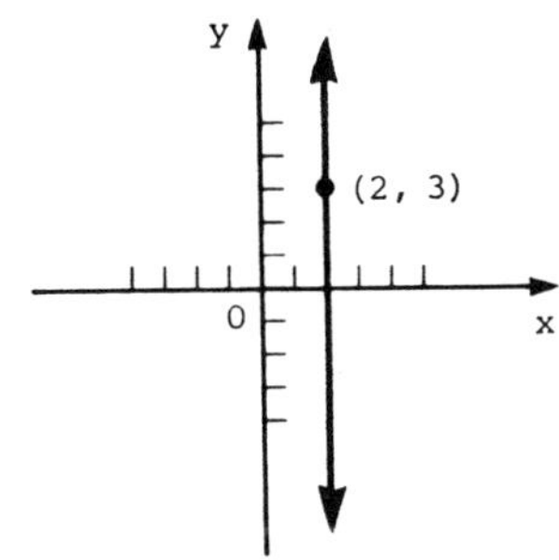

45. 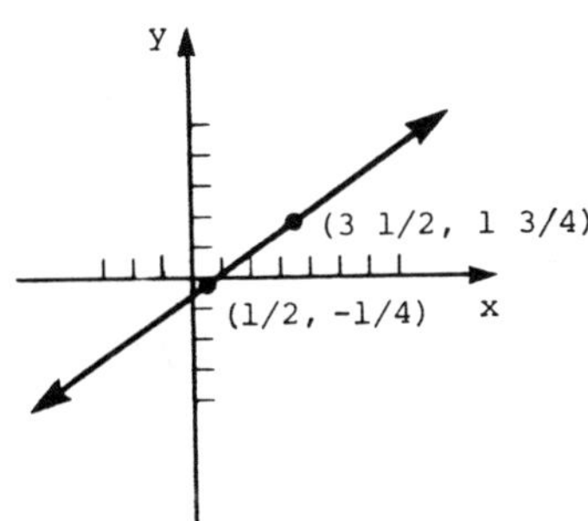

46. 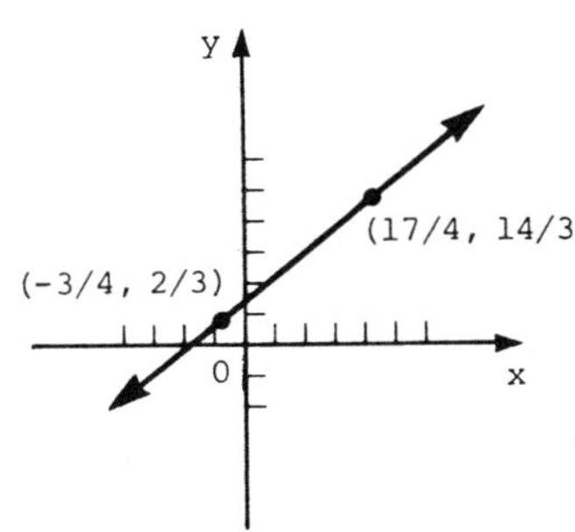

47. $2x - y = 7$ 48. $3x - y = -1$ 49. $2x + y = -4$

50. $4x + y = 3$ 51. $2x - 3y = -9$ 52. $4x - 5y = 28$

53. $3x + 4y = -17$ 54. $5x + 9y = -58$

55. $8x + 11y = 48$ 56. $2x + 5y = -20$

57. $y = -2$ or $0x + y = -2$ 58. $y = 7$ or $0x + y = 7$

59. $x - y = 3$ 60. $x - y = 2$ 61. $5x + 7y = -54$

62. $3x - 5y = -11$ 63. $x - 2y = -5$

64. $3x + 5y = -11$ 65. $3x - 15y = -5$ 66. $72x - 36y = 55$ 67. $4x + y = 6$

68. $3x - y = -9$ 69. $2x - 3y = -15$ 70. $4x + 7y = -42$ 71. $4x - y = -3$

72. $5x + y = 9$ 73. $x - y = 2$ 74. $14x + y = 10$ 75. $x - 4y = -160$

76. 61.25°F

77. (a) 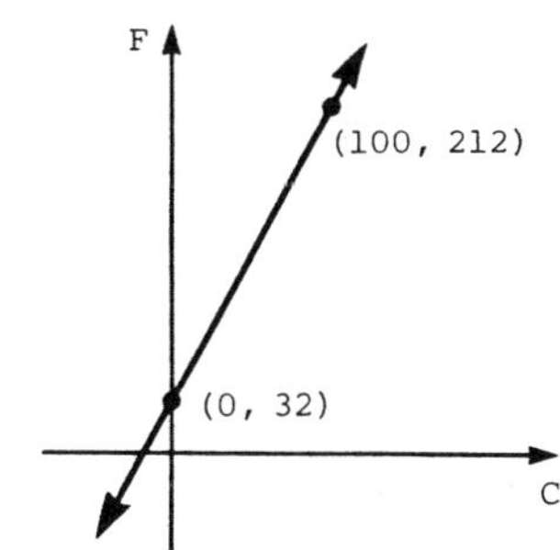

(b) 9/5 (c) $F - 32 = (9/5)(C - 0)$

(d) $C = (5/9)(F - 32)$

(e) $F = 9C/5 + 32$

78. $-40°$ **79.** Parallel **80.** Parallel **81.** Perpendicular **82.** Perpendicular **83.** Parallel **84.** Perpendicular **85.** Perpendicular **86.** Parallel **87.** Neither **88.** Neither

Section 8.3 (page 395)

1. (4, 2) **2.** (1, -5) **3.** (3, 2) **4.** (4, -1) **5.** (2, 2) **6.** (4, -2) **7.** (3, -2) **8.** (4, 1) **9.** (3, -2) **10.** (1, 3) **11.** (0, 0) **12.** (0, 0) **13.** (5, 2) **14.** (7, 5) **15.** (4, 1) **16.** (2, 5) **17.** (-1, -2) **18.** (-3, 1) **19.** (-2, 6) **20.** (2, 1) **21.** (2, -3) **22.** (5, 2) **23.** (4, 4) **24.** (5, 4) **25.** (2, -5) **26.** (-1, 5) **27.** (-9, -11) **28.** (1, 1) **29.** No solution **30.** No solution **31.** No solution **32.** No solution **33.** Same line **34.** Same line **35.** (7, -2) **36.** (-8, 5) **37.** (3.5, -2.8) **38.** (8.1, -2.9) **39.** Let x and y represent the numbers. Then $x + y = 62$ and $x - y = 16$. The numbers are 39 and 23. **40.** Let x represent the larger number and y represent the smaller number. Then $x = y + 12$ and $x = 7y$. The larger number is 14, and the smaller number is 2. **41.** Let x and y represent the side lengths. Since $P = 2L + 2W$, one equation is $54 = 2y + 2x$. The other is $x = 4y - 3$. The dimensions are 21 m by 6 m. **42.** Let x represent the length of the two sides that have the same length and y represent the length of the other side. Then $2x + y = 39$ and $y = 2x - 9$. The equal sides are each 12 cm, and the remaining side is 15 cm. **43.** Let x be the side of the square and y the side of the equilateral triangle. Then $x = y + 2$. The perimeter of a square is given by $P = 4s$, or, here, $P = 4x$. The perimeter of the triangle is $P = a + b + c$, or $P = y + y + y$, or $P = 3y$. Since the perimeter of the square is twice the perimeter of the triangle, $4x = 2(3y)$ or $4x = 6y$. The side of the square is 6 cm long, and the side of the triangle is 4 cm long. **44.** Let x represent the price of a small box and y represent the price of a large box. The equations are $10x + 12y = 34$ and $5x + 10y = 25$. A small box costs $1. **45.** Let x be the number of brown rats and y the number of white rats. Then $2x + 3y = 17$ and $3x + 4y = 24$. The lab should keep 4 brown rats and 3 white rats. **46.** Let x represent the number of units of yarn and y represent the number of units of thread. Then $x + y = 8$ and $2x + y = 14$. The factory should make 6 units of yarn and 2 units of thread. **47.** Let x be the number of dimes and y the number of quarters. Then $x + y = 53$ and $.10x + .25y = 8.45$. He has 32 dimes and 21 quarters. **48.** Let x represent the number of general admission tickets and y represent the number of student tickets. Then $x + y = 325$ and $1.50x + 1y = 380$. 110 general admission and 215 student tickets were sold. **49.** Let x be the number of fives and y the number of tens. Then $x + y = 25$ and $5x + 10y = 165$. The deposit included 17 fives and 8 tens. **50.** Let x represent the cost per pound for peanuts and y represent the cost per pound for cashews. Then $5x + 6y = 11.20$ and $3x + 7y = 10.80$. The store charges $.80 for a pound of peanuts.

Section 8.4 (page 400)

1.

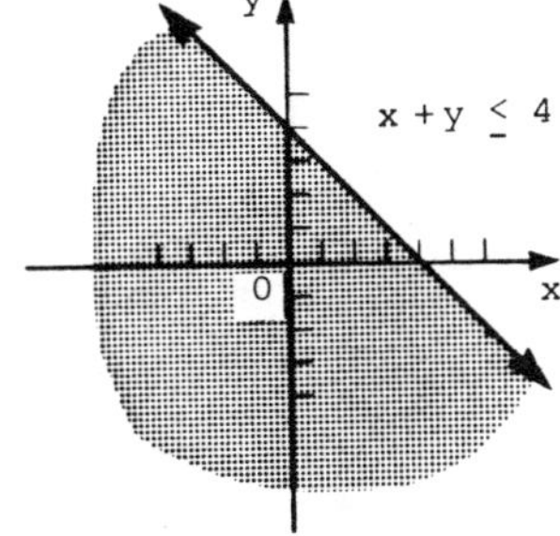

2.

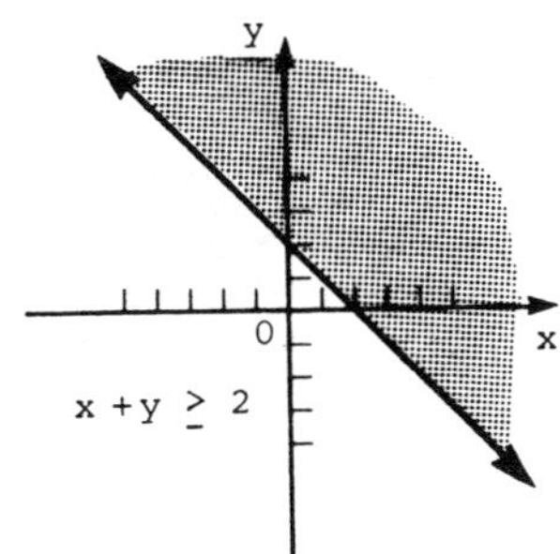

3.

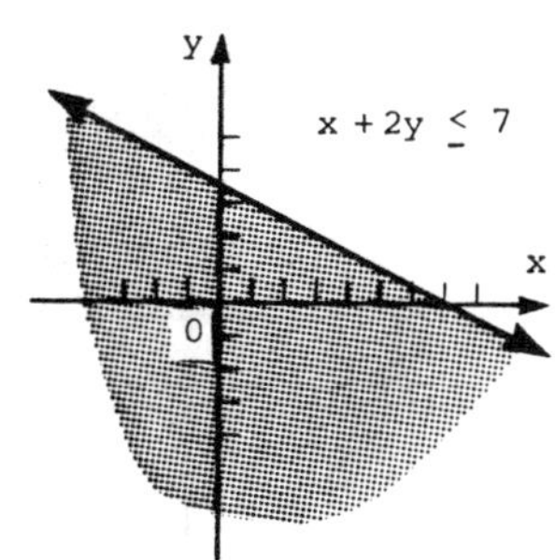

4.

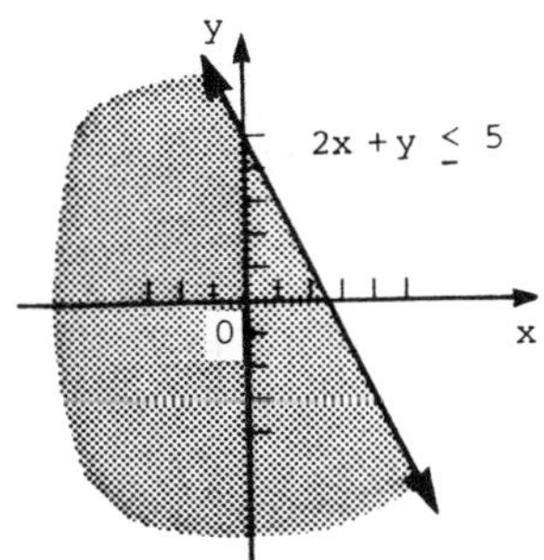

5.

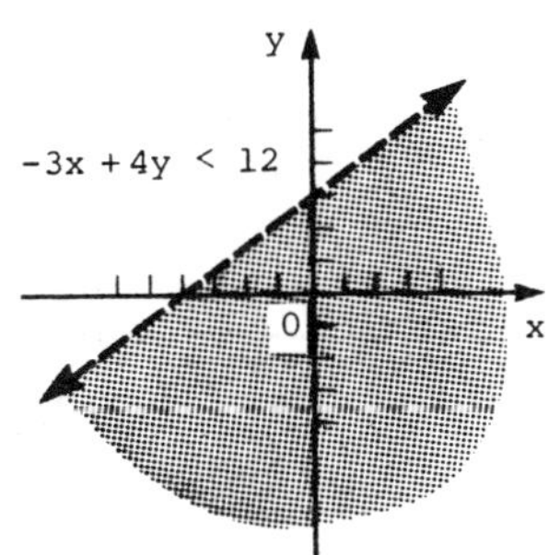

6.

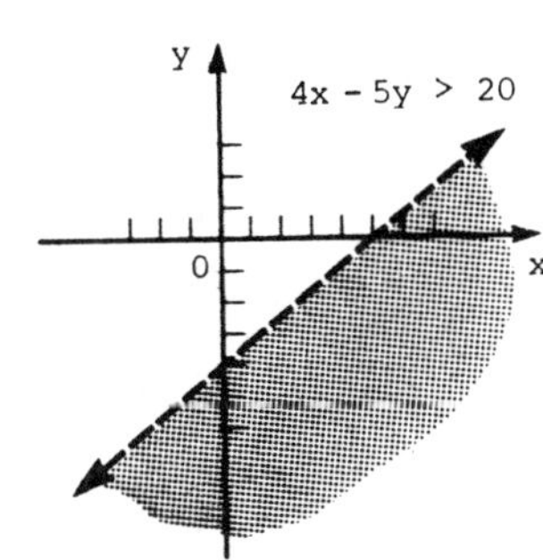

7.

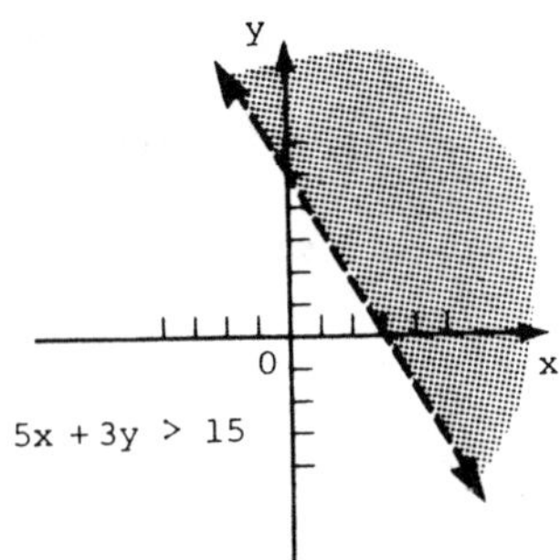

8.

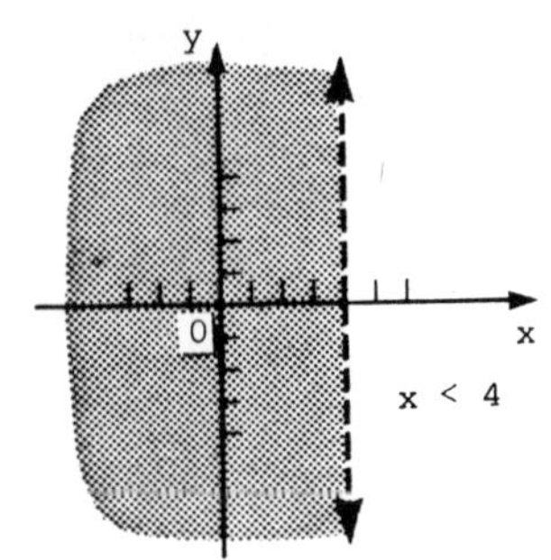

9.

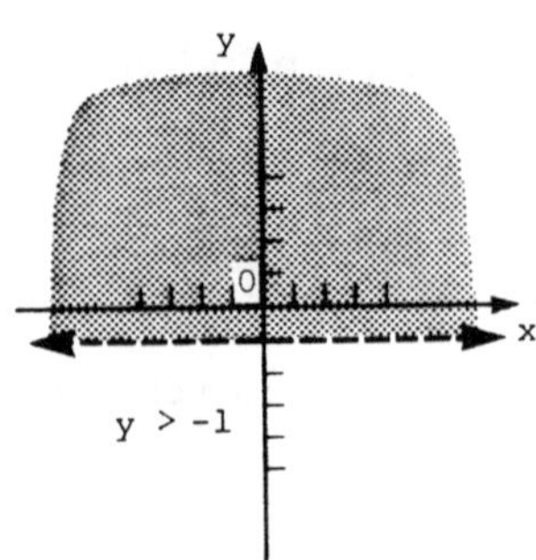

10.

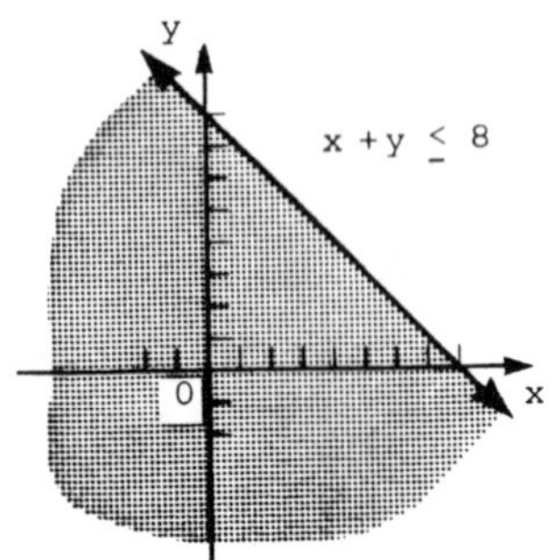

11.

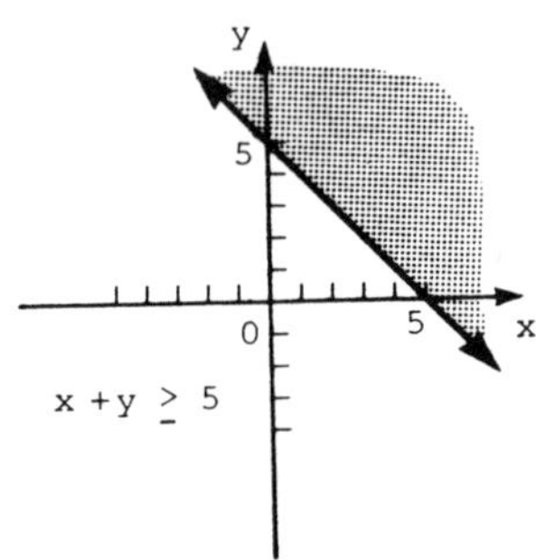

12.

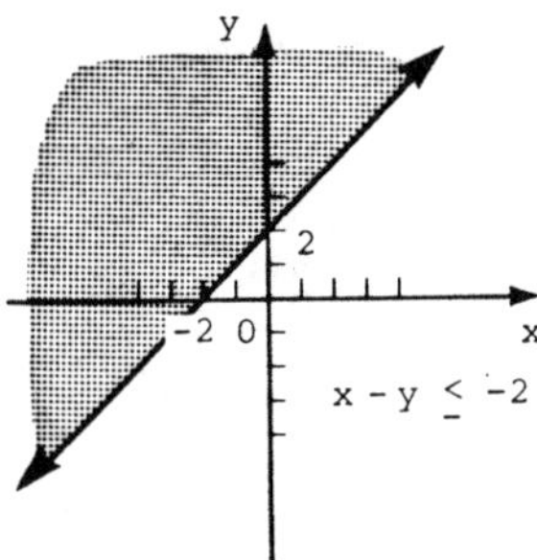

13.

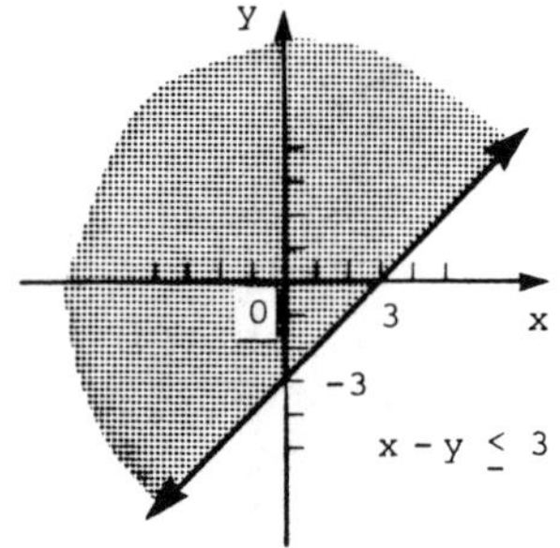

14.

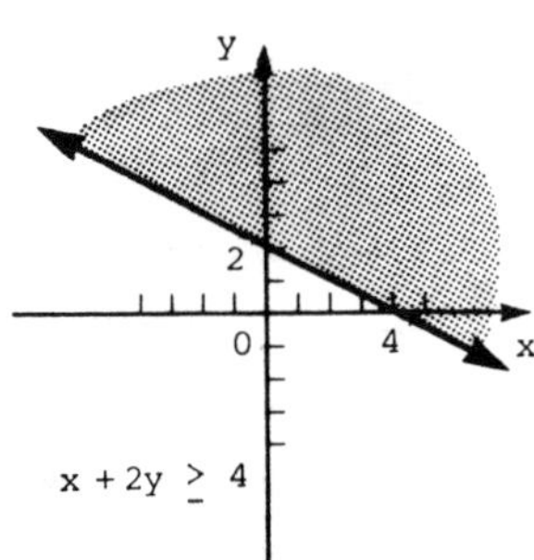

15.

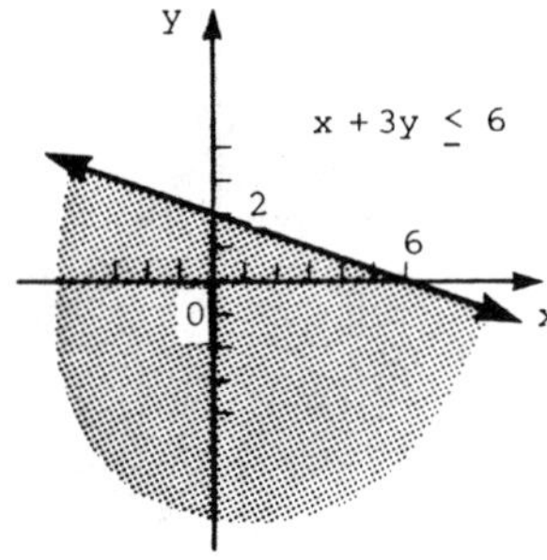

16.

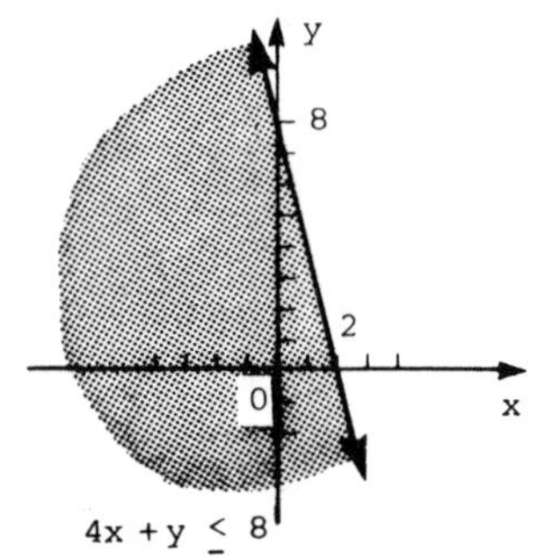

17.

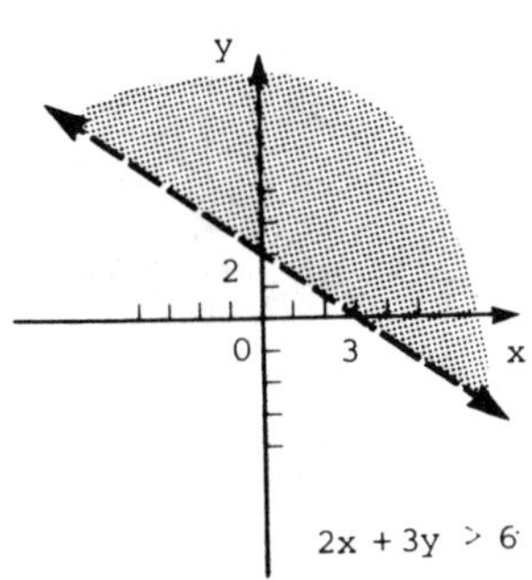

18.

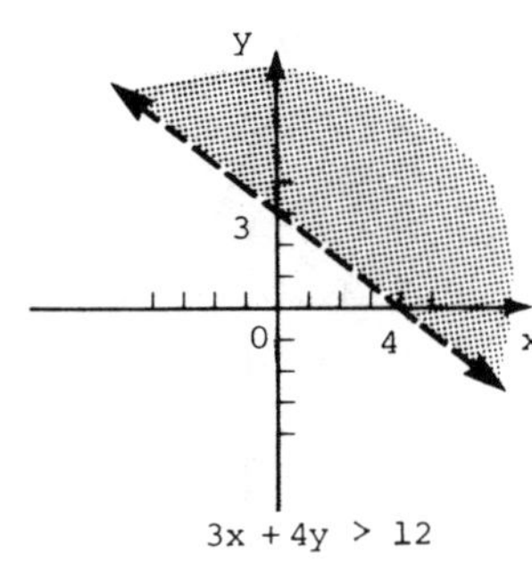

19.

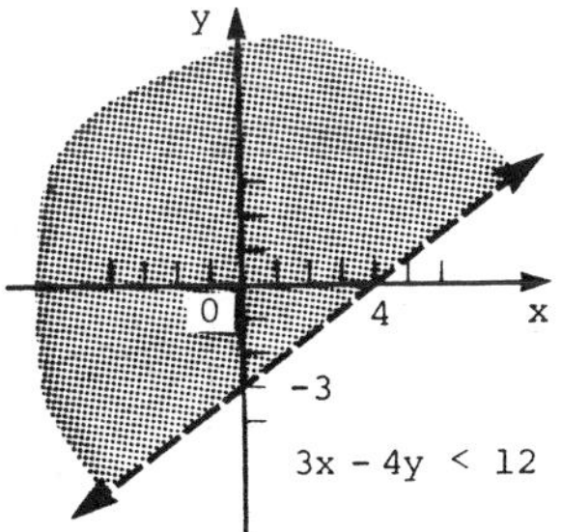

20.

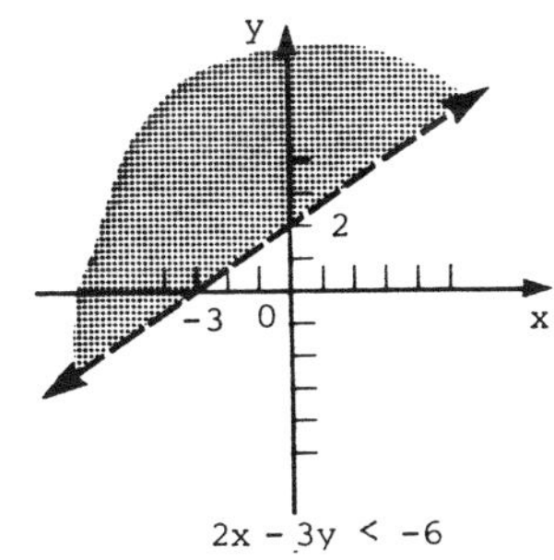

21.

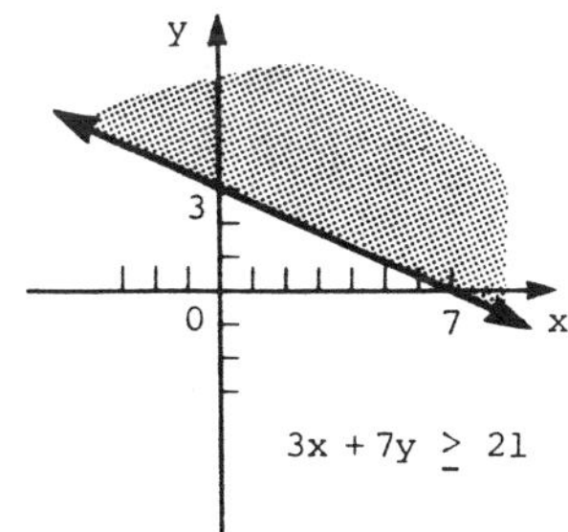

22.

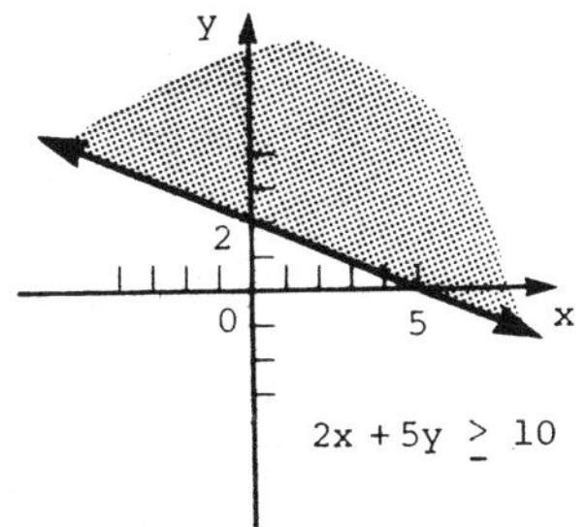

23.

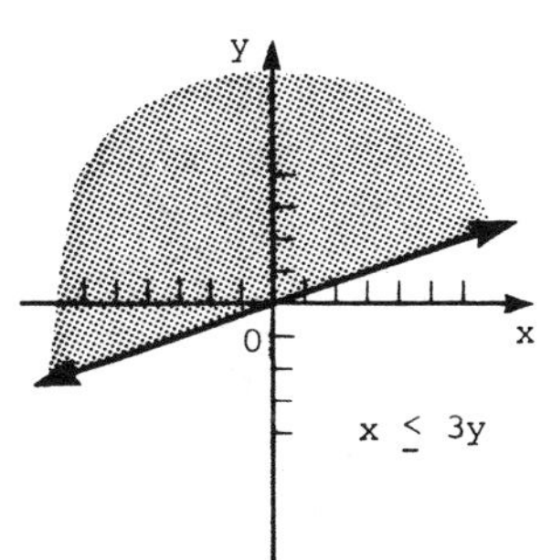

24.

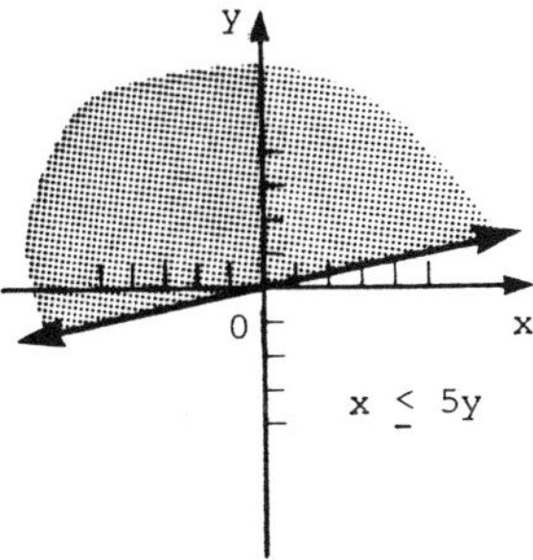

25.

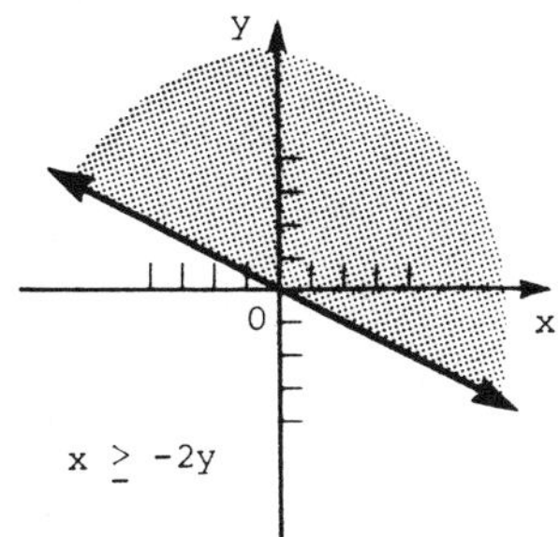

26.

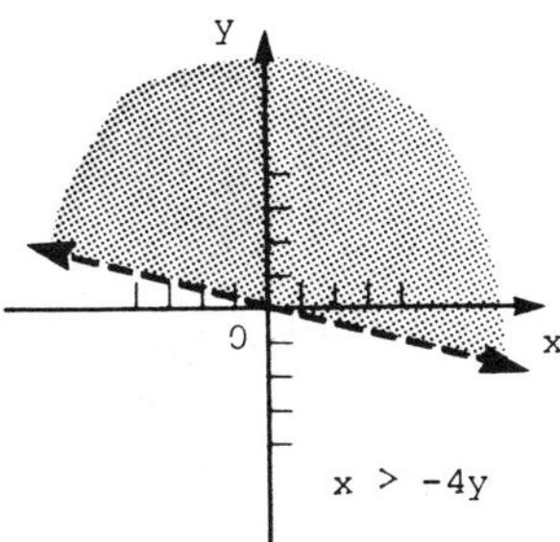

27.

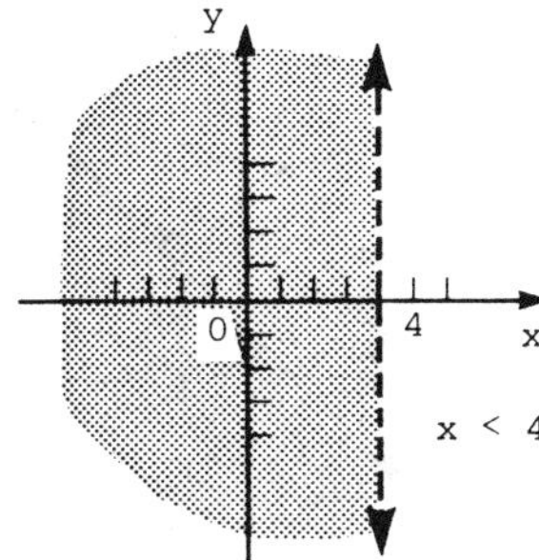

28.

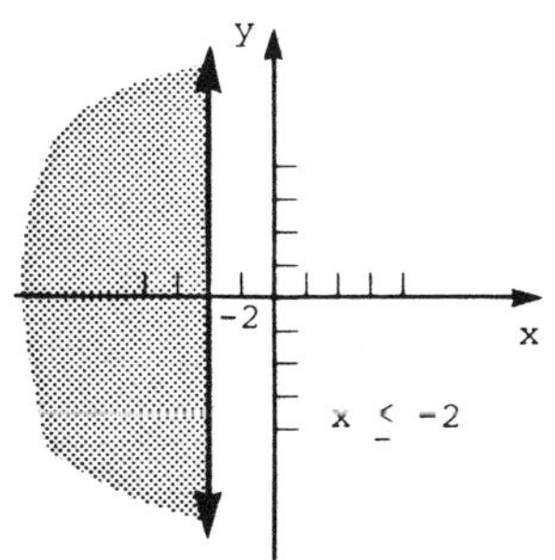

29.

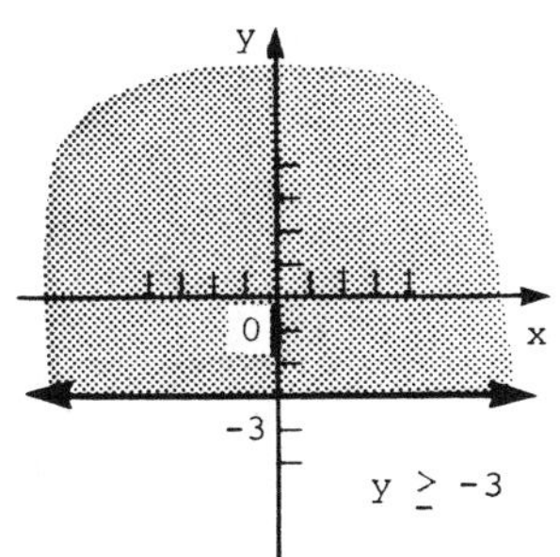

30.

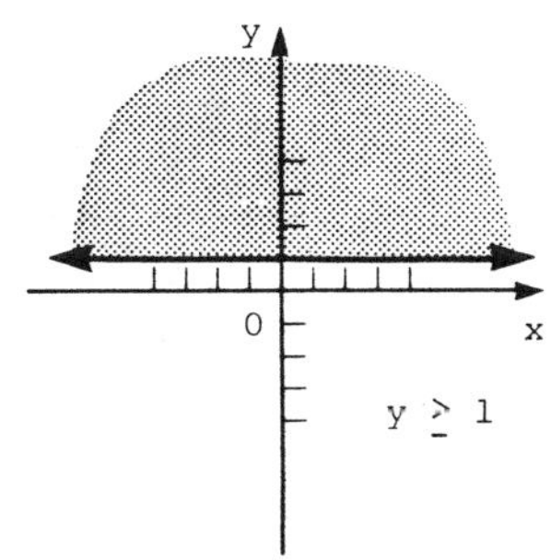

31.

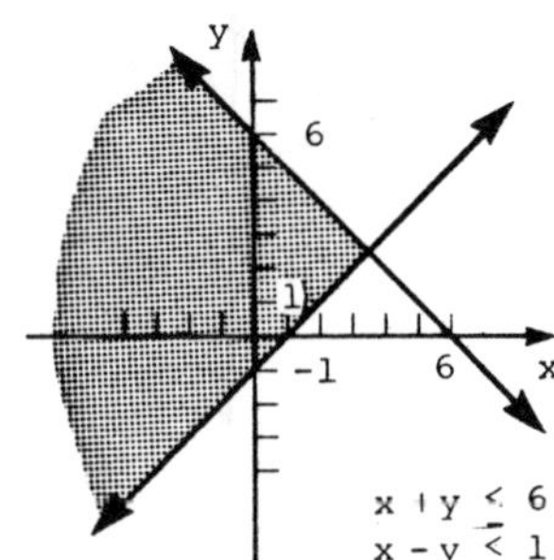

32.

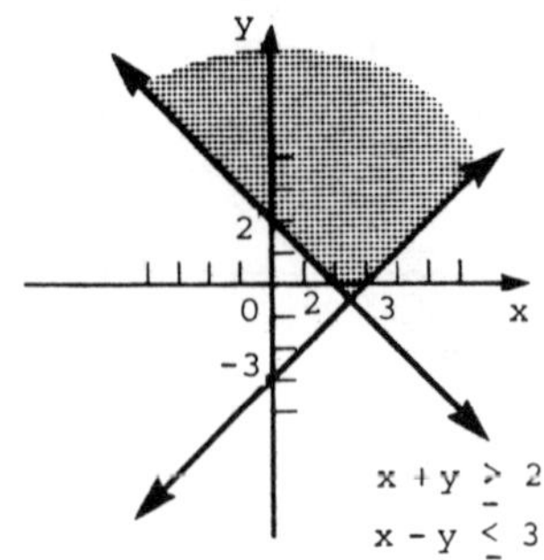

33.

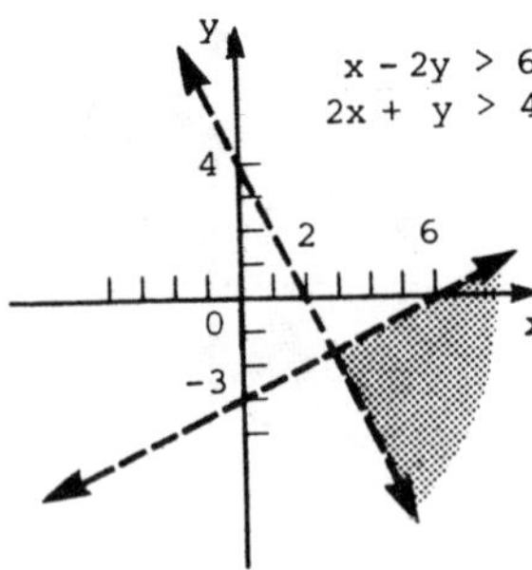

34.

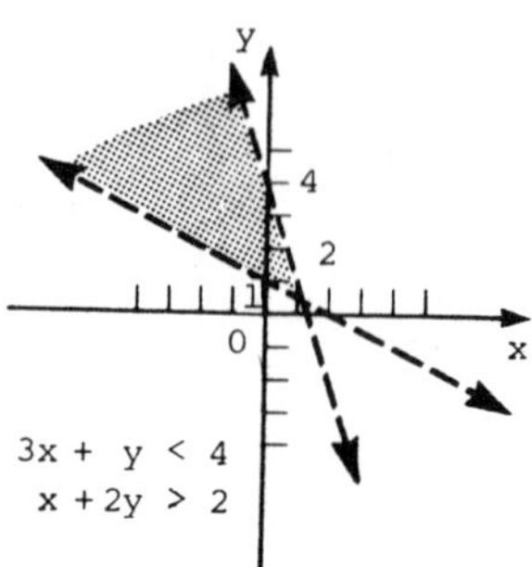

35.

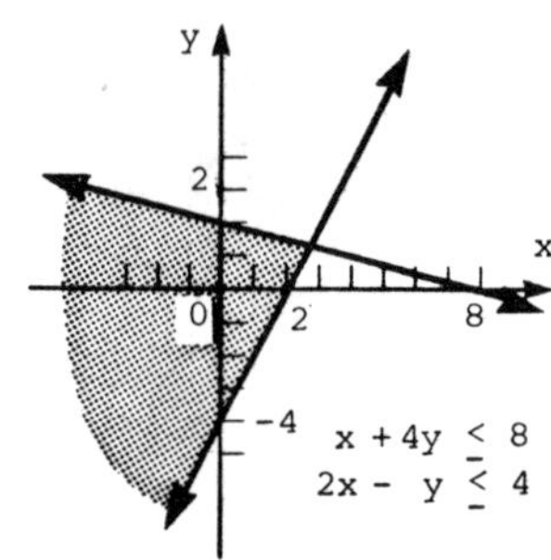

36.

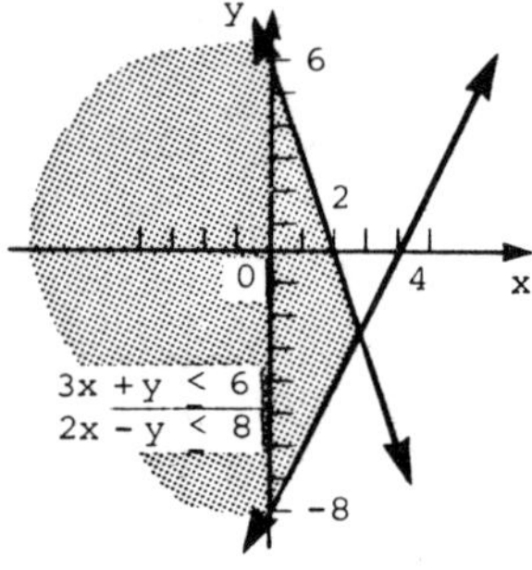

37.

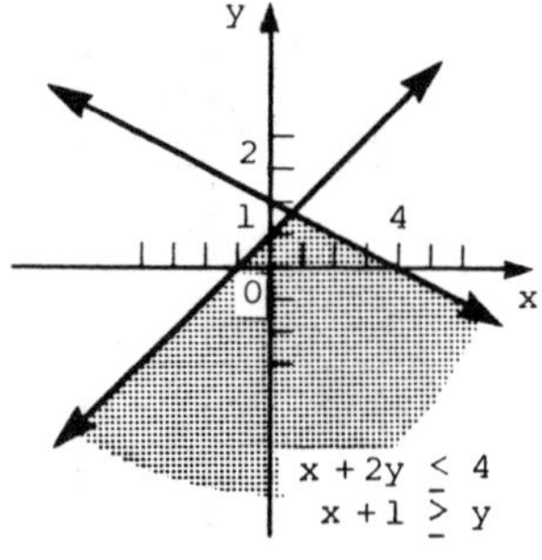

38.

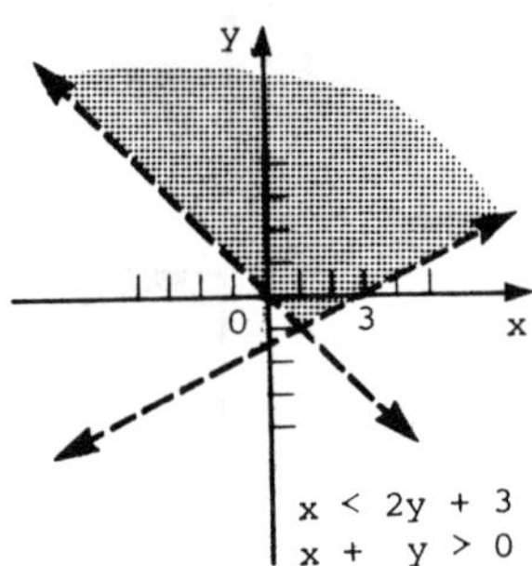

39.

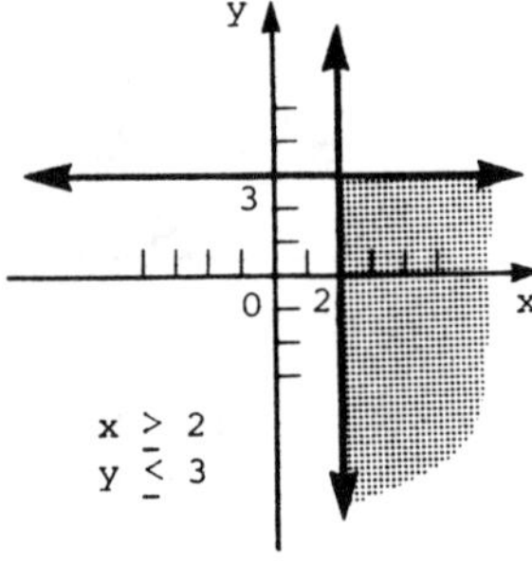

40.

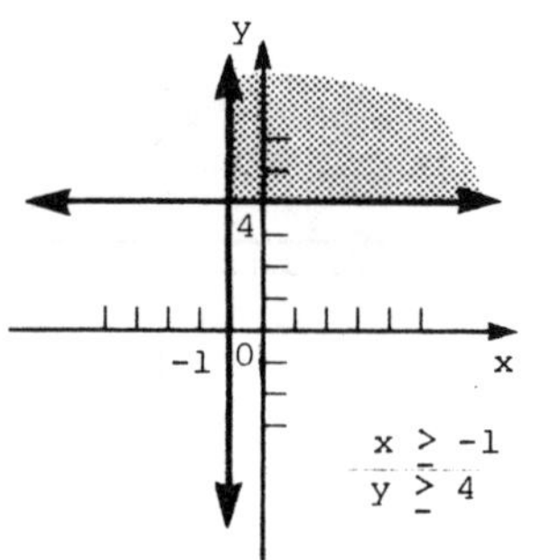

41.

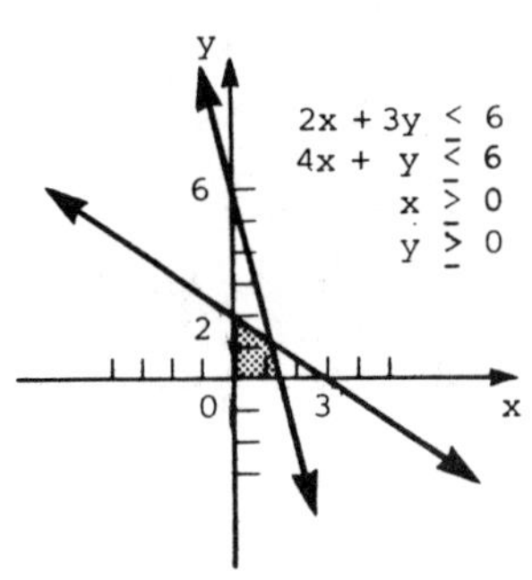

42.

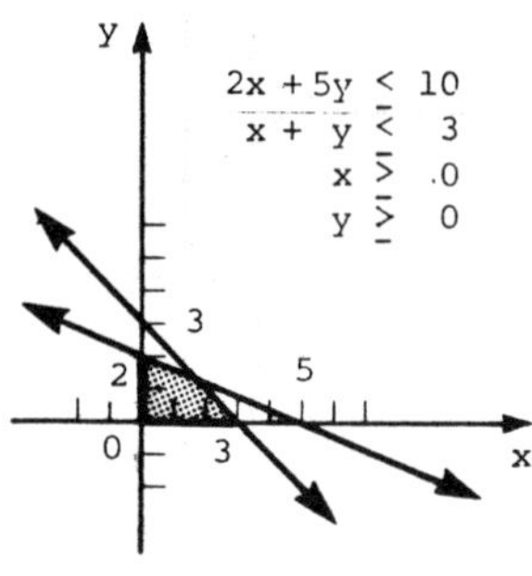

Section 8.5 (page 404)

1. Maximum of 65 at (5, 10); minimum of 8 at (1, 1) **2.** Maximum of 55 at (9, 1); minimum of 8 at (1, 2) **3.** Maximum of 900 at (0, 12); minimum of 0 at (0, 0) **4.** Maximum of 2460 at (6, 18); minimum of 0 at (0, 0) **5.** (6/5, 6/5) **6.** (10/3, 5/3) **7.** (17/3, 5) **8.** (10, 80/3) **9.** (105/8, 25/8) **10.** (15/2, 0) **11.** (a) Maximum of 204 at (18, 2) (b) Maximum of 117 3/5 at (12/5, 39/5) (c) Maximum of 102 at (0, 17/2) **12.** (a) Minimum of 7 at (0, 7/2) (b) Minimum of 10 at (0, 5) (c) Minimum of 19 1/3 at (14/3, 8/3) **13.** $112 profit with 4 pigs and 12 geese **14.** 15 inquiries if 5 units of hats and no whistles are displayed **15.** 8 of #1 and 3 of #2 **16.** $9 profit if 6 ashtrays and 3 cufflink sets are made **17.** 800 bargain sets and 300 deluxe sets; maximum profit is $125,000 **18.** 80 sq ft of window space and 480 sq ft of wall space for a maximum area of 560 sq ft **19.** 150 kg of the half and half mix and 75 kg of the other mix; maximum profit is $1050 **20.** 1 blue vitamin and 3 red vitamins for a cost of 17¢ per day

Section 8.6 (page 414)

1. (3, 9), (4, 10), (5, 11), (6, 12), (7, 13); range: $\{9, 10, 11, 12, 13\}$

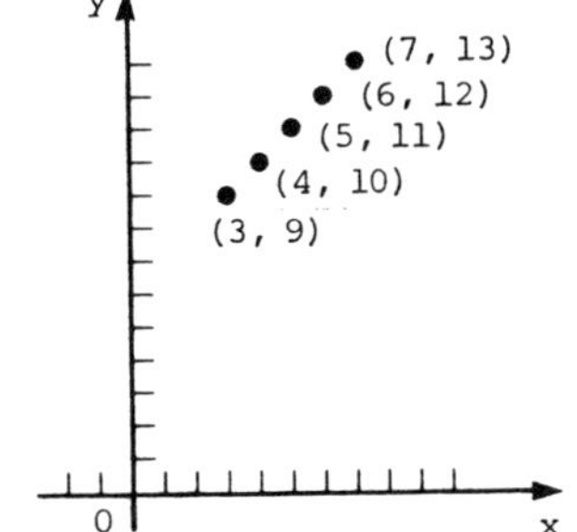

2. (0, 1), (1, 3), (2, 5), (3, 7), (4, 9); range: $\{1, 3, 5, 7, 9\}$

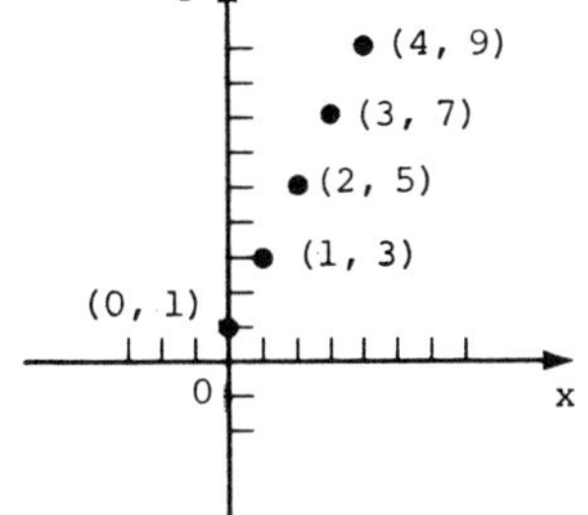

3. (-1, 6), (0, 4), (1, 2), (2, 0), (3, -2), (4, -4); range: {6, 4, 2, 0, -2, -4}

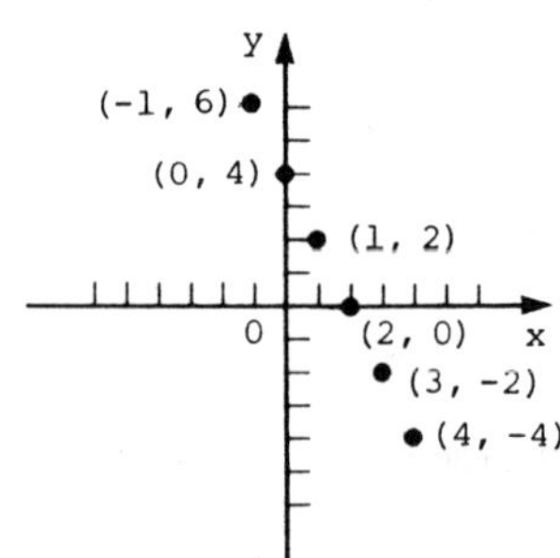

4. (-2, 17), (-1, 13), (0, 9), (1, 5), (2, 1), (3, -3); range: {17, 13, 9, 5, 1, -3}

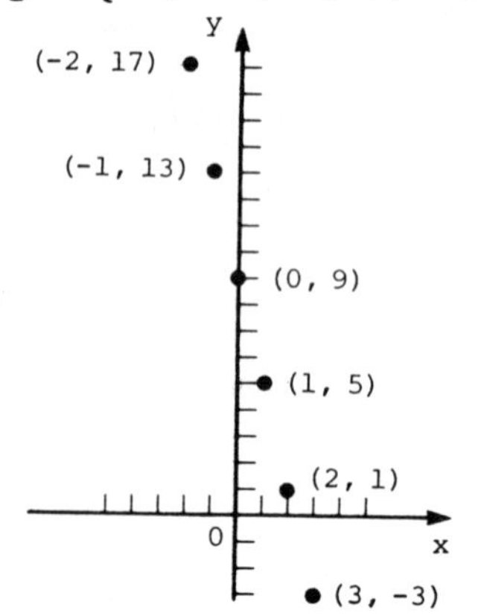

5. (-1, 4), (0, 6), (1, 8), (2, 10), (3, 12), (4, 14), (5, 16); range: {4, 6, 8, 10, 12, 14, 16}

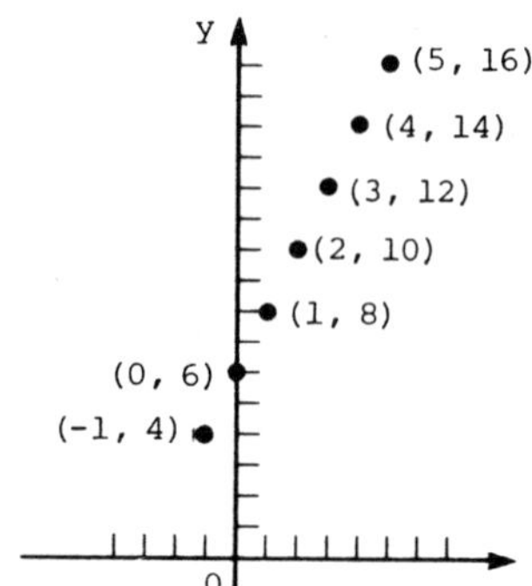

6. (3, 1), (4, 2), (5, 3), (6, 4), (7, 5); range: {1, 2, 3, 4, 5}

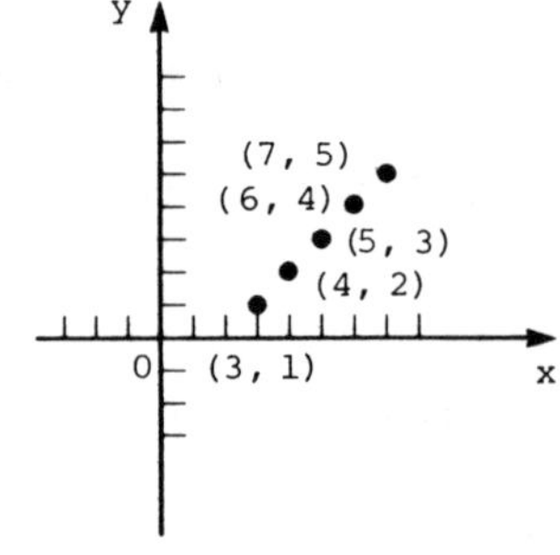

7. (-4, 3), (-2, 5/2), (0, 2), (2, 3/2), (4, 1); range: {3, 5/2, 2, 3/2, 1}

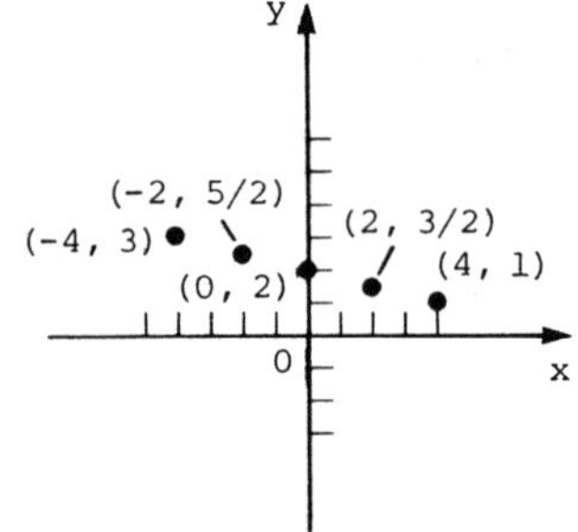

8. (-2, 0), (-1, 1), (0, 2), (1, 3), (2, 4), (3, 5); range: {0, 1, 2, 3, 4, 5}

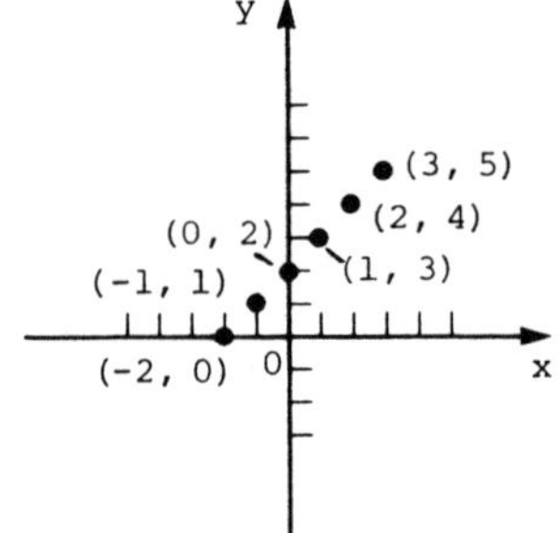

9. (-4, -2), (-2, -1), (0, 0), (2, 1), (4, 2); range: {-2, -1, 0, 1, 2}

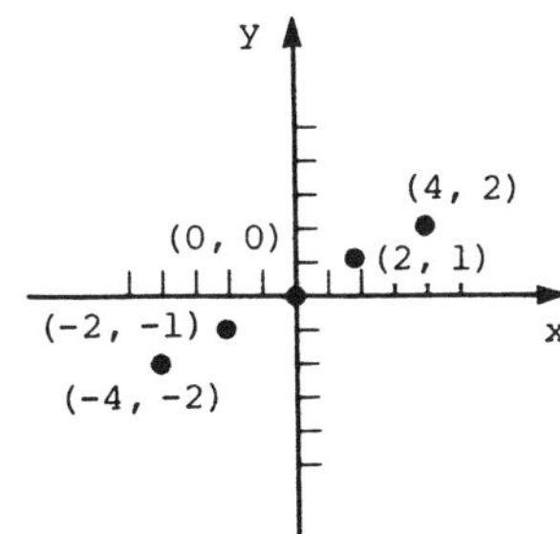

10. (-2, 6), (-1, 3), (0, 0), (1, -3), (2, -6), (3, -9); range: {6, 3, 0, -3, -6, -9}

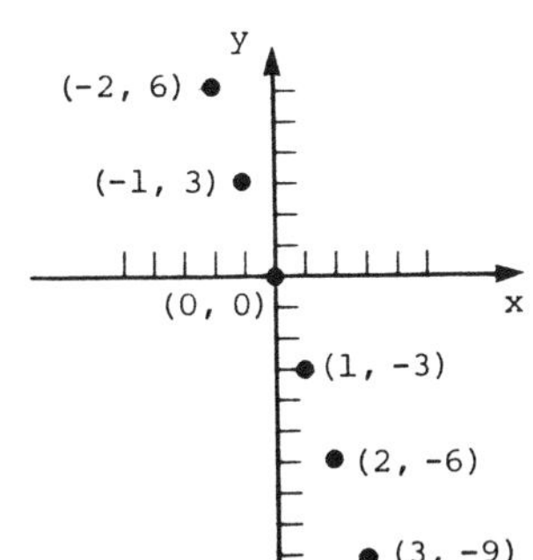

11. (-9, 3), (-6, 2), (-3, 1), (0, 0), (3, -1), (6, -2); range: {3, 2, 1, 0, -1, -2}

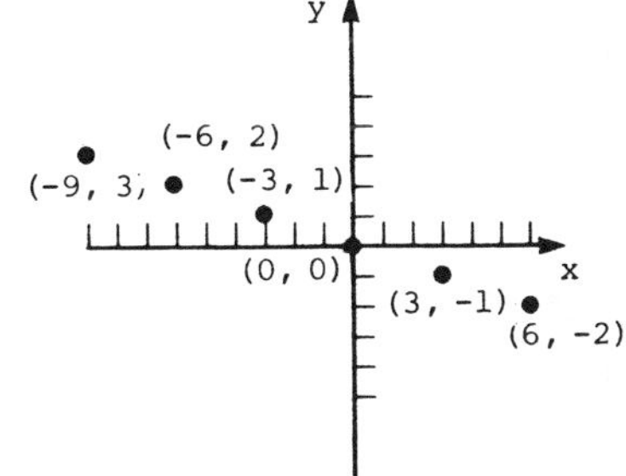

12. (-2, -4), (-1, -2), (0, 0), (1, 2), (2, 4), (3, 6); range: {-4, -2, 0, 2, 4, 6}

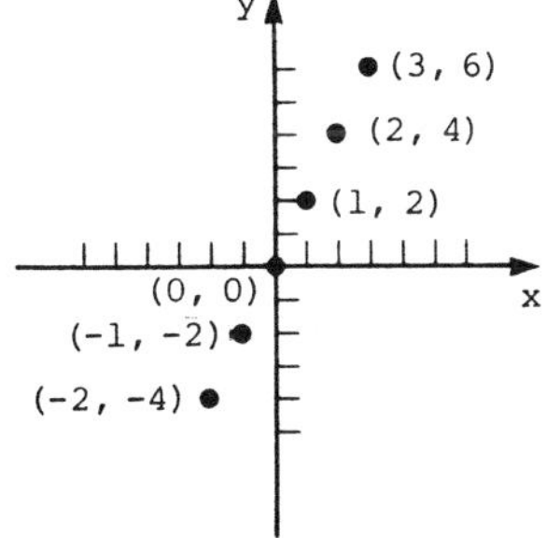

13. (-3, -1/2), (-2, -1), (0, 1), (1, 1/2), (2, 1/3); range: {-1/2, -1, 1, 1/2, 1/3}

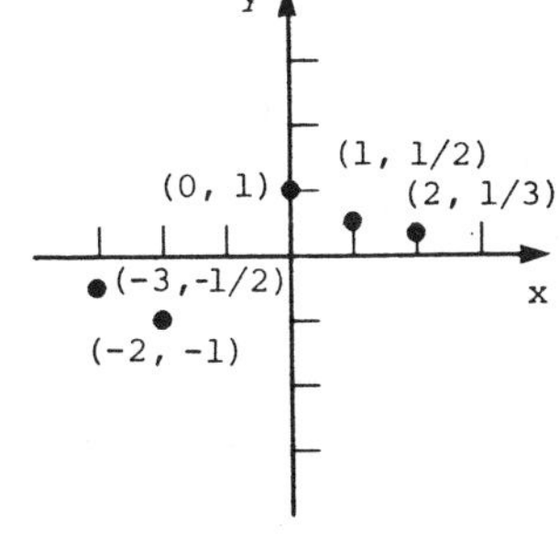

14. (-3, -2/3), (-2, -6/7), (-1, -6/5), (0, -2), (1, -6), (2, 6); range: {-2/3, -6/7, -6/5, -2, -6, 6}

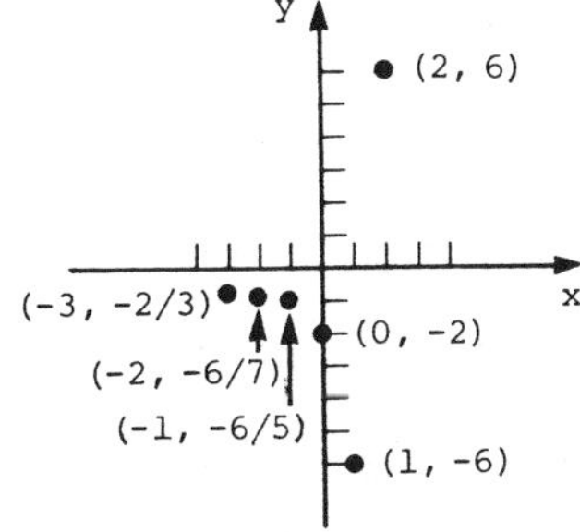

15. (7/8, 24), (3/4, 12), (1/2, 6), (1/4, 4), (0, 3); range: {3, 4, 6, 12, 24}

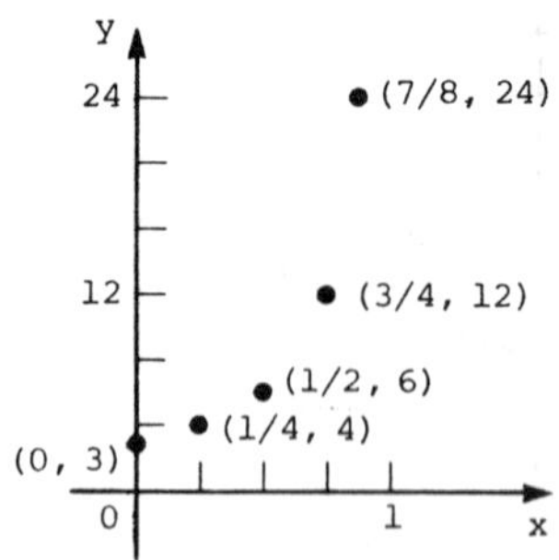

16. (1 7/8, 32), (1 3/4, 16), (1 1/2, 8), (1 1/4, 16/3), (1, 4); range: {32, 16, 8, 16/3, 4}

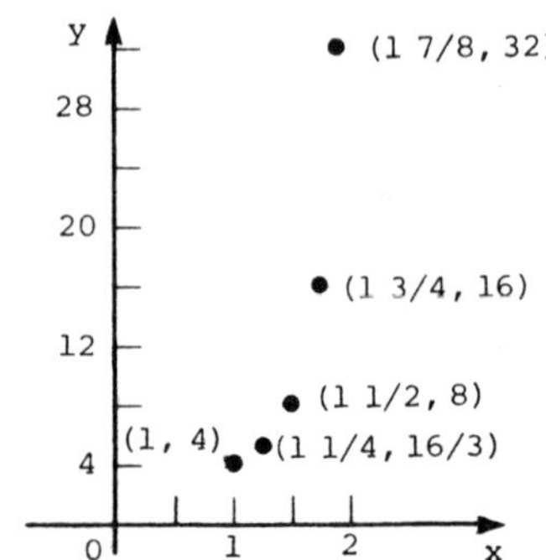

17. (0, 3), (1, 3), (2, 3), (4, 3), (5, 3); range: {3}

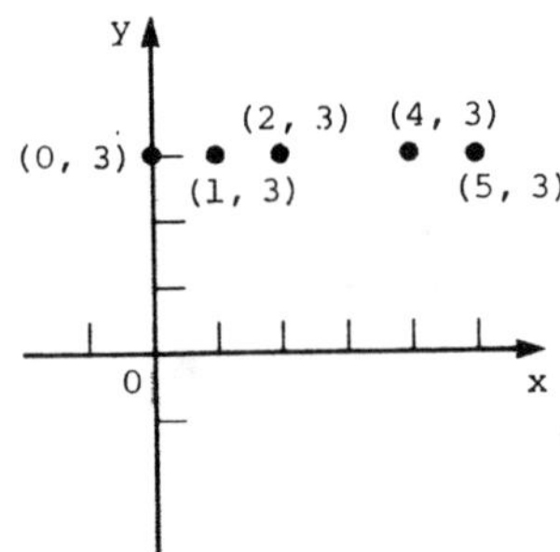

18. (−2, −1), (−1, −1), (0, −1), (1, −1), (2, −1), (3, −1); range: {−1}

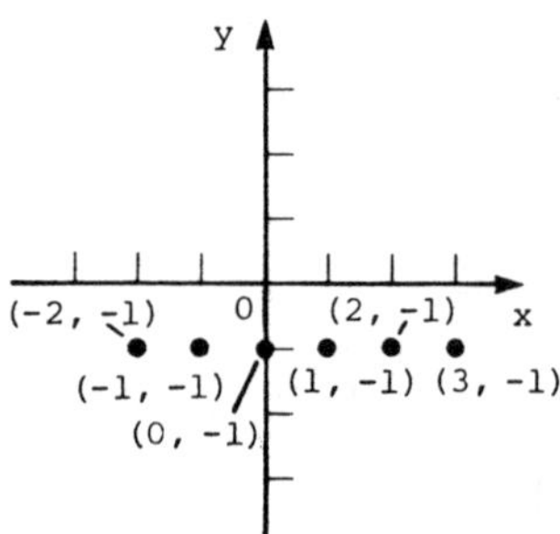

19. f(−2) = 0; f(0) = 2; f(3) = 5

20. f(−2) = 7; f(0) = 5; f(3) = 2

21. f(−2) = −3; f(0) = 1; f(3) = 7

22. f(−2) = −7; f(0) = 3; f(3) = 18

23. f(−2) = 13; f(0) = 9; f(3) = 3

24. f(−2) = 19; f(0) = 3; f(3) = −21

25. f(−2) = −6; f(0) = 0; f(3) = 24

26. f(−2) = 12; f(0) = 0; f(3) = −3

27. f(−2) = 0; f(0) = −6; f(3) = 15

28. f(−2) = 17; f(0) = 1, f(3) = 22

29. f(−2) = 0; f(0) = 2; f(3) = 20

30. f(−2) = 5; f(0) = −3; f(3) = 0

31. f(−2) = 6; f(0) = 8/3; f(3) = 11/6

32. f(−2) = −10; f(0) = 6; f(3) = 0

33. f(−2) does not exist; f(0) = 3/2; f(3) = 3

34. f(−2) = −3; f(0) = −5/3; f(3) does not exist

35. Function

36. Function

37. Function

38. Function **39.** Not a function **40.** Function **41.** Not a function

42. Not a function **43.** Not a function **44.** Function **45.** Function

46. Not a function **47.** Not a function **48.** Not a function

49. (a) \$7 (b) \$10 (c) \$13 (d) \$16 (e) \$7 (f) \$7 (g) \$16 (h) \$22

50. Continue the bars up and to the right. **51.** Function **52.** Function

53. Not a function **54.** Every straight line except vertical straight lines

55. No

56. (a) 16 (b) 11 (c) 6 (d) 1 (e) 8 (f) 24/5 (g) 0 (h) 0

(i) 8 (j) 16 (k)

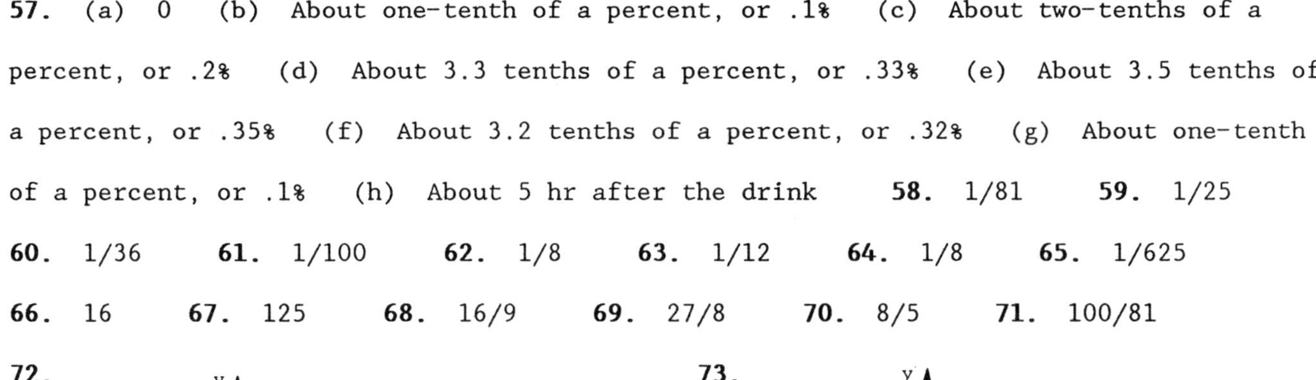

(l) 8 (m) 32/5

57. (a) 0 (b) About one-tenth of a percent, or .1% (c) About two-tenths of a percent, or .2% (d) About 3.3 tenths of a percent, or .33% (e) About 3.5 tenths of a percent, or .35% (f) About 3.2 tenths of a percent, or .32% (g) About one-tenth of a percent, or .1% (h) About 5 hr after the drink **58.** 1/81 **59.** 1/25

60. 1/36 **61.** 1/100 **62.** 1/8 **63.** 1/12 **64.** 1/8 **65.** 1/625

66. 16 **67.** 125 **68.** 16/9 **69.** 27/8 **70.** 8/5 **71.** 100/81

72.

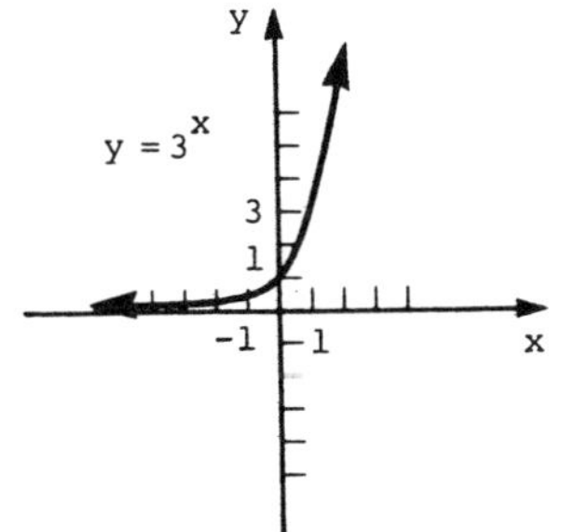

73.

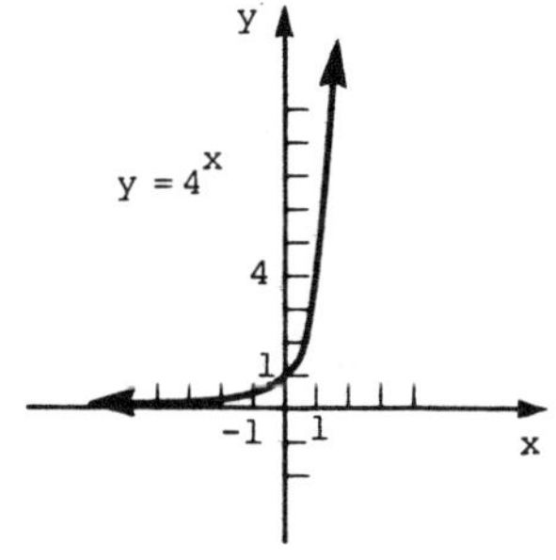

74.

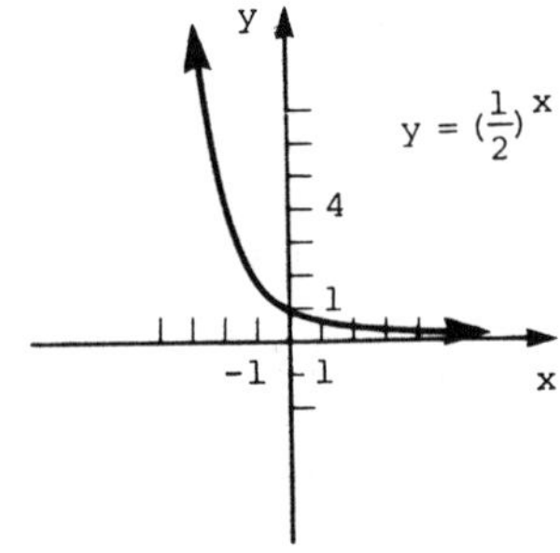

75.

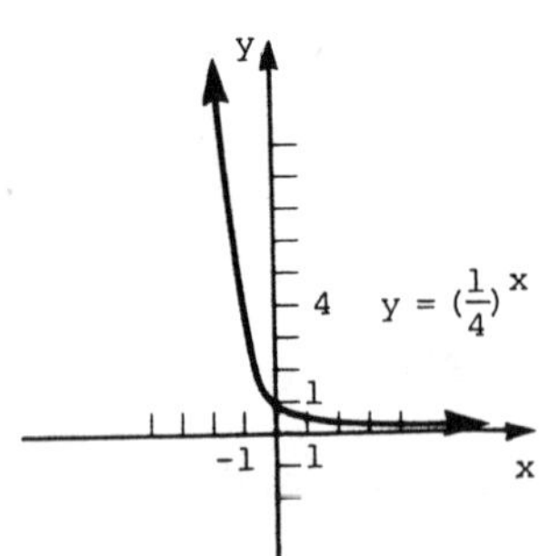

Answers for Exercises 76-89 are approximate.

76. \$2.20; \$3.20; \$4.65 **77.** \$4.20 **78.** \$2.35 **79.** \$1.75 **80.** \$1.80

81. \$2.40 **82.** \$1.45 **83.** \$2.60 **84.** \$4.65 **85.** \$2.50 **86.** \$2400

87. \$46,500 **88.** \$370,000 **89.** \$315,000

An Extension Properties of Exponents (page 418)

1. 4^5 **2.** 9^{10} **3.** 2^3 **4.** 5^6 **5.** $1/12^4$ **6.** $1/3^3$ **7.** $1/5^{10}$

8. $1/6^7$ **9.** 1 **10.** 1 **11.** 1 **12.** −1 **13.** 5^6 **14.** 7^6

15. $1/2^3$ **16.** $1/11^3$ **17.** 6^3 **18.** 1/3 **19.** $1/2^3$ **20.** 9^3 **21.** 2^{18}

22. 4^6 **23.** 5^6 **24.** 6^{12} **25.** $1/7^4$ **26.** $1/3^{14}$ **27.** $1/(2/3)^6$ or $3^6/2^6$

28. $1/(3/5)^3$ or $5^3/3^3$ **29.** 1/9 **30.** 1 **31.** 7^7 **32.** 6^3 **33.** $1/4^8$

34. 6^{22} **35.** $1/8^6$ **36.** 4^{18} **37.** 39 1/4; 39.25 **38.** 43 1/8; 43.125

39. 14 21/64; 14.3281 **40.** 28 25/64; 28.3906 **41.** 323 93/512; 323.182

42. 119 139/512; 119.2715 **43.** 1/6 **44.** 1/7 **45.** $1/9^3$ or 1/729

46. $1/9^3$ or 1/729 **47.** $1/5^3$ or 1/125 **48.** $1/7^4$ or 1/2401 **49.** $1/12^3$ or 1/1728

50. $1/12^4$ or 1/20,736 **51.** 3.47×10^5 **52.** 9.2×10^5 **53.** 1.9×10^{11}

54. 8.25×10^{11} **55.** 4.1×10^{-4} **56.** 5.72×10^{-5} **57.** 9.10004×10^{-1}

58. 2.10003×10^{-2} **59.** 270,000 **60.** 6880 **61.** 507,000,000 **62.** 845

63. .0001377 **64.** .00000211 **65.** .00009 **66.** .0000074

Chapter 8 Test (page 421)

1\.

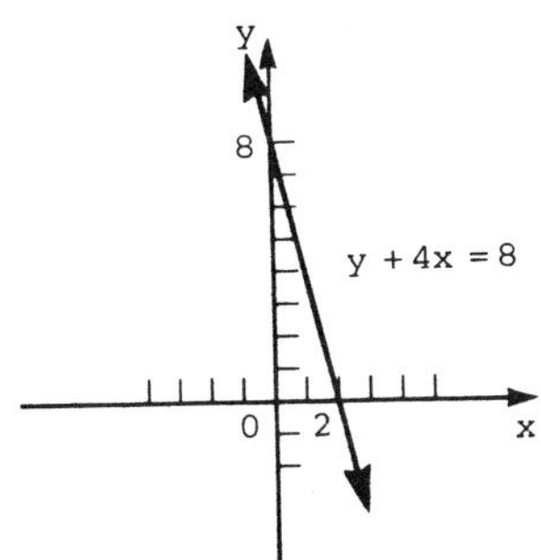

2\.

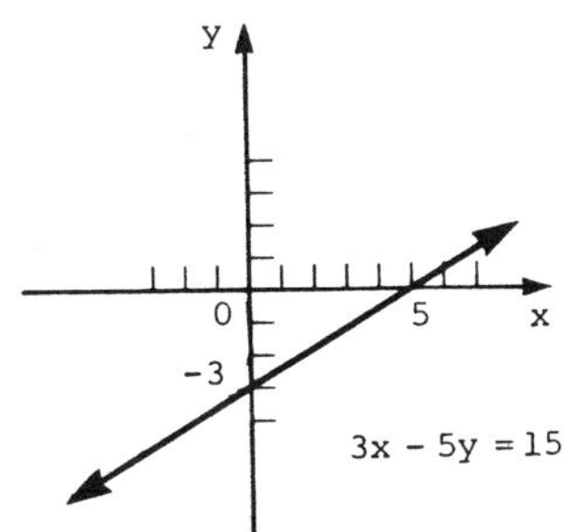

3\.

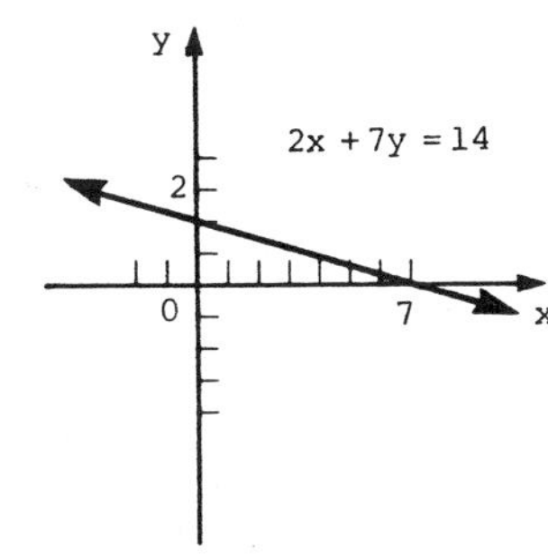

4\.

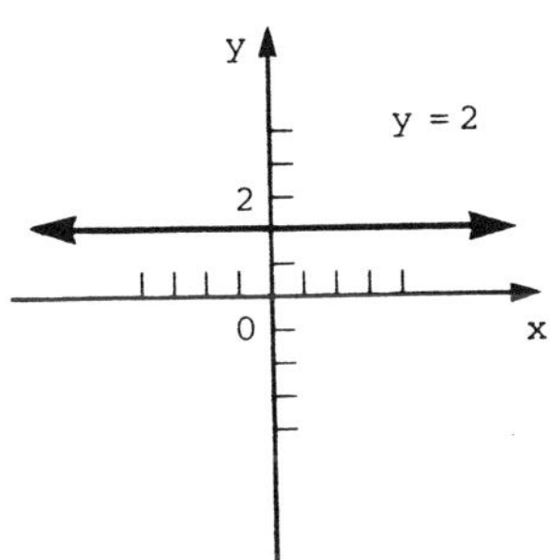

5\.

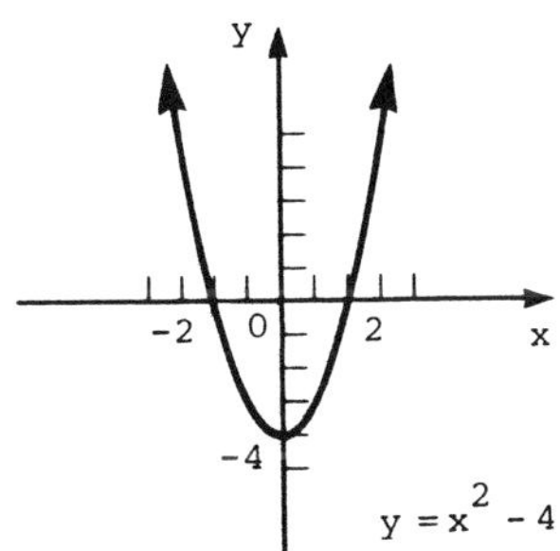

6\.

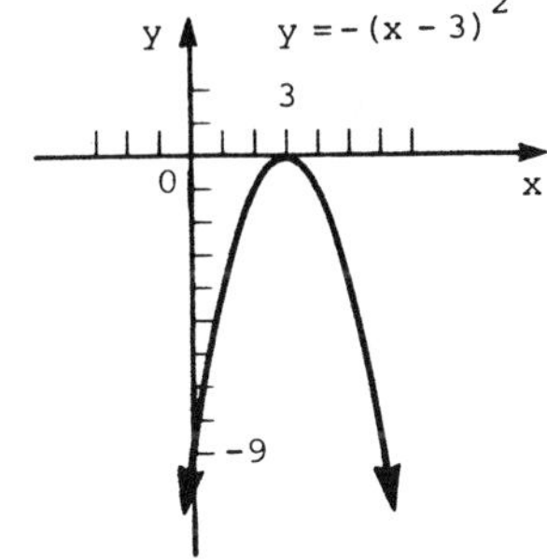

7. $-5/17$ **8.** $5/8$ **9.** $2x - 3y = -26$ **10.** $3x + y = 17$ **11.** $(10, -2)$

12. $(4, 1)$ **13.** $(8, -2)$ **14.** 2 at \$3 and 5 at \$4

15\.

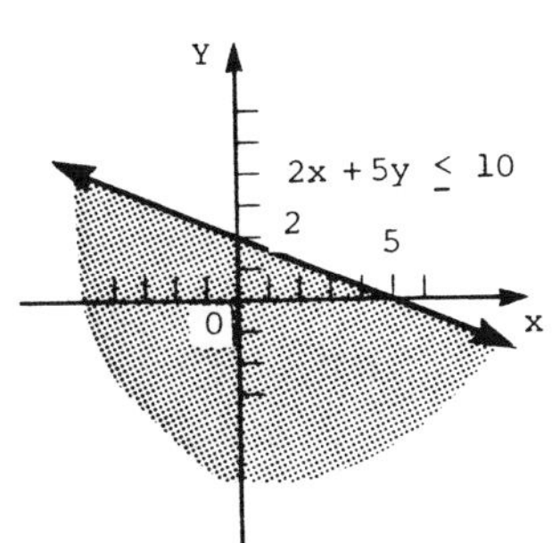

16\.

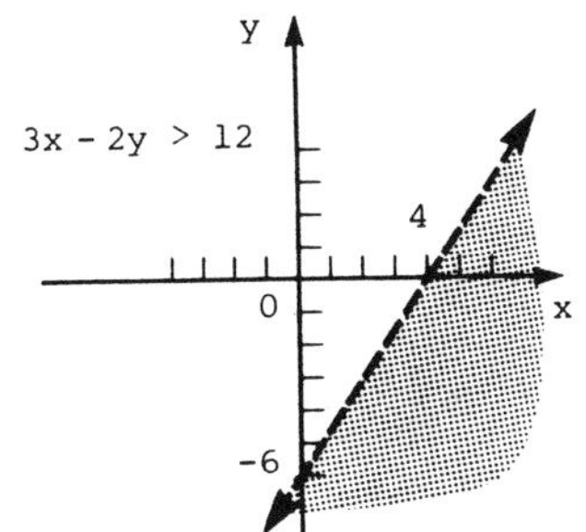

17\.

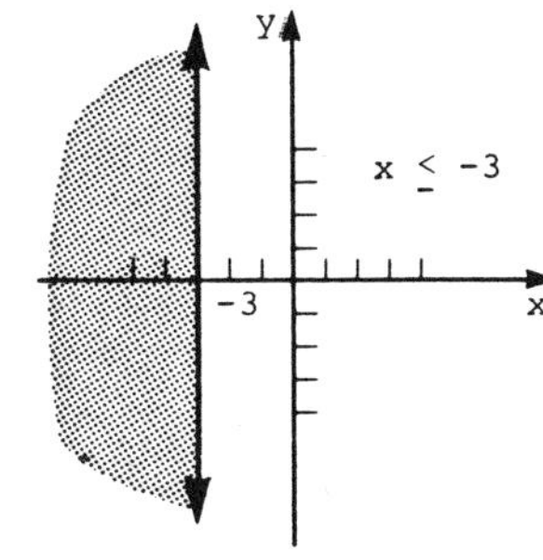

18.

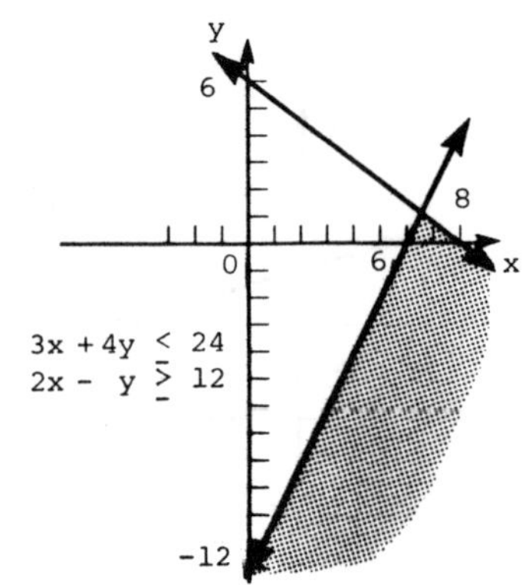

19.

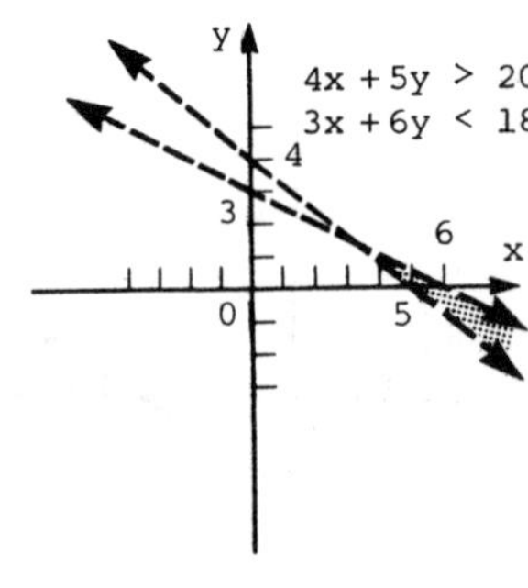

20. Maximum of 13 at (2, 1)

21. f(−1) = 17

22. f(2) = 2

23. f(−3) = 47

24.

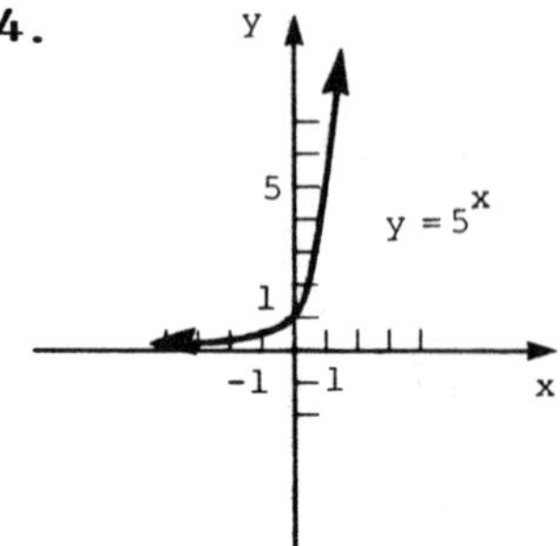

25. The interest alone is approximately $2900.

CHAPTER 9

Section 9.1 (page 431)

1. (a) $\overline{AB}$ (b) 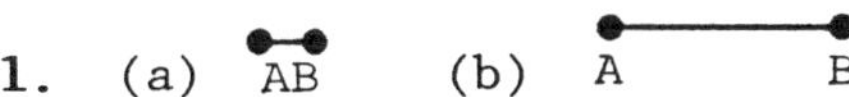

2. (a) $\overrightarrow{BC}$ (b) 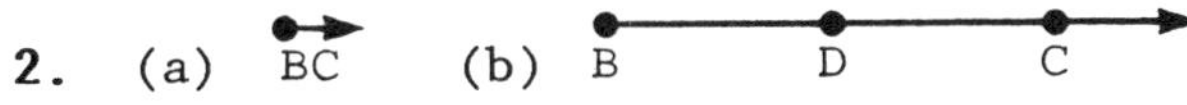

3. (a) $\overrightarrow{CB}$ (b) B D C

4. (a) $\overline{AD}$ (b) A B D

5. (a) $\overset{\circ\!\rightarrow}{BC}$ (b) B D C

6. (a) $\overset{\circ\!\rightarrow}{AD}$ (b) A B D

7. (a) $\overrightarrow{BA}$ (b) A B

8. (a) $\overrightarrow{DA}$ (b) A B D

9. (a) $\overline{CA}$ (b) A B D C

10. (a) $\overline{DA}$ (b) 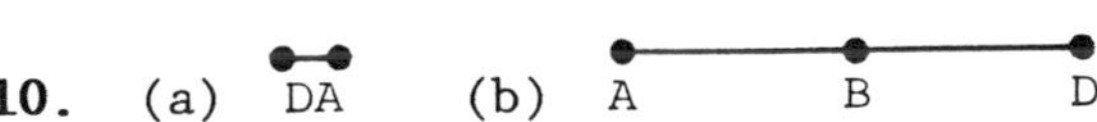

11. 47°; acute 12. 80°; acute 13. 90°; right 14. 115°; obtuse

15. 140°; obtuse 16. 155°; obtuse

17. 18. 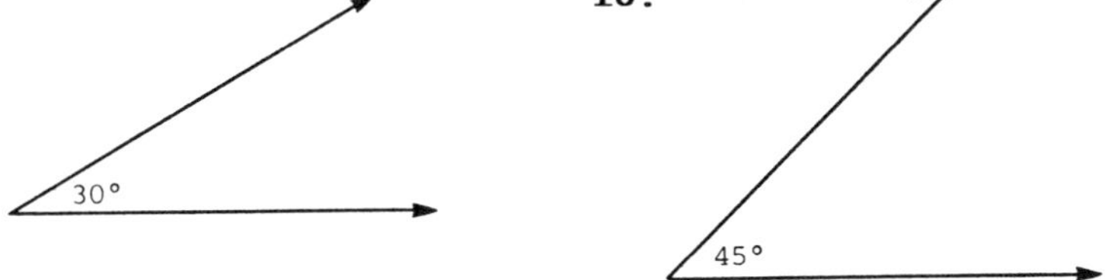

19. 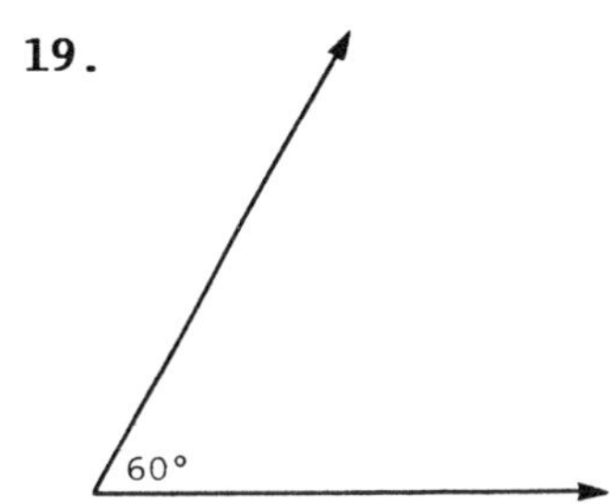

20. 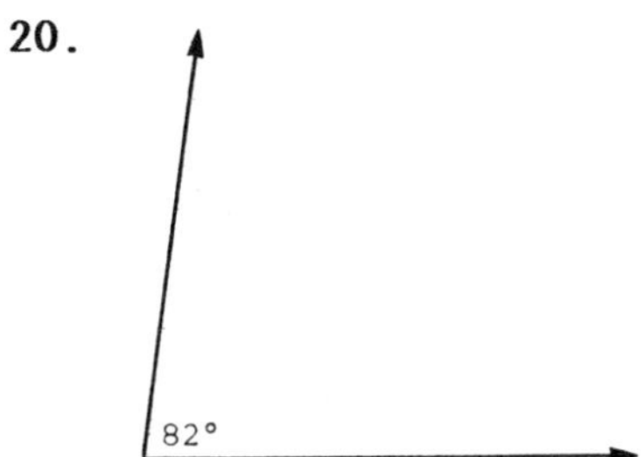

21. 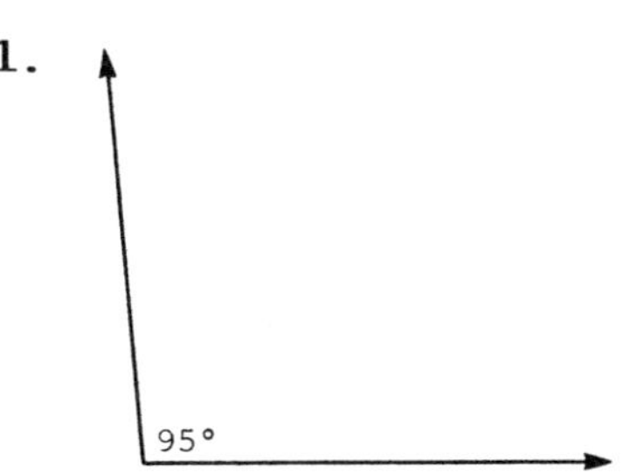

22. 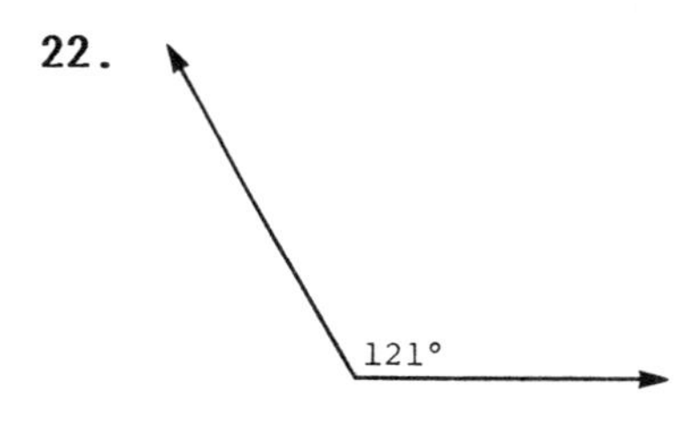

23. CBD and EBA; CBE and DBA 24. SQT and PQR; SQP and TQR

25. (a) 52° (b) 128° 26. (a) 126° (b) 54° 27. 32° 28. 5°

29. 77° 30. 45° 31. 75° 32. 55° 33. 166° 34. 90°

35. $x = 10$; $(7x)° = 70°$ and $(11x)° = 110°$ **36.** $x = 15$; $(2x)° = 30°$ and $(4x)° = 60°$
37. $x = 10$; $(5x + 5)° = 55°$ and $(3x + 5)° = 35°$ **38.** $x = 10$; $(10x + 7)° = 107°$ and $(7x + 3)° = 73°$ **39.** $x = 9$; $(10x + 15)° = 105°$ and $(12x - 3)° = 105°$
40. $x = 10$; $(7x + 5)° = 75°$ and $(3x + 45)° = 75°$ **41.** $x = 27$; $(2x - 5)° = 49°$ and $(x + 22)° = 49°$ **42.** $x = 28$; $(2x + 61)° = 117°$ and $(6x - 51)° = 117°$
43. $x = 47$; $(x + 1)° = 48°$ and $(4x - 56)° = 132°$ **44.** $x = 13$; $(15x - 54)° = 141°$ and $(10x + 11)° = 141°$ **45.** (a) ③ (b) ⑥ (c) ⑦ (d) ⑦; exterior
46. Use the sketch for Exercise 45 to show that angles ③ and ⑤ are supplementary.
(a) measure of ∡③ + measure of ∡④ = 180°, since they form a straight angle.
(b) measure of ∡④ = measure of ∡⑤, since they are alternate interior angles.
(c) measure of ∡③ + measure of ∡⑤ = 180°, by substitution of the result of (b) into the equation in (a). (d) By the result of (c) and the definition of supplementary angles, interior angles on the same side of a transversal are supplementary.
47. $x = 36$; $(5x - 129)° = 51°$ and $(2x - 21)° = 51°$ **48.** $x = 16$; $(11x - 37)° = 139°$ and $(7x + 27)° = 139°$ **49.** (a) 180 (b) 180 (c) 180, 180 (d) 0 (e) 0 (f) ∡③ **50.** 90°, 45° **51.** 55° **52.** 120° **53.** 60° **54.** 60°
55. 60° **56.** 60° **57.** 65° **58.** 55° **59.** 55° **60.** 180°
61. $x = 10$, $y = 30$ **62.** 50°

Section 9.2 (page 439)

1. Both simple and closed **2.** Simple **3.** Closed **4.** Both simple and closed
5. Closed **6.** Simple **7.** Neither **8.** Both simple and closed, and a polygon
9. Both simple and closed, and a polygon **10.** Both simple and closed **11.** Closed
12. Neither **13.** Convex **14.** Not convex **15.** Convex **16.** Convex
17. Not convex **18.** Not convex **19.** 78° **20.** 52° **21.** 60° **22.** 48°
23. 77° **24.** 20° **25.** 74° **26.** 83° **27.** 45° **28.** 104°
29. Acute, scalene **30.** Obtuse, scalene **31.** Acute, equilateral
32. Acute, isosceles **33.** Right, scalene **34.** Obtuse, isosceles

35. Right, isosceles **36.** Right, scalene **37.** Obtuse, scalene

38. Acute, equilateral **39.** Acute, isosceles **40.** Right, scalene

41. True **42.** True **43.** False **44.** True **45.** True **46.** False

47. True **48.** False **49.** (a) 4; $4 \cdot 180° = 720°$ (b) 5; $5 \cdot 180° = 900°$

(c) 6; $6 \cdot 180° = 1080°$ **50.** 2; $s - 2$; $S = (s - 2) \cdot 180°$ **51.** 1260° **52.** 1620°

53. 1800° **54.** 5040° **55.** 6120° **56.** 6840° **57.** 14,940° **58.** 25,380°

59. (e) The sum of the angles of a triangle is 180° (one-half of a complete rotation).

60. $x = 35/8$ **61.** $x = 15$ **62.** $x = 30$ **63.** 0 **64.** $\overline{OA}$, $\overline{OC}$, $\overline{OB}$, $\overline{OD}$

65. $\overline{AC}$, $\overline{DB}$ **66.** $\overline{AC}$, $\overline{BD}$, $\overline{BC}$, $\overline{AB}$ **67.** $\overleftrightarrow{BC}$, $\overleftrightarrow{AB}$ **68.** $\overleftrightarrow{AE}$

69. m(∡①) + m(∡②) + m(∡③) = 180°; m(∡③) + m(∡⑥) = 180°;

m(∡①) + m(∡②) + m(∡③) − [m(∡③) + m(∡⑥)] = 180° − 180°;

m(∡①) + m(∡②) − m(∡⑥) = 0°; m(∡①) + m(∡②) = m(∡⑥)

Section 9.3 (page 445)

1. $c = 17$ **2.** $b = 24$ **3.** $a = 13$ **4.** $b = 7$ cm **5.** $c = 50$ m

6. $b = 96$ km **7.** $a = 20$ ft **8.** $a = 21$ in **9.** $c = 34$ m **10.** $a = 16$ cm

11. $b = 18$ km **12.** Yes **13.** Yes **14.** No **15.** No **16.** No **17.** No

18. $a^2 = 36$; $b^2 = 64$; $c^2 = 100$; $36 + 64 = 100$. The Pythagorean theorem does hold. Thus, the triangle is a right triangle. **19.** $a^2 = 16$; $b^2 = 121$; $c^2 = 144$; $16 + 121 \neq 144$. The Pythagorean theorem does not hold. Thus, the triangle is not a right triangle. **20.** $a = r^2 - s^2 = (4)^2 - (3)^2 = 16 - 9 = 7$; $b = 2rs = 2(4)(3) = 24$; $c = r^2 + s^2 = (4)^2 + (3)^2 = 16 + 9 = 25$ **21.** $a = 13$, $b = 84$, $c = 85$

22. $a = 63$, $b = 16$, $c = 65$ **23.–25.** Answers will vary depending upon the values chosen for r and s. **26.** If $r = 6$ and $s = 8$, a comes out negative, and a triangle can't have a side with a negative length.

27. $a^2 + b^2 = (r^2 - s^2)^2 + (2rs)^2$

$= r^4 - 2r^2s^2 + s^4 + 4r^2s^2$

$= r^4 + 2r^2s^2 + s^4$

$= (r^2 + s^2)^2$

$= c^2$

28. $\sqrt{2x^2 + 4x + 4}$ **29.** $\sqrt{8r}$ or $2\sqrt{2r}$ **30.** $\sqrt{16y - 16}$ or $4\sqrt{y - 1}$ **31.** $\sqrt{3a^2 - 4a + 1}$ **32.** $x = 3$ **33.** $x = 8$

34. $x = 7$ **35.** $x = 12$ **36.** 24 m **37.** 8 cm, 15 cm, 17 cm **38.** 16 m

39. Length 4 cm, width 3 cm **40.** 24 in **41.** 30 ft **42.** 31.6 ft **43.** $74.52

Section 9.4 (page 454)

1. 12 cm^2 **2.** 9 cm^2 **3.** 5 cm^2 **4.** 3 cm^2 **5.** 8 cm^2 **6.** 10 cm^2

7. 4.5 cm^2 **8.** 936 mm^2 **9.** 418 mm^2 **10.** 7.5 m^2 **11.** 8 cm^2

12. 13.5 cm^2 **13.** C = 6.3 cm; A = 3.1 cm^2 **14.** C = 94.2 cm; A = 706.5 cm^2

15. C = 113.0 m; A = 1017.4 m^2 **16.** C = 37.7 m; A = 113.0 m^2 **17.** 20 cm^2

18. 80 cm^2 **19.** 180 cm^2 **20.** 320 cm^2 **21.** (a) 4 (b) 3; 9 (c) 4; 16 (d) n^2 **22.** $320 **23.** $1200 **24.** $156 **25.** $1350

26. $218.50 **27.** $16 **28.** $3 **29.** $1120 **30.** $22.50 **31.** 76.26

32. 124 **33.** 80 **34.** 265.12 **35.** 164.48 **36.** 115 **37.** 132 ft^2

38. 868 cm^2 **39.** 5376 cm^2 **40.** 250 cm^2 **41.** 309.9 ft^2 **42.** 145.3 m^2

43. 244.9 cm^2 **44.** 56.5 cm^2 **45.** 100.5 cm^2 **46.** 6.9 m^2 **47.** 174.7 cm^2

48. 44.5 cm^2 **49.** 448.7 m^2 **50.** 860.8 mm^2 **51.** 117.6 cm^2 **52.** (a) 9 km^2 (b) 500 (c) 4500 km^2 (d) 1/20 **53.** x = 14.5 cm **54.** x = 11 cm

55. x = 7 m **56.** x = 23 in **57.** x = 5 cm **58.** x = 7.5 cm

59. x = 5.1 cm **60.** x = 4 cm **61.** x = 5 in **62.** x = 2.4 cm

63. (a) $a + b$; $a + b$; $a^2 + 2ab + b^2$ (b) $\frac{1}{2}ab$; $2ab$; c^2 (c) $2ab + c^2$ (d) $a^2 + 2ab + b^2$; $2ab + c^2$ (e) $a^2 + b^2$; c^2

64. As the area of a trapezoid, the area is $\frac{1}{2}(a + b)(a + b)$. As the sum of the areas of three triangles, the area is $\frac{1}{2}c^2 + \frac{1}{2}ab + \frac{1}{2}ab$. Setting these two expressions equal to each other and simplifying leads to $a^2 + b^2 = c^2$.

Section 9.5 (page 464)

1. V: 3.8 m^3; SA: 14.8 m^2 **2.** V: 96 cm^3; SA: 128 cm^2 **3.** V: 96 m^3; SA: 130.4 m^2 **4.** V: 45,000 mm^3; SA: 8700 mm^2 **5.** 168 **6.** 160 **7.** 1436.0 m^3 **8.** 267,946.7 mm^3 **9.** 1696.5 cm^3 **10.** 549.5 cm^3 **11.** 1808.6 m^3 **12.** 3297 cm^3 **13.** 65.9 m^3 **14.** 100.5 cm^3 **15.** 1969.1 cm^3 **16.** 305.5 cm^3 **17.** 427.3 cm^3 **18.** 125.6 cm^3 **19.** 508.7 cm^3 **20.** 30.4 cm^3 **21.** 2.1 liters **22.** 1.57 liters **23.** 1.7 liters **24.** 2.46 liters **25.** 74.7 m^3 **26.** 133.3 m^3 **27.** 2,415,766.7 m^3 **28.** 1,461,732.8 m^3 **29.** .5 m^3 **30.** 3663.3 cm^3 **31.** (a) 4.2 m^3 (b) 33.5 m^3 (c) 8 times (d) 113.0 m^3 (e) 27 times **32.** $8100 **33.** $19,200 **34.** $37,500 **35.** .00052 mm^3 **36.** 536.8 m^3 **37.** (a) 4, 4, 6, 8 (b) 6, 8, 12, 14 (c) 8, 6, 12, 14 (d) 12, 20, 30, 32 (e) 20, 12, 30, 32 **38.** 2, E + 2 **39.** x = 2.5 cm **40.** x = 9 cm **41.** x = 9 cm **42.** x = 12 cm **43.** x = 5 cm **44.** x = 10 cm

Section 9.6 (page 470)

1. A and P; C and R; B and Q; AC and PR; CB and RQ; AB and PQ **2.** M and Q; N and R; P and S; PN and RS; MN and QR; MP and QS **3.** X and P; Y and Q; Z and R; XY and PQ; XZ and PR; YZ and QR **4.** Similar **5.** Similar **6.** Not similar **7.** Not similar **8.** Similar **9.** Not similar **10.** P = 78°, M = 46°, A = N = 56° **11.** Q = 42°, P = 90°, B = R = 48° **12.** T = 74°, Y = 28°, Z = W = 78° **13.** B = 106°, A = M = 44° **14.** T = 20°, V = 64°, R = U = 96° **15.** M = X = 52° **16.** a = 5, b = 3 **17.** a = 30, b = 60 **18.** a = 6, b = 7 1/2 **19.** a = 2 **20.** x = 6 **21.** m = 18 **22.** 30 m **23.** 1.75 m **24.** 108 ft **25.** 112.5 ft **26.** 500 m, 700 m **27.** Phoenix to Tucson, 153 km; Tucson to Yuma, 326 km **28.** x = 110 **29.** y = 12 **30.** c = 111 1/9 **31.** m = 85 1/3 **32.** All similar **33.** All similar **34.** Not similar **35.** Not similar

36. The missing side in the first quadrilateral is 40 cm; the missing sides in the second one are 27 cm and 36 cm. **37.** 506 2/3 ft **38.** x = 10, y = 5

39. x = 10, y = 2 **40.** x = 20, y = 10 **41.** x = 8, y = 12 **42.** x = 5/2, y = 5

43. x = 9, y = 6

Section 9.7 (page 476)

1. About 90° **2.** About 90° **3.** About 90° **4.** About 270° **5.** About 295°

6. About 375° **7.** About 300° **8.** About 260° **9.** A is about 40°; B is about 10°; C is about 30°. **10.** A is about 40°; B is about 20°; C is about 15°.

11. A is about 10°; B is about 30°; C is about 40°. **12.** The sum is less than 180°.

13. About 70° **14.** About 115° **15.** About 60° **16.** About 85°

In Exercises 17–24, the answers depend on the size of globe you use. These answers are based on a globe with diameter about 16 in.

17. About 65° **18.** About 50° **19.** About 105° **20.** About 220°

21. About 30° **22.** About 85° **23.** About 70° **24.** About 185°

Section 9.8 (page 484)

1. C **2.** A, E **3.** A, E **4.** B, D **5.** A, E **6.** A, E **7.** B, D

8. C **9.** B, D **10.** B, D **11.** No **12.** Yes **13.** Yes **14.** 0

15. 1 **16.** 0 **17.** 1, 2, or 3, depending on the pretzel **18.** 1 **19.** 1

20. 1 **21.** 2 **22.** 0 **23.** 1 **24.** 1 **25.** 0 **26.** 1 **27.** 2

28. 2 even, 2 odd **29.** 0 even, 6 odd **30.** 0 even, 6 odd **31.** 3 even, 4 odd

32. 15 even, 0 odd

33. Traversible **34.** Not traversible **35.** Traversible

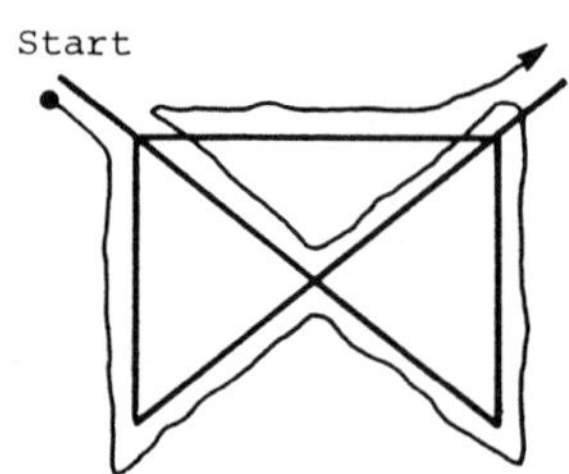

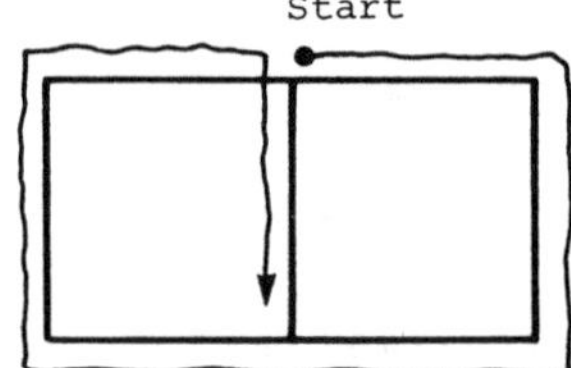

36. Traversible

Start

37. Not traversible

38. Traversible

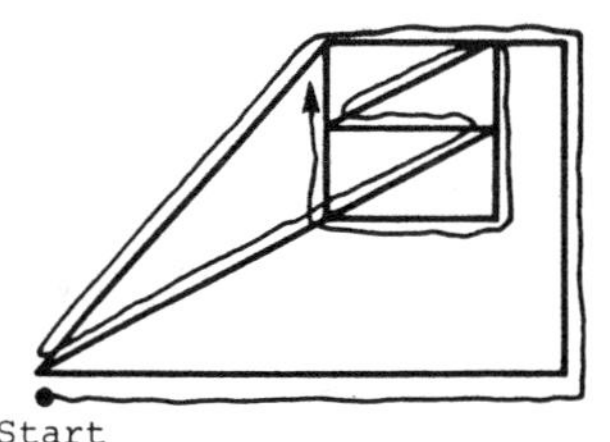

39. Yes **40.** No **41.** Yes **42.** No

Chapter 9 Test (page 490)

1.

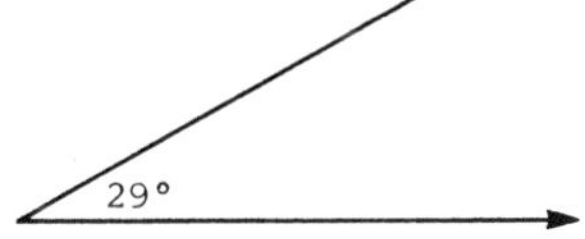

2.

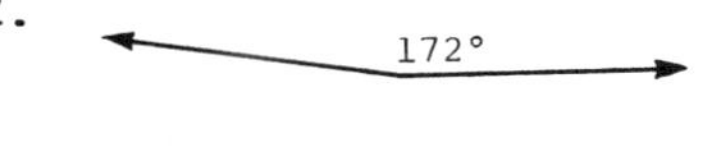

3. 106° **4.** 90°

5. x = 17 **6.** y = 11

7. C = 111° **8.** x = 10

9. 16 **10.** Both simple and closed **11.** Neither

12. 72 **13.** 60 **14.** 68 **15.** 180 **16.** $152 **17.** $54,000

18. 650 m^2 **19.** 2915.1 m^2 **20.** 57 cm^2 **21.** 904.32 **22.** 864 **23.** 336

24. 1582.56 **25.** x = 11.5 m **26.** 301.44 m^3 **27.** p = 8, q = 10

28. n = 60, m = 45 **29.** r = 108/7 **30.** k = 14

CHAPTER 10

Section 10.1 (page 502)

1. AA, AB, AC, AD, AE, BA, BB, BC, BD, BE, CA, CB, CC, CD, CE, DA, DB, DC, DD, DE, EA, EB, EC, ED, EE; 25 ways **2.** CA, CB, CD, CE, EA, EB, EC, ED; 8 ways **3.** AC, AE, BC, BE, CA, CB, CD, DC, DE, EA, EB, ED; 12 ways **4.** AB, AC, AD, AE, BA, BC, BD, BE, CA, CB, CD, CE, DA, DB, DC, DE, EA, EB, EC, ED; 20 ways **5.** ACE, AEC, BCE, BEC, DCE, DEC; 6 ways **6.** ACB, ACD, AEB, AED, BCA, BCD, BEA, BED, DCA, DCB, DEA, DEB; 12 ways **7.** ABC, ABD, ABE, ACD, ACE, ADE, BCD, BCE, BDE, CDE; 10 ways **8.** ABC, ABD, ABE, ACD, ADE, BCD, BDE; 7 ways **9.** (1, 1); 1 way **10.** (2, 1), (1, 2); 2 ways **11.** (3, 1), (2, 2), (1, 3); 3 ways **12.** (4, 1), (3, 2), (2, 3), (1, 4); 4 ways **13.** (5, 1), (4, 2), (3, 3), (2, 4), (1, 5); 5 ways **14.** (6, 1), (5, 2), (4, 3), (3, 4), (2, 5), (1, 6); 6 ways **15.** (6, 2), (5, 3), (4, 4), (3, 5), (2, 6); 5 ways **16.** (6, 3), (5, 4), (4, 5), (3, 6); 4 ways **17.** (6, 4), (5, 5), (4, 6); 3 ways **18.** (6, 5), (5, 6); 2 ways **19.** (6, 6); 1 way **20.** (2, 1), (1, 2), (4, 1), (3, 2), (2, 3), (1, 4), (6, 1), (5, 2), (4, 3), (3, 4), (2, 5), (1, 6), (6, 3), (5, 4), (4, 5), (3, 6), (6, 5), (5, 6); 18 ways **21.** (1, 1), (3, 1), (2, 2), (1, 3), (5, 1), (4, 2), (3, 3), (2, 4), (1, 5), (6, 2), (5, 3), (4, 4), (3, 5), (2, 6), (6, 4), (5, 5), (4, 6), (6, 6); 18 ways **22.** (4, 1), (3, 2), (2, 3), (1, 4), (5, 1), (4, 2), (3, 3), (2, 4), (1, 5), (6, 1), (5, 2), (4, 3), (3, 4), (2, 5), (1, 6), (6, 2), (5, 3), (4, 4), (3, 5), (2, 6), (6, 3), (5, 4), (4, 5), (3, 6); 24 ways **23.** (5, 1), (4, 2), (3, 3), (2, 4), (1, 5), (6, 1), (5, 2), (4, 3), (3, 4), (2, 5), (1, 6), (6, 2), (5, 3), (4, 4), (3, 5), (2, 6); 16 ways

24.

		Second digit					
		0	1	2	3	4	5
	1	10	11	12	13	14	15
First	2	20	21	22	23	24	25
digit	3	30	31	32	33	34	35
	4	40	41	42	43	44	45
	5	50	51	52	53	54	55

25. 15 **26.** 15

27. 10 **28.** 25

29.

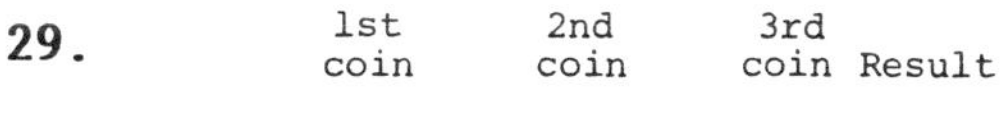

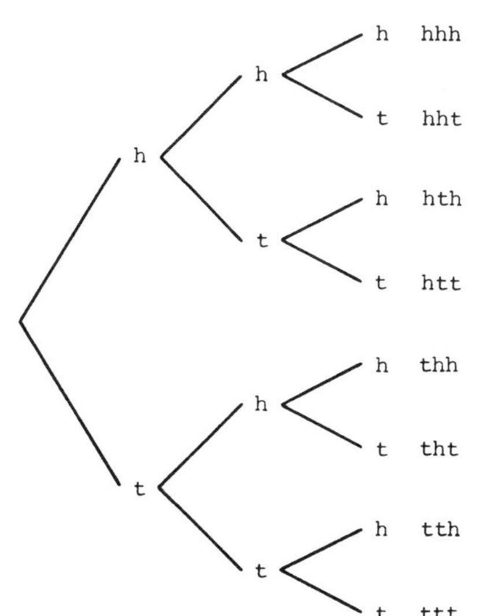

(a) hhh, hht, hth, thh (b) hhh

(c) hht, hth, htt, thh, tht, tth, ttt

(d) htt, tht, tth, ttt

30.

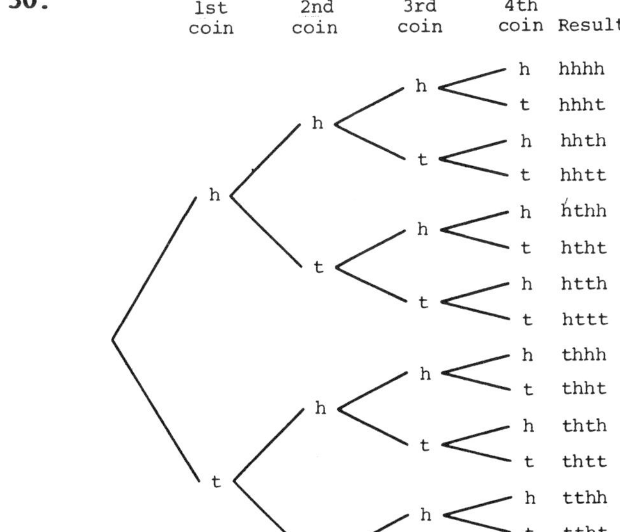

(a) tttt

(b) hhhh, hhht, hhth, hhtt, hthh, htht, htth, thhh, thht, thth, tthh

(c) httt, thtt, ttht, ttth, tttt

(d) hhhh, hhht, hhth, hhtt, hthh, htht, htth, httt, thhh, thht, thth, thtt, tthh, ttht, ttth

31.

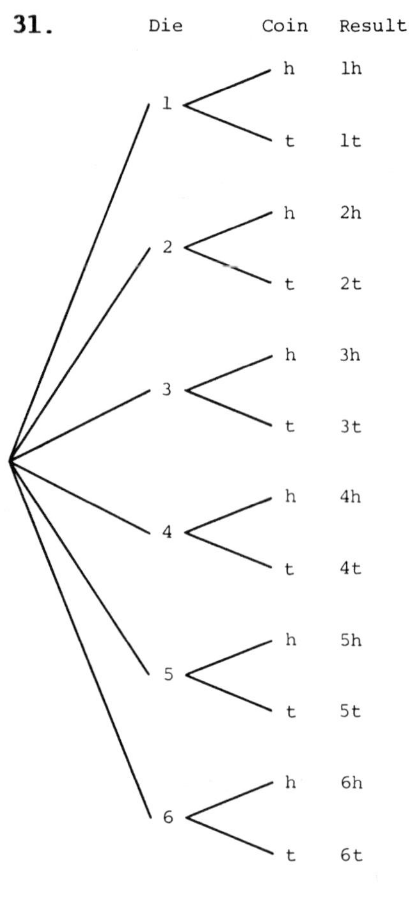

32.

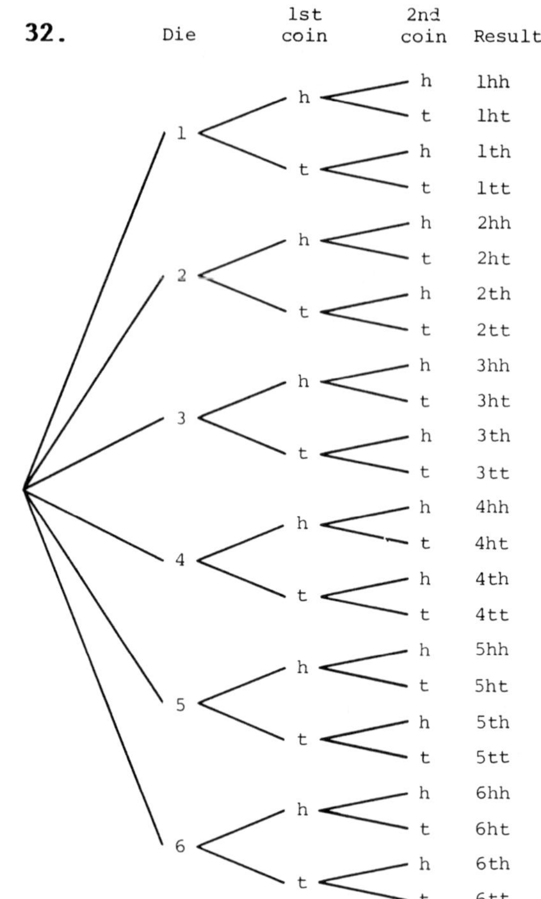

33. 16 **34.** 17 **35.** 17 **36.** 21 **37.** 8 **38.** 12 **39.** 8

40. 20 **41.** 46 **42.** 31 **43.** 15 **44.** 21

45. He has 10 choices.

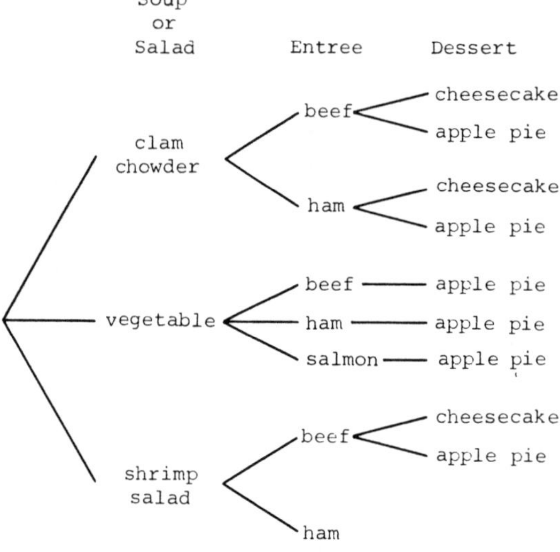

Section 10.2 (page 506)

1. When a task consists of two or more parts, the number of ways of completing the task is the product of the numbers of ways of completing the various parts.

2. $2^4 = 16$ **3.** $6^2 \cdot 2^3 = 288$ **4.** $2^6 = 64$ **5.** $2^{12} = 4096$ **6.** $4^{10} = 1,048,576$

7. $8^2 \cdot 10^5 = 6,400,000$ **8.** $9 \cdot 10^8 = 900,000,000$ **9.** $2^5 = 32$

10. $4 \cdot 5 \cdot 6 \cdot 3 \cdot 3 \cdot 2 \cdot 2 \cdot 2 = 8640$ **11.** $3 \cdot 2 \cdot 2 \cdot 2 = 24$ **12.** $3 \cdot 2 = 6$ **13.** $2 \cdot 2 \cdot 3 \cdot 2 \cdot 2 \cdot 2 = 96$

14. $3 \cdot 4 \cdot 2 = 24$ **15.** $26^2 \cdot 9^2 \cdot 10^2 = 5,475,600$ **16.** $18 \cdot 25 \cdot 24 \cdot 23 \cdot 22 = 5,464,800$

17. $5 \cdot 6^2 = 180$ **18.** $5 \cdot 6 \cdot 2 = 60$ **19.** $5 \cdot 6 \cdot 3 = 90$ **20.** $3 \cdot 6^2 = 108$

21. $5^2 \cdot 4 = 100$ **22.** $4^7 = 16,384$ **23.** $3^7 = 2187$ **24.** $2 \cdot 4^4 = 512$

25. $7^4 = 2401$ **26.** $3 \cdot 2 \cdot 2 \cdot 6 \cdot 4 \cdot 5 = 1440$ **27.** $2 \cdot 2 \cdot 6 \cdot 4 = 96$ **28.** $4 \cdot 5 = 20$

29. $2(3 \cdot 2 \cdot 6 \cdot 4 \cdot 1) = 288$

30. (a) 6 (b) 5 (c) 4 (d) 3 (e) 2 (f) 1; then $6 \cdot 5 \cdot 4 \cdot 3 \cdot 2 \cdot 1 = 720$

31. (a) 5 (b) 2 (c) 4 (d) 3 (e) 2 (f) 1; then $5 \cdot 2 \cdot 4 \cdot 3 \cdot 2 \cdot 1 = 240$

32. (a) 3 (b) 3 (c) 2 (d) 2 (e) 1 (f) 1; then $3 \cdot 3 \cdot 2 \cdot 2 \cdot 1 \cdot 1 = 36$

33. (a) 6 (b) 3 (c) 2 (d) 2 (e) 1 (f) 1; then $6 \cdot 3 \cdot 2 \cdot 2 \cdot 1 \cdot 1 = 72$

Section 10.3 (page 516)

1. $3 \cdot 2 \cdot 1 = 6$ **2.** $9 \cdot 8 \cdot 7 \cdot 6 \cdot 5 \cdot 4 \cdot 3 \cdot 2 \cdot 1 = 362,880$ **3.** $362,880 - 6 = 362,874$

4. $6! = 720$ **5.** $9 \cdot 6 = 54$ **6.** $362,880/6 = 60,480$ **7.** $3! = 6$

8. $362,880/720 = 504$ **9.** $362,880/(6 \cdot 6!) = 362,880/(6 \cdot 720) = 362,880/4320 = 84$

10. 8 **11.** $4 \cdot 3 = 12$ **12.** $10 \cdot 9 \cdot 8 = 720$ **13.** $7 \cdot 6 \cdot 5 \cdot 4 \cdot 3 = 2520$

14. $6 \cdot 5 \cdot 4 \cdot 3 \cdot 2 \cdot 1 = 720$ **15.** 1 **16.** $13 \cdot 12 \cdot 11 = 1716$ **17.** $15 \cdot 14 \cdot 13 \cdot 12 \cdot 11 = 360,360$ **18.** $12 \cdot 11 \cdot 10 \cdot 9 \cdot 8 \cdot 7 = 665,280$ **19.** $25 \cdot 24 \cdot 23 \cdot 22 = 303,600$

20. $30 \cdot 29 \cdot 28 \cdot 27 \cdot 26 \cdot 25 \cdot 24 \cdot 23 \cdot 22 \cdot 21 = 109,027,350,432,000$ **21.** $8 \cdot 7 \cdot 6 = 336$

22. $4 \cdot 3 \cdot 2 \cdot 1 = 24$ **23.** $12 \cdot 11 = 132$ **24.** 1 **25.** $18 \cdot 17 \cdot 16 \cdot 15 \cdot 14 = 1,028,160$

26. $16 \cdot 15 \cdot 14 \cdot 13 \cdot 12 \cdot 11 \cdot 10 \cdot 9 = 518,918,400$ **27.** 362,880 **28.** 87,178,291,200

29. $5! = 120$ **30.** $8! = 40,320$ **31.** $P(8, 3) = 336$ **32.** $P(10, 3) = 720$

33. $6! = 720$ **34.** $P(6, 4) = 360$ **35.** $P(7, 2) = 42$ **36.** $2 \cdot P(25, 2) = 1200$

37. 2•P(25, 3) = 27,600 **38.** 7! = 5040 **39.** 6!/2! = 360 **40.** 10!/(3!•2!•2!) = 151,200 **41.** P(26, 5)•P(10, 8)•P(26, 2) = 9,309,396,096,000,000 **42.** P(26, 5)•P(10, 8)•P(21, 2) = 6,015,302,092,800,000 **43.** (a) 11! = 39,916,800 (b) 6!•5! = 86,400 (c) 6!•5! = 86,400 (d) 6•6!•5! = 518,400 (e) 2•6!•5! = 172,800 **44.** (a) 9! = 362,880 (b) 5!•4! = 2880 (c) 8! = 40,320 (d) 4•3•7! = 60,480 (e) 6•4!•5! = 17,280 **45.** (a) P(8, 5) = 6720 (b) P(15, 5) = 360,360 (c) P(5, 2)•P(2, 1)•P(8, 2) = 2240 (d) 2•P(13, 2)•1 = 3432 (e) P(8, 3)•P(5, 2) = 6720 **46.** (a) 7! = 5040 (b) P(7, 5) = 2520 (c) 4!•3! = 144 (d) 3•2•5! = 720 (e) 4•6! = 2880

Section 10.4 (page 522)

1. 15 **2.** 56 **3.** 210 **4.** 495 **5.** 1 **6.** 1 **7.** 1 **8.** 2002 **9.** 184,756 **10.** 3,268,760 **11.** 1,715,884,494,940 **12.** 2,250,829,575,120 **13.** No. Size-6 subsets cannot be selected from a size-4 set. **14.** No. Size-12 subsets cannot be selected from a size-8 set. **15.** 15 **16.** 8 **17.** 252 **18.** 4845 **19.** 133,784,560 **20.** 7,307,872,110 **21.** C(50, 4) = 230,300 **22.** C(20, 10) = 184,756 **23.** C(100, 4) = 3,921,225 **24.** C(5, 2) = 10 **25.** C(12, 3) = 220 **26.** C(10, 5) = 252 **27.** C(12, 4) = 495 **28.** C(10, 4) = 210 **29.** C(6, 4)•C(8, 3) = 15•56 = 840 **30.** 7•C(10, 2) = 7•45 = 315 **31.** C(5, 2) = 10 **32.** C(5, 2) − 1 = 10 − 1 = 9 **33.** C(14, 8) = 3003 **34.** 0 (Impossible) **35.** C(12, 5) = 792 **36.** C(40, 5) = 658,008 **37.** C(12, 2)•C(40, 3) = 652,080 **38.** C(13, 1)•C(13, 2)•C(13, 2) = 79,092 **39.** C(26, 5) = 65,780 **40.** C(13, 5) = 1287 **41.** C(6, 2) = 6!/(2!•4!) = 15 and C(6, 4) = 6!/(4!•2!) = 15 **42.** C(10, 7) = 120 and C(10, 3) = 120 **43.** C(n, r) = n!/[r!•(n − r)!] and C(n, n − r) = n!/[(n − r)!•(n − (n − r))]! = n!/[(n − r)!•r!] = n!/[r!•(n − r)!] **44.** C(16, 6) = 8008 **45.** C(3, 2)•C(5, 2)•C(8, 2) = 840 **46.** C(3, 1)•C(5, 2)•C(8, 3) = 1680 **47.** C(8, 3)•C(8, 3) = 3136 **48.** C(8, 6) = 28 **49.** 0 (Impossible) **50.** C(8, 6) = 28

51. C(20, 3)•C(10, 2) = 51,300 **52.** C(5, 3) = 10 **53.** C(5, 4) = 5

54. (a) C(12, 6)•C(6, 6) = 924•1 = 924 (b) C(12, 4)•C(8, 4)•C(4, 4) = 495•70•1 = 34,650 (c) C(12, 3)•C(9, 3)•C(6, 3)•C(3, 3) = 220•84•20•1 = 369,600
(d) C(12, 2)•C(10, 2)•C(8, 2)•C(6, 2)•C(4, 2)•C(2, 2) = 66•45•28•15•6•1 = 7,484,400

55. C(20, 6)•C(14, 5)•C(9, 4)•C(5, 3)•C(2, 2) = (38,760)(2002)(126)(10)(1) = 97,772,875,200

56. C(40, 8)•C(32, 8)•C(24, 8)•C(16, 8)•C(8, 8) = (76,904,685)(10,518,300)(735,471)(12,870)(1) = 7,656,714,453,150,000,000,000,000

Section 10.5 (page 528)

1. 32 - 1 = 31 **2.** 32 - (1 + 5) = 26 **3.** 2^8 - 1 = 256 - 1 = 255

4. 2^8 - (1 + 8) = 247 **5.** 256 - (1 + 8) = 247 **6.** 6 **7.** 3 + 2 + 1 = 6

8. 6 + 6 - 1 = 11 **9.** 36 - (1 + 2) = 33 **10.** 36 - 6 = 30

11. 635,013,559,600 - 1 = 635,013,559,599 **12.** 635,013,559,600 - 4 = 635,013,559,596

13. 635,013,559,600 - C(40, 13) = 622,980,336,720

14. 635,013,559,600 - [C(39, 13) + 1] = 626,891,134,155 **15.** 9•10•10•6 = 5400

16. (5•10^3 - 1) + (9•10•1^2) - 49 = 5040 **17.** 2^{15} - (1 + 15) = 32,768 - 16 = 32,752

18. 2^{15} - [C(15, 13) + C(15, 14) + C(15, 15)] = 32,647

19. 2^{15} - [C(15, 0) + C(15, 1) + C(15, 2) + C(15, 14) + C(15, 15)] = 32,631

20. 65 + 40 - 18 = 87 **21.** 100 - (47 + 18 + 22) = 13 **22.** 13 + 26 - 13 = 26

23. 12 + 26 - 6 = 32 **24.** 1 in each suit: 4•1 = 4 **25.** 9 in each suit: 4•9 = 36

26. Within each suit there are C(13, 5) = 1287 different hands. Of these, 1 is a royal flush and 9 are straight flushes. 4(1287 - 10) = 4(1277) = 5108

27. The total number containing 5 successive denominations is 10•4^5 = 10,240. Of these, 36 are straight flushes and 4 are royal flushes. 10,240 - (36 + 4) = 10,200

28. 5•6•3 = 90 **29.** 5•6•1 = 30 **30.** 5•1•1 = 5

31. 5•1•1 = 5 end in 00; 5•1•1 = 5 end in 25; 5•1•1 = 5 end in 50; 5 + 5 + 5 = 15

33. 13 + 12 + 20 - 3 - 5 - 12 + 3 = 28 **34.** 13 + 4 + 26 - 1 - 13 - 2 + 1 = 28

Section 10.6 (page 534)

1. P(7, 3) = 210 **2.** P(7, 2) = 42 **3.** 3•P(6, 2) = 90 **4.** C(5, 4) = 5
5. 0 (Impossible) **6.** C(5, 2)•C(3, 2) = 30 **7.** C(5, 3)•C(3, 1) = 30
8. C(5, 1)•C(3, 3) = 5 **9.** C(5, 1)•C(3, 3) = 5 **10.** C(5, 4)•C(3, 0) + C(5, 3)•C(3, 1) = 35 **11.** C(4, 2) = 6 **12.** $5^3 = 125$ **13.** $5^2 \cdot 2 = 50$
14. 5•4•3 = 60 **15.** $40^3 = 64{,}000$ **16.** C(8, 2) = 28 **17.** C(8, 5) = 56
18. C(11, 5) = 462 **19.** C(8, 3)•C(11, 2) = 3080 **20.** C(8, 3)•C(11, 2) + C(8, 4)•C(11, 1) + C(8, 5)•C(11, 0) = 3906 **21.** 8•8•1 + 8•9•1 = 136
22. C(10, 5)•C(12, 5)•10! = 724,250,419,200 **23.** 2•P(10, 5)•P(12, 5) = 5,748,019,200
24. 6•P(10, 5)•P(12, 5) = 17,244,057,600 **25.** C(8, 5) = 56
26. C(1, 1)•C(7, 4) = 35 **27.** 56 - C(6, 3) = 36 **28.** C(5, 3) = 10
29. SSSDD, SSDSD, SSDDS, SDSSD, SDDSS, DSSSD, DSSDS, DSDSS, DDSSS **30.** C(5, 1) = 5
31. C(5, 2)•C(5, 3)•C(5, 4) = 500 **32.** 3!•C(5, 2)•C(5, 3)•C(5, 4) = 3000
33. C(14, 3) = 364 **34.** C(3, 1)•C(6, 1)•C(5, 1) = 90 **35.** C(3, 3) = 1
36. C(3, 2)•C(6, 1) = 18 **37.** C(6, 2)•C(5, 1) = 75 **38.** C(6, 1)•C(5, 2) = 60
39. C(5, 3) = 10 **40.** None **41.** C(13, 3) = 286 **42.** C(4, 3) = 4
43. 0 (Impossible) **44.** 4•4•4 = 64 **45.** C(5, 4) = 5 **46.** 0 (Impossible)
47. C(5, 2)•C(3, 2) = 30 **48.** C(5, 1)•C(3, 3) = 5 **49.** C(5, 3)•C(3, 1) = 30
50. C(5, 3)•C(3, 1) + C(5, 4)•C(3, 0) = 35 **51.** 5 + 0 = 5 **52.** C(5, 4)•C(3, 0) + C(5, 3)•C(3, 1) + C(5, 2)•C(3, 2) = 65 **53.** There are 13 choices for the denomination of the 4-of-a-kind hand and 48 choices for the fifth card. 13•48 = 624
54. 13•36 = 468

Chapter 10 Test (page 537)

1. 11

2.

		Second digit			
		0	2	4	6
	1	10	12	14	16
First digit	3	30	32	34	36
	4	40	42	44	46
	5	50	52	54	56
	6	60	62	64	66

3.

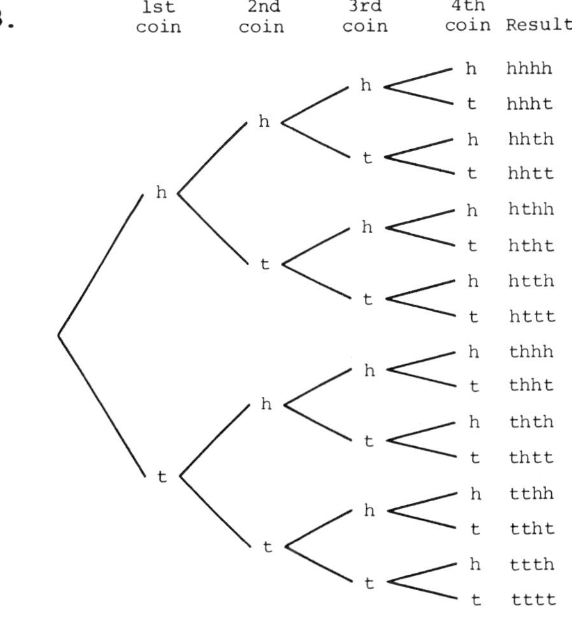

4. $4 \cdot 6 \cdot 2 = 48$ **5.** $4 \cdot 4 \cdot 1 = 16$ **6.** $7 \cdot 8^3 = 3584$ **7.** $7 \cdot 8^2 \cdot 4 = 1792$

8. $7 \cdot 7 \cdot 6 \cdot 5 = 1470$ **9.** $7 \cdot 8^2 \cdot 1 = 448$ **10.** $3^6 = 729$ **11.** $6!/3!2! = 60$

12. 24 **13.** 360 **14.** 6 **15.** 720 **16.** 120 **17.** 56 **18.** 1

19. $6! = 720$ **20.** $5 \cdot 6 = 30$ **21.** (a) 6720 (b) 1320 **22.** 126 **23.** 1

24. $C(100, 5) = 75,287,520$ **25.** $C(13, 5) = 1287$ **26.** $C(13, 1) \cdot C(13, 2) \cdot C(26, 2) = 329,550$ **27.** $C(26, 0) \cdot C(26, 5) + C(26, 1) \cdot C(26, 4) + C(26, 2) \cdot C(26, 3) = 1,299,480$

28. 4 **29.** $2^{12} - (1 + 12) = 4083$ **30.** $C(52, 13) - C(39, 13) = 635,013,559,600 - 8,122,425,444 = 626,891,134,156$ **31.** $C(1, 1) \cdot C(5, 2) = 10$

32. $C(2, 2) \cdot C(4, 1) = 4$ **33.** $C(2, 1) \cdot C(4, 2) = 12$ **34.** $C(2, 2) \cdot C(4, 1) + C(2, 0) \cdot C(4, 3) = 8$ **35.** $C(4, 3) = 4$

CHAPTER 11

Section 11.1 (page 549)

1. Deterministic **2.** Random **3.** Random **4.** Deterministic **5.** Random **6.** Random **7.** Deterministic **8.** Random **9.** 1/6 **10.** 1/2 **11.** 2/3 **12.** 1/3 **13.** 2/3 **14.** 1/4 **15.** 1/13 **16.** 1/26 **17.** 1/52 **18.** 3 to 10 **19.** 1 to 12 **20.** 1 to 1 **21.** 1 to 51 **22.** 36/2,598,960 = 3/216,580 ≈ .00001385 **23.** 624/2,598,960 = 1/4165 ≈ .00024 **24.** (624/13)/2,598,960 = 1/54,145 ≈ .00001847 **25.** 1,098,240/2,598,960 = 352/833 ≈ .42257 **26.** (1,098,240/13)/2,598,960 = 352/10,829 ≈ .03250531 **27.** 2,593,852 to 5108, or 648,463 to 1277 **28.** 2,598,960 - 36 to 36, or 216,577 to 3 **29.** 2,596,406 to 2554, or 1,298,203 to 1277 **32.** .97 **33.** .68 **34.** Subjective **35.** Classical **36.** Subjective **37.** Empirical **38.** Classical **39.** Subjective **40.** Subjective **41.** 1/P(8, 3) = 1/336 **42.** 1•1•1•3•2•1/(3•2•1•3•2•1) = 1/6 **43.** 1/3! = 1/6 **44.** 3•3•2•2•1•1/(6•5•4•3•2•1) = 1/20 **45.** 4•3!•3!/6! = 1/5 **46.** 2•3!•3!/6! = 1/10 **47.** C(7, 5)/C(10, 5) = 1/12 **48.** C(10, 4)/C(12, 4) = 14/33 **49.** 3/(9•10) = 1/30 **50.** 29 to 1 **51.** [C(5, 2)•C(4, 1) + C(5, 3)•C(4, 0)]/C(9, 3) = 25/42 **52.** C(39, 13) = 8,122,425,444 **53.** C(5, 5)•C(34, 8) = 18,156,204 **54.** C(5, 5)•C(34, 8)/C(39, 13) = 18,156,204/8,122,425,444 = 341/152,551

Section 11.2 (page 558)

1. S = {1, 2, 3, 4} **2.** E = {2, 3, 4} **3.** n(E)/n(S) = 3/4 **4.** 3 to 1

5.

		2nd die 1	2	3	4
	1	(1, 1)	(1, 2)	(1, 3)	(1, 4)
1st	2	(2, 1)	(2, 2)	(2, 3)	(2, 4)
die	3	(3, 1)	(3, 2)	(3, 3)	(3, 4)
	4	(4, 1)	(4, 2)	(4, 3)	(4, 4)

6.

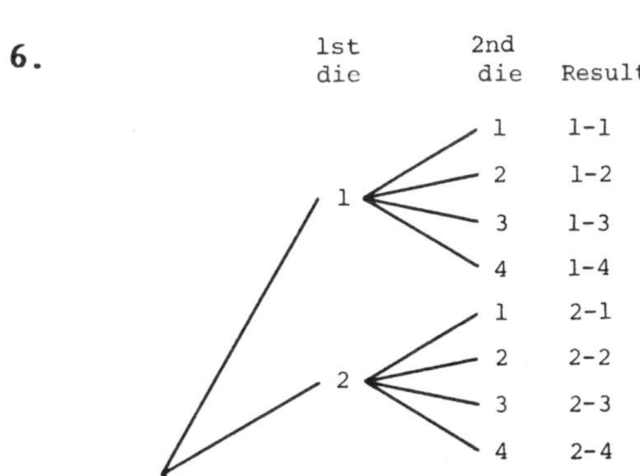

7. S = {(1, 1), (1, 2), (1, 3), (1, 4), (2, 1), (2, 2), (2, 3), (2, 4), (3, 1), (3, 2), (3, 3), (3, 4), (4, 1), (4, 2), (4, 3), (4, 4)} **8.** $4^4 = 256$ **9.** $2^4 = 16$

10. 16/256 = 1/16 **11.** 16 to 256 - 16, or 16 to 240, or 1 to 15 **12.** 15 to 1

15. 5/(5 + 2) = 5/7 **16.** 1/13 **17.** $(.8)^2 = .64$ **18.** $(.8)^3 = .512$

19. $(.2)^3 = .008$

20.

		2nd die					
		1	2	3	4	5	6
	1	2	3	4	5	6	7
	2	3	4	5	6	7	8
1st	3	4	5	6	7	8	9
die	4	5	6	7	8	9	10
	5	6	7	8	9	10	11
	6	7	8	9	10	11	12

21. 11 (2 through 12) **22.** 0

23. 1/36 **24.** 2/36 = 1/18

25. 3/36 = 1/12 **26.** 4/36 = 1/9

27. 5/36 **28.** 6/36 = 1/6

29. 5/36 **30.** 4/36 = 1/9

31. 3/36 = 1/12 **32.** 2/36 = 1/18 **33.** 1/36 **34.** (a) Worker is male (b) Worker has worked five or more years (c) Worker is female and has worked less than five years (d) Worker has worked less than five years or contributes to a voluntary retirement plan (e) Worker is female or does not contribute to a voluntary retirement plan (f) Worker has worked five or more years and does not contribute to a voluntary retirement plan **35.** (a) Person is not overweight (b) Person smokes or has a family history of heart disease (c) Person has a family history of heart disease and is overweight (d) Person does not smoke and has a family history of heart disease (e) Person smokes or is not overweight (f) Person does not have a family history of heart disease or is not overweight **36.** (a) E' (b) $E \cap F$ (c) $E' \cap F'$ (d) $E \cap F'$ (e) $(E \cap F') \cup (E' \cap F)$ (f) $E \cup F$ **37.** (a) E' (b) $E' \cap F'$ (c) $E \cap F$ (d) $E \cap F'$ (e) $(E \cup F) \cap (E \cap F)'$ **38.** $\{\ \}$, $\{r\}$, $\{s\}$, $\{t\}$, $\{r, s\}$, $\{r, t\}$, $\{s, t\}$, $\{r, s, t\}$ **39.** $n_1 \cdot n_2 = n_1n_2$ **40.** $s_1 \cdot s_2 = s_1s_2$ **41.** $s_1s_2/(n_1n_2)$ **42.** s_1/n_1 **43.** s_2/n_2 **44.** $s_1s_2/(n_1n_2)$ **45.** $5 \cdot 6^2 = 180$ **46.** $5 \cdot 6 \cdot 2 = 60$ **47.** 120/180 = 2/3 **48.** $n(E') = a - b$ **49.** $P(E) = b/a$; $P(E') = (a - b)/a$ **50.** $P(E) = b/a$; $1 - P(E') = 1 - [(a - b)/a] = [a - (a - b)]/a = b/a$ **51.** 1 - .06 = .94 **52.** $(.94)^{10} \approx .54$ **53.** $1 - (.94)^{10} \approx .46$ **54.** About 73 to 27 **55.** 3/4 **56.** 1/4 **57.** 1/4 **58.** 2/4 = 1/2 **59.** 1/4 **60.** The pattern is the same. Red (R) corresponds to heads (h), and white (r) corresponds to tails (t). **61.** 12 **62.** $12/29 \approx .41$ **63.** (1/2)(1/2) = 1/4 = .25; .25 and .41 are quite different. **64.** 11 **65.** 4 **66.** $4/28 \approx .14$ **68.** The sizes of the various regions are proportional to the numbers of ways those sums can occur in the sample space. **69.** 40° **70.** 60° **71.** 30° **72.** 10° **73.** Divide the circle into two parts, the part for boy being slightly larger than the part for girl, in the ratio of 105 to 100. **74.** For example, assign "wise advice" to 1, 2, 3, and 4 and "unwise advice" to 5 and 6.

Section 11.3 (page 567)

1. 4/52 = 1/13 **2.** 26/52 = 1/2 **3.** 2/52 = 1/26 **4.** 26/52 + 4/52 - 2/52 = 7/13 **5.** 13/52 = 1/4 **6.** 4/52 = 1/13 **7.** 1/52 **8.** 4/52 + 13/52 - 1/52 = 4/13 **9.** 28 to 24, or 7 to 6 **10.** 16 to 36, or 4 to 9 **11.** 15/36 = 5/12 **12.** 18/36 = 1/2 **13.** 9/36 = 1/4 **14.** 18/36 + 15/36 - 9/36 = 2/3 **15.** .08 **16.** .28 **17.** .50 **18.** .77 **19.** .13 **20.** 72 to 28, or 18 to 7 **21.** .41 **22.** .67 **23.** .21 **24.** .87 **25.** .79 **26.** .46

27. $P(E_1) + P(E_2) + \ldots + P(E_n)$
$= P(E_1 \cup E_2 \cup \ldots \cup E_n)$ *Special addition rule of probability*
$= P(S)$ *The union of the E's is the sample space*
$= 1$ *The sample space has probability 1*

28. $A \cup B$ **29.** $P(A) + P(B)$ **30.** $(26/52)(25/51) = 25/102$

31. $(26 \cdot 26)/(52 \cdot 51) = 13/51$ **32.** $13/51 + 13/51 = 26/51$

33. 1277/2,598,960 + 624/2,598,960 = 1901/2,598,960

34. 2554/2,598,960 + 3744/2,598,960 = 3149/1,299,480

35. 144/2,598,960 = 3/54,145 **36.** 143/16,660 ≈ .00858

42. For example, assign 1 to white and 2, 3, and 4 to red, simply ignoring 5s and 6s.

43. For example, assign 1 to white and 2, 3, and 4 to red.

Section 11.4 (page 574)

1. $C(4, 0)(1/2)^0(1/2)^4 = 1/16$ **2.** $C(4, 1)(1/2)^1(1/2)^3 = 1/4$

3. $C(4, 2)(1/2)^2(1/2)^2 = 3/8$ **4.** $C(4, 3)(1/2)^3(1/2)^1 = 1/4$

5. $C(4, 4)(1/2)^4(1/2)^0 = 1/16$ **6.** $C(5, 0)(1/2)^0(1/2)^5 = 1/32$

7. $C(5, 1)(1/2)^1(1/2)^4 = 5/32$ **8.** $C(5, 2)(1/2)^2(1/2)^3 = 5/16$

9. $C(5, 3)(1/2)^3(1/2)^2 = 5/16$ **10.** $C(5, 4)(1/2)^4(1/2)^1 = 5/32$

11. $C(5, 5)(1/2)^5(1/2)^0 = 1/32$ **12.** $C(5, 0)(1/6)^0(5/6)^5 = 3125/7776 \approx .402$

13. $C(5, 1)(1/6)^1(5/6)^4 = 3125/7776 \approx .4019$ **14.** $C(5, 2)(1/6)^2(5/6)^3 = 625/3888 \approx .161$ **15.** $C(5, 3)(1/6)^3(5/6)^2 = 250/7776 \approx .0322$

16. $C(5, 4)(1/6)^4(5/6)^1 = 25/7776 \approx .003$ **17.** $C(5, 5)(1/6)^5(5/6)^0 = 1/7776 \approx .0001$

18. $C(3, 1)(1/5)^1(4/5)^2 = 48/125 = .384$ **19.** $1 - C(3, 0)(1/5)^0(4/5)^3 = 1 - 64/125 = 61/125 \approx .488$ **20.** $C(4, 0)(.320)^0(.680)^4 \approx .214$ **21.** $C(4, 1)(.320)^1(.680)^3 \approx .402$

22. $C(4, 2)(.320)^2(.680)^2 \approx .284$ **23.** $C(4, 3)(.320)^3(.680)^1 \approx .089$

24. $C(4, 4)(.320)^4(.680)^0 \approx .010$ **25.** $1 - C(4, 0)(.320)^0(.680)^4 \approx 1 - .214 = .786$

26. .214 + .402 + .284 = .900

27.

x	P(x)
0	1/8
1	3/8
2	3/8
3	1/8

28. 3/8 + 3/8 = 3/4

29. 3/8 + 1/8 = 1/2

30. 1/8 + 3/8 = 1/2

31.

x	P(x)
0	27/64
1	27/64
2	9/64
3	1/64

32. 9/64 + 1/64 = 5/32 **33.** 27/64 + 27/64 = 27/32

34. $C(5, 2)(3/13)^2(10/13)^3 \approx .242$ **35.** 18/50 = 9/25 = .36

36. $C(3, 2)(1/2)^2(1/2)^1 = 3/8 = .375$ **37.** 18/50 = 9/25 = .36

38. 13/50 = .26 **39.** 19/50 = .38 **40.** P(0 points) = .40; P(1 point) = (.60)(.40) = .24; P(2 points) = (.60)(.60) = .36. These values are all close to the empirical values. **41.** 1/1024 **42.** 45/1024 **43.** 45/1024 **44.** 0

45. 210/1024 = 105/512 **46.** (210 + 120 + 45 + 10 + 1)/1024 = 193/512

47. (1024 - 252)/1024 = 193/256 **48.** 252/1024 = 63/256

Section 11.5 (page 583)

1. 1/3 **2.** 2/3 **3.** 0 **4.** 1 **5.** 5/15 = 1/3 **6.** 1/6 **7.** 0

8. 6/8 = 3/4 **9.** 12/51 = 4/17 **10.** 4/51 **11.** 25/51 **12.** 11/51

13. 4/51 **14.** 26/51 **15.** 25/51 **16.** 0 **17.** 1/3 **18.** 2/3

19. 3/10 **20.** 1/6 **21.** 1/3 **22.** 0/4 = 0 **23.** 4/6 = 2/3 **24.** 2/3

25. Yes **26.** (a) Probability of check, given deposit: 50/70 = 5/7 (b) Probability of no deposit, given check: 30/80 = 3/8 (c) Probability of no check, given no deposit: 10/40 = 1/4 (d) Probability of no check, given deposit: 20/70 = 2/7 (e) Probability of not both check and deposit: 60/110 = 6/11 **27.** (a) Probability of new and satisfied: 300/1000 = 3/10 (b) Probability of new or not satisfied: 550/1000 = 11/20 (c) Probability of new, given satisfied: 300/750 = 2/5 (d) Probability of used, given satisfied: 450/750 = 3/5 (e) Probability of satisfied, given used: 450/600 = 3/4 (f) Probability of not satisfied, given used: 150/600 = 1/4 **28.** 15/30 = 1/2

29. 5/20 = 1/4 **30.** 6/16 = 3/8 **31.** 14/20 = 7/10 **32.** 25/36

33. (30/50)•(29/49) = 87/245 **34.** (20/50)•(14/49) = 4/35 **35.** (20/50)•(19/49) + (16/50)•(15/49) + (14/50)•(13/49) = 401/1225 **36.** (30/50)•(29/49) = 87/245

37. (20/50)•(30/49) = 12/49 **38.** (20/50)•(30/49) + (30/50)•(20/49) = 24/49

39. .6 **40.** .4 **41.** .95 **42.** .05 **43.** .9 **44.** .1

45. (.6)(.95) = .57 **46.** (.4)(.9) = .36 **47.** .57 + .36 = .93

48. 1 - .93 = .07 **49.** .57/.93 ≈ .61 **50.** .03/.07 ≈ .43

51. 1 - .973 = .027 **52.** 1 - .944 = .056 **53.** 1 - .905 = .095

54. 1 - .859 = .141

Section 11.6 (page 590)

1. 3.5 **2.** $0 **3.** Yes **4.** No (Expected net winnings: -3/4¢) **5.** -$1/37 ≈ -2.7¢ **6.** -$.05 = -5¢ **7.** 2/5 **8.** 1/2 **9.** No (Expected net winnings: -20.6¢) **10.** $25,000 at age 30 (This choice produces an expected inheritance of $22,500, while the other choice yields $21,000.) **11.** $4500 **12.** $18,000 profit **13.** 118 **14.** 1.11¢ **15.** No, it favors the player slightly. **16.** Column 5: 25,000, 60,000, 16,000 **17.** Column 6: 22,000, 51,000, 30,000, 60,000, 46,000 **18.** Column 7: C, C, C, B, C, A, B **19.** $106,500 **20.** About -15¢ **21.** 31.73 **22.** 11.82 **23.** 21.98 **24.** 40.02

Section 11.7 (page 596)

1. 6 **2.** 10 **3.** 6 **4.** 35 **5.** 56 **6.** 84 **7.** 120 **8.** 45

9. C(5, 3)/C(9, 3) = 5/42 **10.** 0 **11.** C(3, 3)/C(9, 3) = 1/84

12. [C(5, 2)•C(1, 1)]/C(9, 3) = 5/42 **13.** [C(5, 2)•C(3, 1)]/C(9, 3) = 5/14

14. [C(3, 2)•C(5, 1)]/C(9, 3) = 5/28 **15.** [C(3, 2)•C(1, 1)]/C(9, 3) = 1/28

16. [C(5, 1)•C(1, 1)•C(3, 1)]/C(9, 3) = 5/28 **17.** C(5, 2) = 10 **18.** C(2, 2) = 1

19. C(2, 1)•C(3, 1) = 6 **20.** C(5, 2) - C(2, 2) = 9

21. [C(1, 1)•C(6, 2)]/C(7, 3) = 3/7 **22.** 1 - [C(4, 3)/C(6, 3)] = 1 - (4/20) = 4/5

23. 10/32 = 5/16 **24.** 70/256 = 35/128 **25.** 126/512 + 84/512 = 105/256

26. 210/1024 + 120/1024 + 45/1024 + 10/1024 + 1/1024 = 193/512

27. The entries of row n give the numbers of subsets of the various sizes in a set of size n, so the sum of the entries in row n is the total number of subsets, or 2^n.

28. $2^{11} = 2048$ **29.** 6, 16, .375 **30.** 20, 64, .313 **31.** 70, 256, .273

32. Not to happen (since its probability of happening is often less than .5)

33. ..., 15, 21, 28, 36, 45, ...; these are the triangular numbers.

34. ..., 8, 13, 21, 34, ...; a number in this sequence is the sum of the two preceding terms. This is the Fibonacci sequence. **35.** The rows of Tartaglia's rectangle correspond to the diagonals of Pascal's triangle.

36.

```
          1
        1   1
      1   0   1
    1   1   1   1
  1   0   0   0   1
1   1   0   0   1   1
```

In rows 2 and 4, every entry, except for the beginning and ending 1s, is 0. (This is because the corresponding entries in the original triangle were all even.)

37. Row 8 **38.** 255

Chapter 11 Test (page 599)

1. 2/3 **2.** 1/4 **3.** 1/26 **4.** 3/13 **5.** 8/13 **6.** 1/2 **7.** 1/3

8. 1 **9.** 3 to 1 **10.** 25 to 1 **11.** 11 to 2 **12.** Empirical

13. Subjective **14.** Classical **15.** 1/4 **16.** 3/4 **17.** 1/2 **18.** 25/102

19. 77/102 **20.** 26/51 **21.** 25/51

22.

		2nd parent N	2nd parent n
1st parent	N	NN	Nn
1st parent	n	nN	nn

23. 1/4 **24.** 1/2

25. 1/6 **26.** 1/3

27.

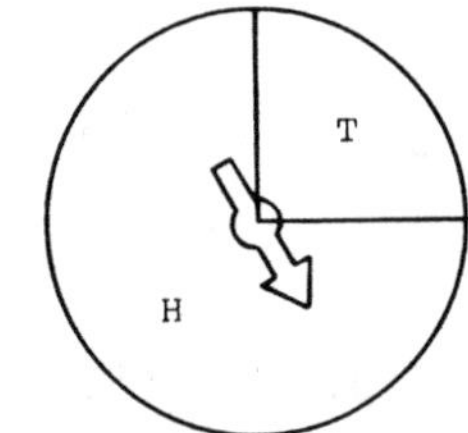

28.

x	P(x)
0	0
1	3/10
2	6/10
3	1/10

29. 9/10

30. 9/5 = 1.8

31.

```
                  1
                1   1
              1   2   1
            1   3   3   1
          1   4   6   4   1
        1   5  10  10   5   1
      1   6  15  20  15   6   1
    1   7  21  35  35  21   7   1
```

32. 5 **33.** 35 **34.** (21 + 7 + 1)/128 = 29/128

CHAPTER 12

Section 12.1 (page 608)

1. (d)

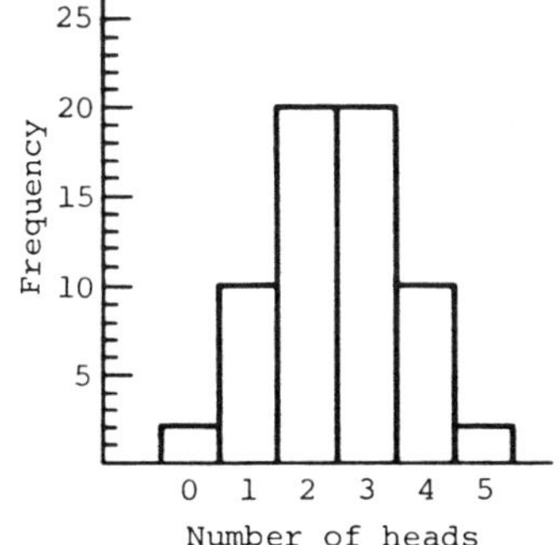

2. (d)

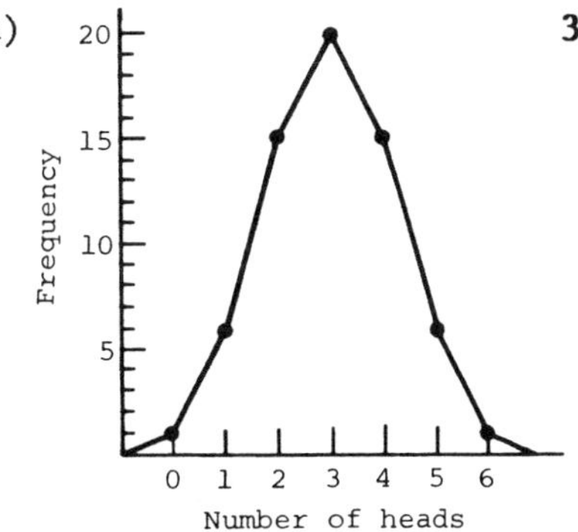

3. (a) 4 (b) 3 (c) 6

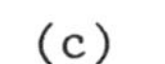

(d) 3 (e) 5 (f) 9

(g)

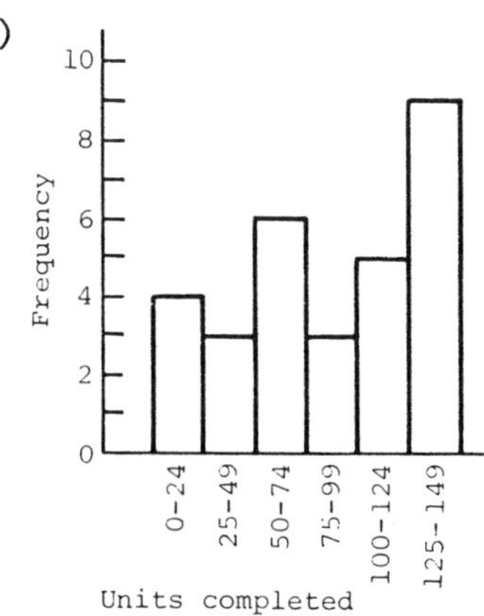

4. (a)

Temperature	Frequency
70-74	2
75-79	1
80-84	3
85-89	2
90-94	5
95-99	5
100-104	6
105-109	4
110-114	2

(b)

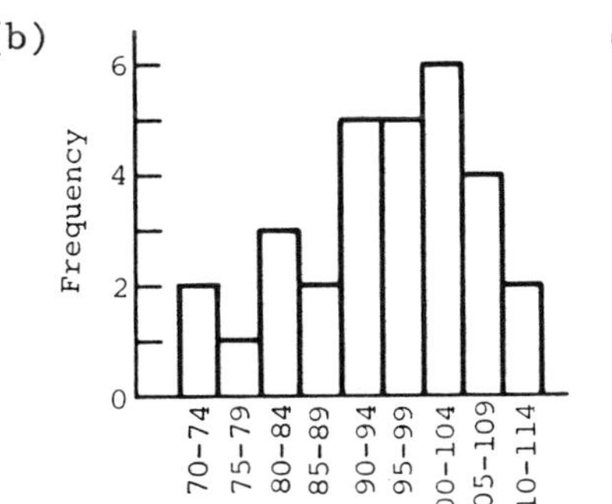

(c)

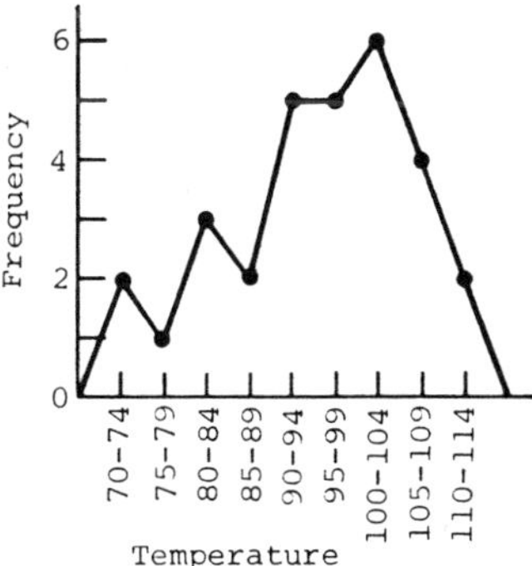

5. (a)

Number sold	Frequency
1-5	11
6-10	14
11-15	11
16-20	7
21-25	8
26-30	5
31-35	2
36-40	2

(b)

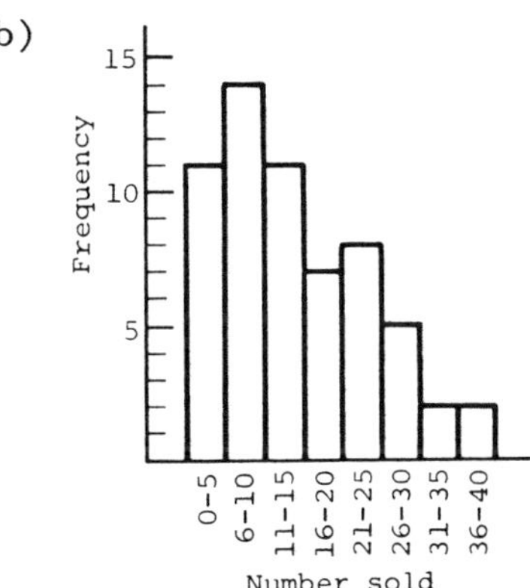

6. (a) One possibility:

IQ	Frequency
91–95	1
96–100	3
101–105	5
106–110	7
111–115	12
116–120	9
121–125	7
126–130	4
131–135	2

(b)

7. (a) Air (b) 23.75% (c) 5.7

8. (a) About 50% (b) About 70%

9. (a) Nine-year-olds (b) Eleven-year-olds

10.

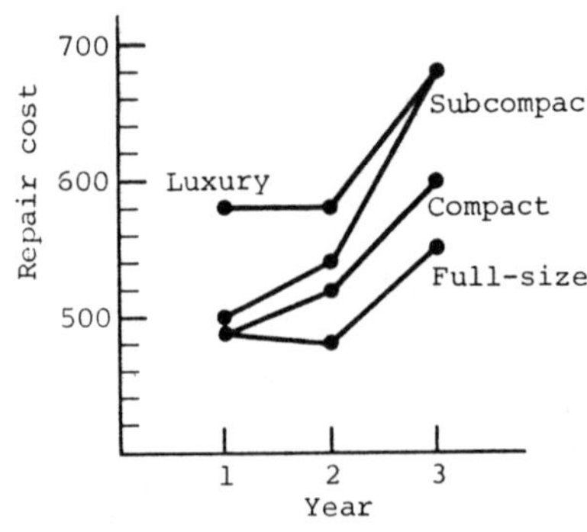

11. Dollar amount: 140;
percent of total: 20, 15, 15, 5, 10;
degrees of a circle: 54, 36, 18

12. (a)

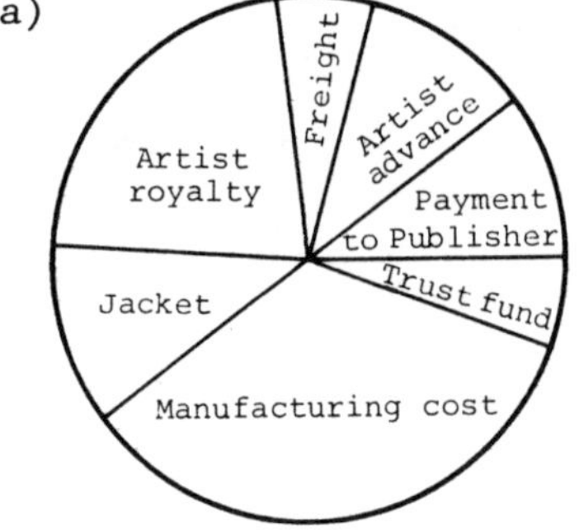

(b) $.99

13. Tax and investment

14. 15.0%

15. "Found attractive residence for sale" and "Worried about rents increasing"

16. Twice as important

17. (a) 64% (b) 25%

18. Equity from previous home

19. Loan from relatives

20.

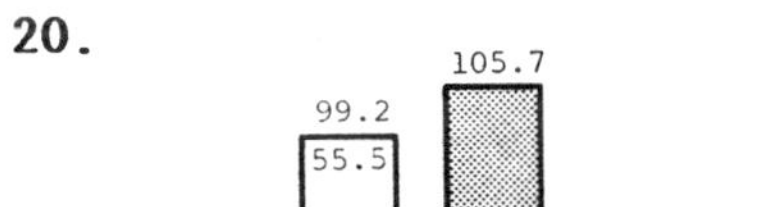

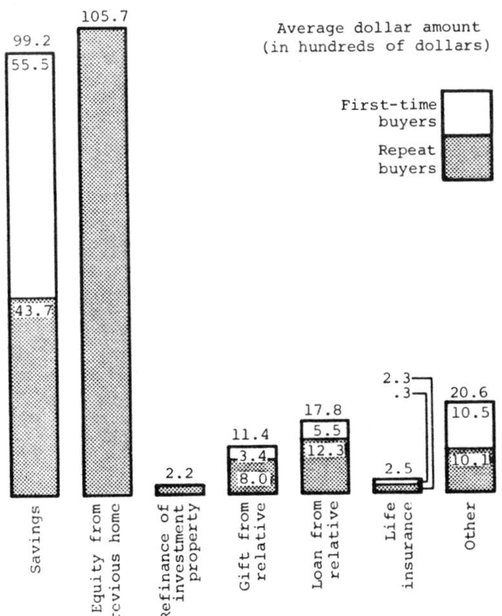

Section 12.2 (page 619)

1. 14 **2.** 51 **3.** 60.3 **4.** 55.8 **5.** 27,955 **6.** 37,127 **7.** 7.7 **8.** 52.6 **9.** .1 **10.** .4 **11.** $39,418 **12.** $776,333 **13.** $657,125 **14.** $559,280 **15.** 22 ft **16.** $750,000 **17.** 51 **18.** 612 **19.** 130 **20.** 508 **21.** 49 **22.** 1056 **23.** 562 **24.** 14.5 **25.** 29.1 **26.** .65 **27.** 9 **28.** 32 **29.** 64 **30.** 97 **31.** 68 and 74 **32.** 162 and 165 **33.** No mode **34.** No mode **35.** 6.1 and 6.3 **36.** 12.75 **37.** 6 **38.** 3 **39.** 3 **40.** 3 **41.** Median **42.** Mode **43.** (a) 6.7 (b) 5 (c) 3 **44.** (a) 13.3 (b) 13.5 (c) 15 **45.** (a) 17.4 (b) 17 (c) 23 **46.** (a) 30.2 (b) 30 (c) 29 and 33 **47.** (a) 118.8 (b) 119 (c) 123 **48.** (a) 299.4 (b) 305.5 (c) 307 **49.** $30,000 **50.** $28,000 **51.** 2.6 **52.** 2.6 **53.** 11.3, 10.2, 9.9 **54.** Median **55.** All except 18.6 **56.** For example: 2, 6, 7 **57.** For example: 3, 5, 7, 9 **58.** For example: 3, 4, 10, 15 **59.** 84 **60.** 99 **61.** 28.82 mpg **62.** 27.83 mpg

63. m represents the median; m = 58.5 **64.** m represents the median; m = 109

65. m represents the mean; m = 68.7 **66.** m represents the mean; m = 4.43

67. x = 8 **68.** x = 33

Section 12.3 (page 628)

1. 6; $\sqrt{5} \approx 2.2$ **2.** 14; $\sqrt{32.5} \approx 5.7$ **3.** 12; $\sqrt{22} \approx 4.7$ **4.** 9; $\sqrt{11.333} \approx 3.4$

5. 53; $\sqrt{475.3} \approx 21.8$ **6.** 58; $\sqrt{438.3} \approx 20.9$ **7.** 46; $\sqrt{258.4} \approx 16.1$

8. 42; $\sqrt{152} \approx 12.3$ **9.** 24; $\sqrt{66} \approx 8.1$ **10.** 56; $\sqrt{424.4} \approx 20.6$

11. 30; $\sqrt{139.7} \approx 11.8$ **12.** 35; $\sqrt{239.2} \approx 15.5$ **13.** 2.4; $\sqrt{.899} \approx .9$

14. 4.8; $\sqrt{2.99} \approx 1.7$ **15.** 3; $\sqrt{.788} \approx .9$ **16.** 4; $\sqrt{1.63} \approx 1.3$

17. 3/4 = .75 **18.** 24/25 = .96 **19.** 5/9 ≈ .556 **20.** 209/225 ≈ .929

21. 93.8% **22.** 97.2% **23.** 85.9% **24.** 91.8% **25.** 3/4 = .75

26. 8/9 ≈ .889 **27.** 15/16 = .9375 **28.** 24/25 = .96 **29.** 1/4 = .25

30. 4/25 = .16 **31.** 1/9 ≈ .111 **32.** (a) \$320, \$184.50 (b) 6 (c) 6 (d) At least 5.25 **33.** (a) 25.5, 7.2 (b) Forever Power (c) Forever Power

34. (a) 12.5 (b) −3.0 (c) 4.9 (d) 4.2 (e) 15.5 (f) 7.55 and 23.45

Section 12.4 (page 636)

1. Discrete **2.** Discrete **3.** Continuous **4.** Continuous **5.** Discrete

6. Continuous **7.** 50 **8.** 84 **9.** 97 or 98 **10.** 16 **11.** 68 **12.** 95

13. 13 or 14 **14.** 81 or 82 **15.** 68 **16.** 5 **17.** 50% **18.** 50%

19. 16% **20.** 68% **21.** 95% **22.** 99.7% **23.** .15% **24.** .15%

25. 49.4% **26.** 45.4% **27.** 17.4% **28.** 29.1% **29.** 45.6% **30.** 47.9%

31. 49.9% **32.** 49.7% **33.** 7.7% **34.** 24.4% **35.** 47.3% **36.** 11.3%

37. 92.4% **38.** 33.2% **39.** 32.6% **40.** 95.2% **41.** 1.64 **42.** Any of these: −2.34, −2.33, −2.32, −2.31 (A more accurate table of normal curve areas would enable us to be more specific.) **43.** −1.03 or −1.04 **44.** .67 **45.** 5000

46. 5000 **47.** 4330 **48.** 4770 **49.** 640 **50.** 6370 **51.** 9920

52. 9770 **53.** 20 **54.** 1840 **55.** 84.1% **56.** 37.1% **57.** 37.8%

58. 79.4% **59.** 2.3% **60.** .047 or 4.7% **61.** .159 or 15.9%

62. .047 or 4.7% **63.** .006 or .6% **64.** 0% **65.** .994 or 99.4%

66. 2150 units **67.** 189 units **68.** 1430 units **69.** .006 **70.** .159

71. .432 **72.** 182 people **73.** \$58.62, \$45.89 **74.** .888

75. .082 **76.** About 2 eggs **77.** 6.7% **78.** 24.1% **79.** 38.4%

80. The freshman class, since a large group of students is more likely to produce a normal distribution of test scores **81.** 82 **82.** 78 **83.** 70 **84.** 66

85. 99.7 **86.** 101.0 **87.** 105.3 **88.** 109.3 **89.** 90.1 **90.** 87.2

91. 85.9 **92.** 81.7 **93.** 79.3 **94.** 75.8 **95.** 70.1 **96.** 64.5

97. (a) At least 36% (b) 78.8% **98.** A distribution that is known to be normal has a higher concentration of items near the mean than many other kinds of distributions.

Section 12.5 (page 643)

1. 19.8% **2.** 17.4% **3.** 12.1% **4.** 2.8% **5.** 2.4% **6.** 1.9%

7. 90.3% **8.** 2.7% **9.** 86.7% **10.** .1% **11.** 9.6% **12.** 5.9%

13. 7.6% **14.** 8.5% **15.** 64.4% **16.** 64.4% **17.** 1.5% **18.** 5.4%

19. 7.5% **20.** .6% **21.** .1% **22.** 0% **23.** 2.7% **24.** 40.8%

25. .995 **26.** .864

An Extension How to Lie with Statistics (page 648)

1. We have no way of telling. **2.** We can't tell; there is no scale.

3. We can tell only that it rises and then falls. **4.** Again, there is no scale.

5. 28% **6.** The actual decrease (\$2.40 to \$1.72) is about 28%, but the artist for the magazine reduced *each* dimension of the original figure by 28%. This causes the area to decrease by about 50%, thus giving a false impression.

7. How long have Toyotas been sold in the United States? How do other makes compare? **8.** The tobacco is 44% fresher than what? **9.** The dentists preferred Trident Sugarless Gum to what? Which and how many dentists were surveyed? What percentage responded? **10.** So what - a Volvo is a much smaller car than a Continental, and should have a smaller turning radius. **11.** Just how quiet *is* a glider, really? **12.** There is no scale. We can't tell if the increase is substantial or not. **13.** The maps convey their impressions in terms of *area* distribution, whereas personal income distribution may be quite different. The map on the left probably implies too high a level of government spending, while that on the right implies too low a level. **14.** It turns out that there were *three* women students, and just *one* had married a faculty member. **15.** By the time the figures were used, circumstances may have changed greatly. (The Navy was much larger.) Also, New York City was most likely not typical of the nation as a whole. **16.** When Huff's book was written, those three states had the best system for reporting these diseases. **17.** (b) **18.** (c) **19.** (c) **20.** (a) **21.** (a) $m = 1$, $a = 6$, $c = 3$ (b) There should be 1.4 managers, 5 agents, and 3 clerical employees. **22.** (a) $d = 2$, $f = 4$, $a = 7$, $s = 7$ (b) There should be 2 deans, 4 full professors, 6.5 associate professors, and 7.5 assistant professors.

Section 12.6 (page 657)

1. (a) $y' = .3x + 1.5$ (b) $r = .20$ (c) 2.4 decimeters

2. (a) $y' = .556x - 17.8$ (b) 48.9° (c) $r = 1$ (The experimental points must lie perfectly along a line.) **3.** (a) $y' = 3.35x - 78.4$ (b) 123 lb (c) 156 lb (d) $r = .66$

4. (a)

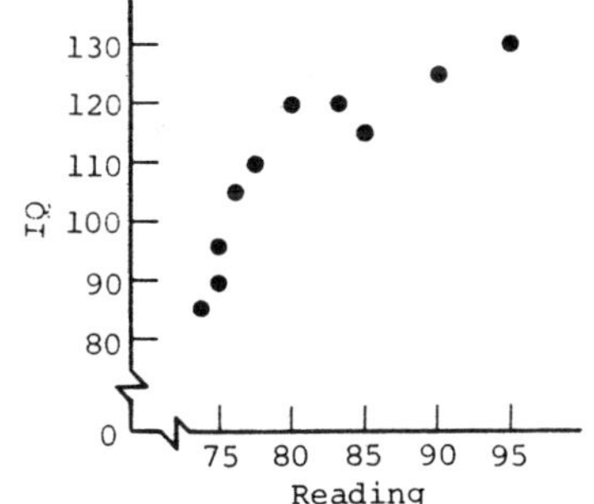

(b) y′ = −51 + 2x (c) 79

5. y′ = 8.06x + 49.52; r = .996

6. (a)

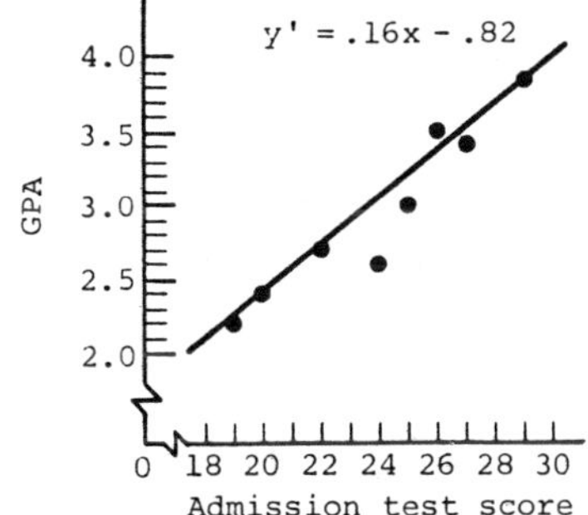

(b) y′ = .16x − .82

(c) About 3.7

(d) r = .95

Chapter 12 Test (page 660)

1. Frequencies: 3, 2, 4, 3, 3, 5

2.

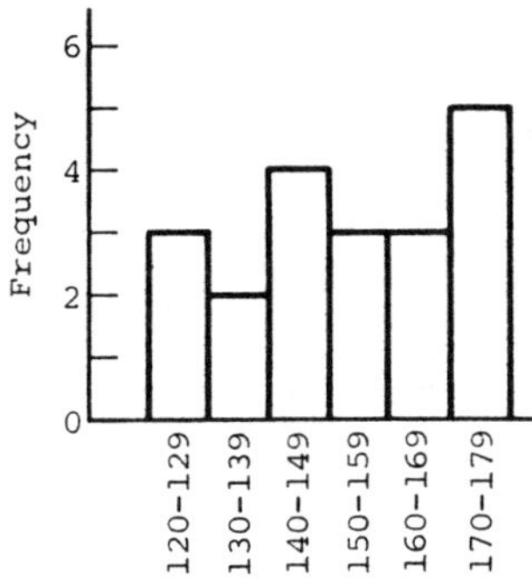

3. 65 **4.** 11.25 **5.** 27; 29

6. 41; 39 and 41 **7.** 18; $\sqrt{48.5} \approx 7.0$

8. 67; $\sqrt{569.1} \approx 23.9$ **9.** 15.9%

10. 97.7% **11.** 81.8% **12.** .422

13. .884 **14.** .069 **15.** 38.2%

16. 42.1% **17.** 66.1% **18.** .9%

19. 4.8% **20.** 7.69 **21.** 9

22. 9 **23.** 6 **24.** $\sqrt{4.08} \approx 2.02$

25. (a) y′ = 3.9x − 7.9 (b) 15.5 (c) r = .998

CHAPTER 13

Throughout this chapter, there are exercises that call for the use of a table or a calculator. Due to table limitations, accuracy may be limited by use of tables.

Section 13.1 (page 671)

1. \$90 **2.** \$600 **3.** \$102 **4.** \$412.50 **5.** \$93.33 **6.** \$150

7. \$580.82 **8.** \$85.33 **9.** \$250 **10.** \$60.94 **11.** \$13,375 **12.** \$190.80

13. \$1262.50 **14.** \$7996 **15.** \$11,469.90 **16.** \$30,557.77 **17.** \$1583.92

18. \$18,295.20 **19.** \$5057.08 **20.** \$28,760 **21.** \$589.58 **22.** \$587.77

23. \$817.15 **24.** \$3883.48; \$1513.48 **25.** \$28,600.50; \$21,100.50

26. \$11,064.50; \$7614.50 **27.** (a) \$259.70 (b) \$265.30 (c) \$268.20

28. (a) \$1674.00 (b) \$1703.20 (c) \$1718.00 **29.** (a) \$2210.40 (b) \$2240.80 (c) \$2256.00 **30.** (a) \$8803.50 (b) \$9015.00 (c) \$9126.00

31. Quarterly - but not by much **32.** \$11,901.75 **33.** \$11,114.05

34. (a) \$15,869.00; \$16,084.00 (b) \$215 **35.** \$40,223.00 **36.** About 24 yr

37. About 18 yr **38.** About 15 yr **39.** About 12 yr **40.** About 10 yr

41. About 7 yr **42.** (a) 14 yr (b) 10 yr (c) 8 yr (d) 6 yr

43. (a) \$150,000 (b) \$300,000 **44.** (a) \$3.38 (b) \$6.76 **45.** (a) \$27.96 (b) \$55.92 **46.** (a) \$2.12 (b) \$4.24 **47.** (a) \$69.90 (b) \$139.80

49. \$4287.75; \$1526.75 **50.** \$8085.43; \$4162.43 **51.** \$15,128.78; \$3520.78

52. \$6369.86; \$883.86 **53.** \$15,467.75; \$5835.21 **54.** \$4286.65; \$1427.42

55. \$680.60 **56.** \$7556.68 **57.** \$15,968.13 **58.** \$13,375.37

59. \$19,108.48 **60.** \$45,702.42 **61.** \$186.22 **62.** \$6555.28

63. \$2010.31 **64.** \$6086.42 **65.** \$4764.17 **66.** \$3519.53 **67.** \$93,475.42

68. \$16,832.44

Section 13.2 (page 681)

1. $4.41 **2.** $8.00 **3.** $2.73 **4.** $15.35 **5.** $9.52 **6.** $17.66

7.

Month	Unpaid balance at beginning of month	Finance charge	Purchases during month	Returns	Payment	Unpaid balance at end of month
February	$297.11	$5.05	$ 86.14	0	$50	$338.30
March	338.30	5.75	109.83	$15.75	60	378.13
April	378.13	6.43	39.74	0	72	352.30
May	352.30	5.99	56.29	18.09	50	346.49

8.

Month	Unpaid balance at beginning of month	Finance charge	Purchases during month	Returns	Payment	Unpaid balance at end of month
October	$554.19	$ 9.42	$128.72	$ 23.15	$125	$544.18
November	544.18	9.25	291.64	0	170	675.07
December	675.07	11.48	147.11	17.15	150	666.51
January	666.51	11.33	27.84	139.82	200	365.86

9.

Month	Unpaid balance at beginning of month	Finance charge	Purchases during month	Returns	Payment	Unpaid balance at end of month
August	$ 822.91	$13.99	$155.01	$38.11	$100	$ 853.80
September	853.80	14.51	208.75	0	75	1002.06
October	1002.06	17.04	56.30	0	90	985.40
November	985.40	16.75	190.00	83.57	150	958.58

10.

Month	Unpaid balance at beginning of month	Finance charge	Purchases during month	Returns	Payment	Unpaid balance at end of month
March	$1522.83	$25.89	$308.13	$74.88	$250	$1531.97
April	1531.97	26.04	488.35	0	350	1696.36
May	1696.36	28.84	134.99	18.12	175	1667.07
June	1667.07	28.34	157.72	0	190	1663.13

11. $1.96 **12.** $.99 **13.** $1.35 **14.** $4.21 **15.** $2.07 **16.** $6.13

17. $12.44 **18.** $26.91 **19.** $772.63; $15.45 **20.** $113.88; $2.28

21. $221.44; $4.43 **22.** $312.91; $6.26 **23.** $682.02; $13.64

24. $139.71; $2.79 **25.** (a) $10.80 (b) $9.93 **26.** (a) $21.40 (b) $18.40
27. $275 **28.** $1525 **29.** $63.54 **30.** $6000 **31.** $2880 **32.** $8880
33. $185 **34.** $125 **35.** $999; $130.53 **36.** $17.12; $17.51
37. $349.20; $87.30 **38.** $504; $108.50 **39.** $52; $37.67 **40.** $891; $99.75
41. $399.65; $183.09 **42.** $61.65; $95.52 **43.** $277.50 **44.** $84.93

Section 13.3 (page 688)

1. 14 1/2% **2.** 14 1/2% **3.** 15 1/2% **4.** 14 1/2% **5.** $66.67
6. $144.44 **7.** $163.33 **8.** $208.33 **9.** $18; 14 1/2% **10.** $1334; 17%
11. 30% **12.** 12% **13.** 18% **14.** 13.2% **15.** 5% **16.** 12%–15%
17. $1.50 **18.** $481.38 **19.** $2.40 **20.** $11.94 **21.** $24.87
22. $274.08 **23.** $10.51 **24.** $5.14 **25.** $56.35 **26.** $21 **27.** $45.66
28. (a) $36.67 (b) $416.93 **29.** $81.08 **30.** $1.94

Section 13.4 (page 695)

1. $632.50 **2.** $379.20 **3.** $354.48 **4.** $603.72 **5.** $503.09
6. $234.02 **7.** $536.40 **8.** $416.91 **9.** $452.57 **10.** $353.60
11. $520.71 **12.** $443.60 **13.** $801.27 **14.** $334.63 **15.** $664.88
16. $767.61 **17.** 360 **18.** $148,176 **19.** $108,176 **20.** The total interest
21. $402.50 **22.** $592.50 **23.** (a) $94,900 (b) $163,300 **24.** $68,400
25. $7789.82 **26.** $174.82 **27.** $59,825.18 **28.** $59,626.24 **29.** Month 297
30. Month 298 **31.** (a) $515.48 (b) $507.50 (c) $7.98 (d) $43,492.02
32. (a) $564.06 (b) $552.50 (c) $11.56 (d) $50,988.44 **33.** (a) $616.01
(b) $585.00 (c) $31.01 (d) $58,468.99 (e) $616.01 (f) $584.69 (g) $31.32
(h) $58,437.67 **34.** (a) $819.84 (b) $800.00 (c) $19.84 (d) $63,980.16
(e) $819.84 (f) $799.75 (g) $20.09 (h) $63,960.07 **35.** $939.74
36. $1254.95 **37.** $833.18 **38.** $620.95 **39.** $773.71 **40.** $1002.12

Section 13.5 (page 703)

1. $64.875 **2.** $24.75 **3.** $38.625 **4.** +$.375 **5.** $90.375 **6.** $24.25

7. $1.04 **8.** $1.20 **9.** $41.375 **10.** $53.375 **11.** 430,800 shares

12. 59,300 shares **13.** 2.2% **14.** 4.9% **15.** $9437.50 **16.** $7837.50

17. $7600 **18.** $10,875 **19.** $11,250 **20.** $3637.50 **21.** $13,107.19

22. $13,722.19 **23.** $46,432.50 **24.** $39,155 **25.** $2675.25 **26.** $4969.69

27. $38,334.88 **28.** $10,746.94 **29.** $25,641.97 **30.** $31,735.59

31. $10,054.48 **32.** $36,305.81 **33.** $35,272.27 **34.** $25,307.86

35. $10,791.25 **36.** $5337.50

Chapter 13 Test (page 705)

1. $78.40 **2.** $300 **3.** $1898.30 **4.** $14,719.45 **5.** $9347.54

6. $8.25 **7.** $540 **8.** $70.56 **9.** $105 **10.** $61.39 **11.** 16%

12. 15% **13.** 16% **14.** $9.63 **15.** $829.50 **16.** $817.19 **17.** $676.12

18. $26 3/4 or $26.75 **19.** 74,500 shares **20.** $15,525

CHAPTER 14

Section 14.1 (page 718)

1. No 2. Yes; (c) repetition 3. Yes; (b) much calculation 4. Yes; (a) speed 5. Yes; (b) much calculation 6. Yes; (b) much calculation 7. No 8. Yes; (a) speed 9. Yes; (c) repetition 10. Yes; (b) much calculation 11. Yes; (c) repetition 12. Yes; (c) repetition 13. Yes; (a) speed 14. Yes; (a) speed 15. Yes; (b) much calculation 16. Yes; (c) repetition 17. Yes; (c) repetition 18. No 19. Yes; (c) repetition 20. Yes; (b) much calculation 21. Yes; (b) much calculation 22. Yes; (b) much calculation 23. Yes; (b) much calculation 24. Yes; (c) repetition 25. Yes; (c) repetition 26. Yes; (b) much calculation 27. Yes; (b) much calculation 28. Yes; (b) much calculation 29. Yes; (b) much calculation 30. Yes; (c) repetition 31. Yes; (c) repetition 32. No 33. No 34. Yes; (c) repetition 35. No 36. Yes; (b) much calculation 37. (b) programming error; (2) run-time 38. (c) data error 39. (a) machine error 40. (f) overconfidence in computers 41. (e) theft 42. (d) privacy error 43. (c) data error 44. (b) programming error; (1) syntax 45. (a) machine error 46. (f) overconfidence in computers 47. (b) programming error; (1) syntax 48. (d) privacy error 49. (e) theft 50. (a) machine error 51. (a) machine error 52. (c) data error 53. (b) programming error; (2) run-time 54. (d) privacy error 55. (f) overconfidence in computers 56. (d) privacy error 57. (c) data error 58. (e) theft 59. (a) programming the computer 60. (a) programming the computer 61. (b) preparing and inputting data 62. (d) modifying an existing program 63. (b) inputting data 64. (c) interpreting output 65. (c) interpreting output 66. (a) programming the computer 67. (d) modifying an existing program 68. (c) inputting data

Section 14.2 (page 727)

1. Gets information and instructions into the computer **2.** Oversees the flow of information within the computer, activating the other components at appropriate times **3.** Performs the appropriate arithmetic operations on numerical data within the computer **4.** Stores information and instructions within the computer **5.** Gets information out of the computer in some usable form **6.** Punched cards, paper tape, magnetic tape, magnetic ink reader, optical scanner, floppy disk, hard disk, and keyboard are methods of input. **7.** Silicon chip, magnetic core, magnetic tape, magnetic drum, magnetic disk, and bubble memory are memory devices. **8.** Card reader, tape punch, magnetic tape unit, automatic typewriter, high-speed printer, graphic plotter, CRT, and engineering drawing unit are output devices. **9.** RAM and ROM **10.** RAM's memory, unlike ROM's, is cleared when the power switch is turned off. RAM stores programs, data files, and other information entered by the operator, while ROM's memory can't be altered by the operator. **11.** 632 **12.** 59,430,000 **13.** 8,201,400,000

14. 9,100,000,000,000 **15.** -8,490,000,000,000 **16.** -142,830,000,000,000,000

17. .000034 **18.** .00000000597 **19.** .0000000014962 **20.** -.0025

21. 3.0E + 12 **22.** 8.74E + 11 **23.** -1.5E + 16 **24.** -9.876E + 10

25. 9.741E - 09 **26.** 3.85972E - 05 **27.** 1.539E - 08 **28.** 4.34E - 10

29. -5.0E - 11 **30.** -8.76921114E - 05 **31.** Business **32.** Scientific

Section 14.3 (page 733)

1. Valid **2.** Not valid **3.** Valid **4.** Not valid **5.** Not valid **6.** 14

7. -40 **8.** -26 **9.** 1000 **10.** 4 **11.** 100 **12.** LET A = X + Y - Z*W

13. LET A = 2*X - 3*Y **14.** LET A = 2 ↑ 3 **15.** LET A = (2 + B)/(C - 5)

16. LET A = (X - 2*(Y - Z))/(3*X + W) **17.** LET A = ((B + C)/(D*E)) ↑ (1/2)

18. LET K3 = (R ↑ 3 + X ↑ 2)/(Y ↑ 2 - M ↑ 4)

19.

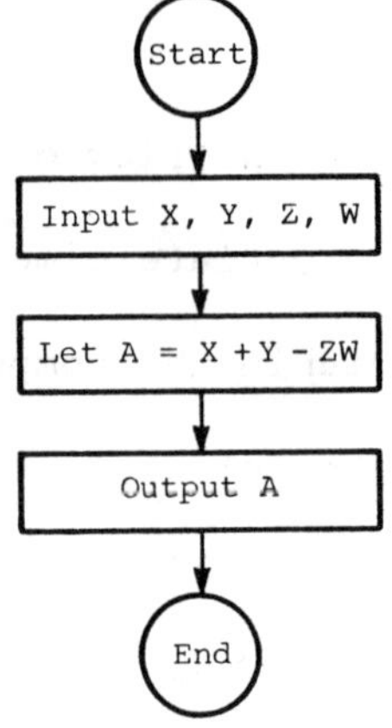

20.

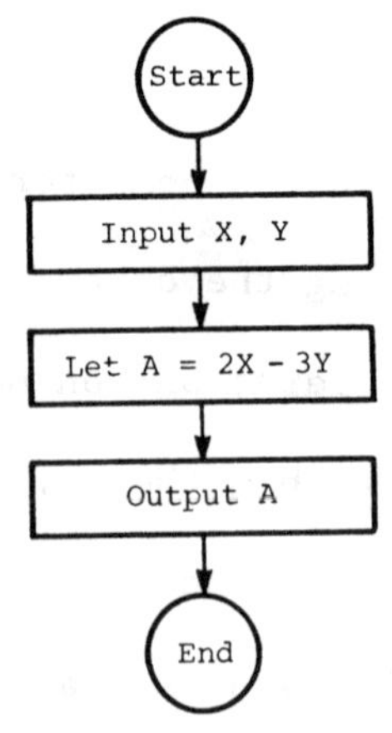

21.

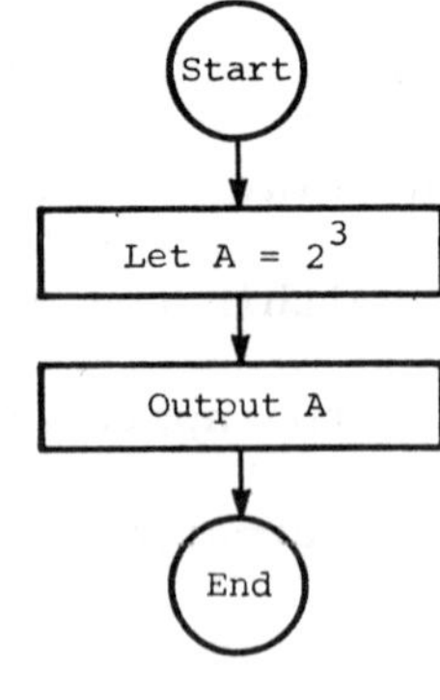

22.

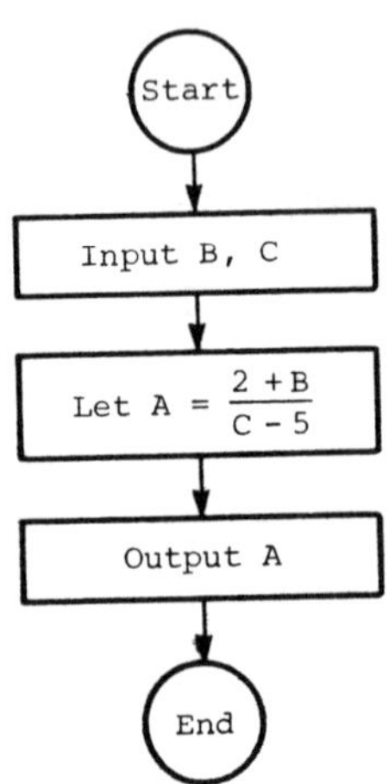

23.

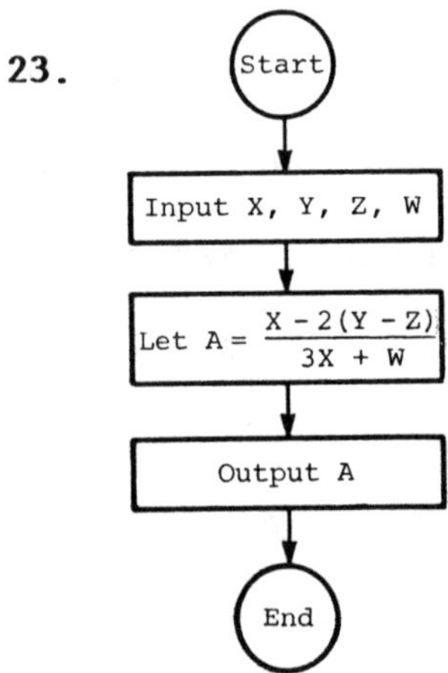

24.

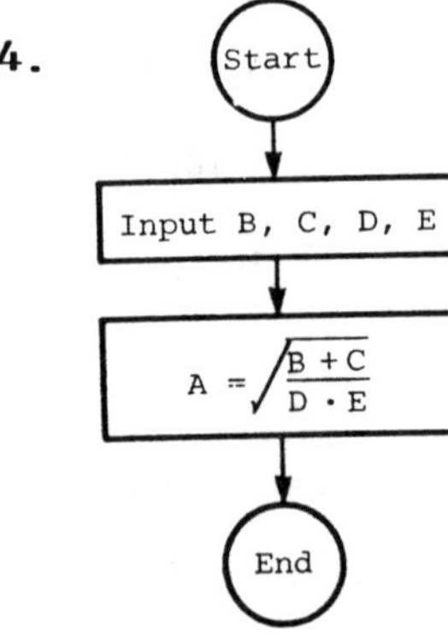

25.

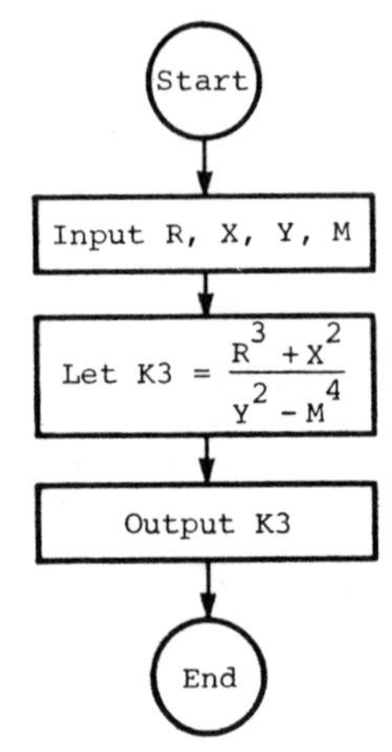

26. 25 **27.** 81 **28.** 125 **29.** 729

30. 53 **31.** 427 **32.** 5 9 53 427

33.

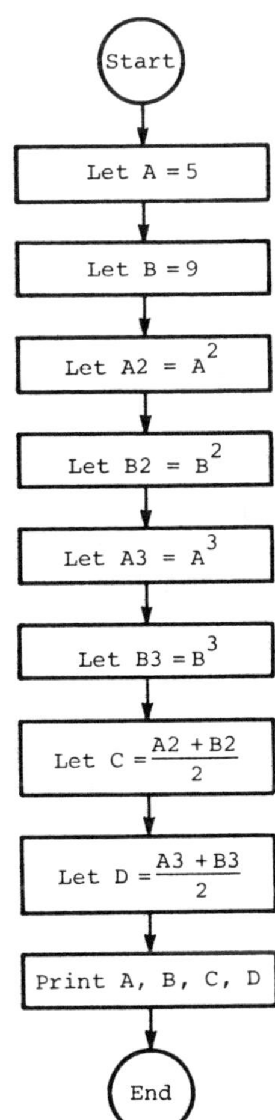

34. 20 **35.** Z = 1.9

36. THE VALUE OF X IS 5

37. 4.8 3.6 4 **38.** Y has no value.

39. XAB is not a valid variable name.

40. There is no END statement.

41. The line numbers are out of sequence.

42. Line 30 is missing a right parenthesis.

43. Line 8 is missing quotation marks between EQUALS and ;.

44. AV is not a valid variable name.

45.

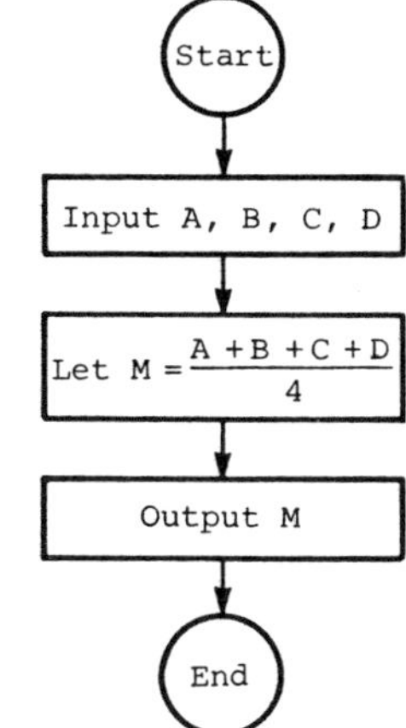

46.

```
10 LET A = 3
20 LET B = 7
30 LET C = 4
40 LET D = 2
50 LET X = (A + B)/2
60 LET Y = (C + D)/2
70 LET T = X ↑ Y
80 PRINT T
90 END
```

47.
```
10  LET T = ((3 + 7)/2) ↑ ((4 + 2)/2)
20  PRINT T
30  END
```

48.
```
10  PRINT ((3 + 7)/2) ↑ ((4 + 2)/2)
20  END
```

49. Change line 80 to:
```
80  DATA 100,50,0
```

50.
```
TOTAL SALARY FOR THE WEEK IS
 180.78 DOLLARS
```

51.
```
10  READ A,B,C
20  LET M = (A + B + C)/3
30  PRINT M
40  DATA 7,12,20
50  END
```

52. 2

53. 23.5   28.4   24.9   25.6   2.1

54. The number 60 would be printed. This could be the perimeter of a triangle with sides of lengths 20, 25, and 15.

55. The number 150 would be printed. This could be the area of a triangle of base 25 and height 12.

Section 14.4 (page 740)

1. All the counting numbers through 30, together with their square roots, would be printed.

2. One possible solution is shown here.

(a)

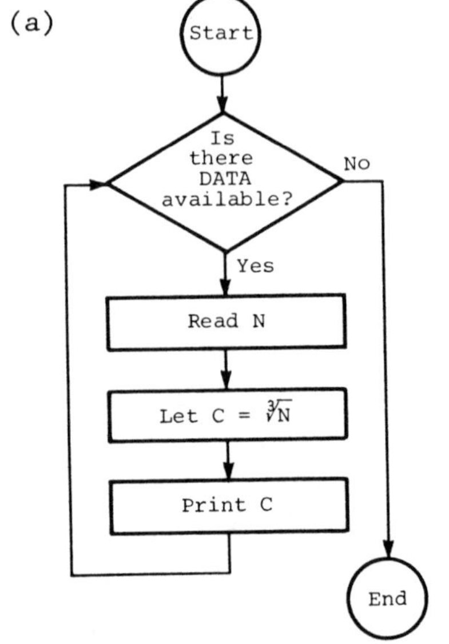

(c)

Start

Let N = 0

Let N = N + 1

Let C = $\sqrt[3]{N}$

Print C

Is N < 10?

Yes

No

End

(b)
```
10  READ N
20  LET C = N ↑ (1/3)
30  PRINT C
40  GO TO 10
50  DATA 1,2,3,4,5,6,7,8,9,10
60  END
```

(d)
```
10  FOR N = 1 TO 10
20     LET C = N ↑ (1/3)
30     PRINT C
40  NEXT N
50  END
```

3. 1 **4.** The value of N is changed from 1 to 2. **5.** 1 1 **6.** 2 1.41421

7. Indefinitely, or until someone stops its execution **8.** Three: X1, X2, S

9. 1, 1, 2 **10.** 3 **11.** 1, 1, 2, 3, 5, 8, 13, 21, 34, 55

12. The Fibonacci sequence **13.** 70 DATA 10,5,6 **14.** 70 DATA 7,5,4

15. 70 DATA 1,2,5 **16.** 70 DATA 10,10,10

17.

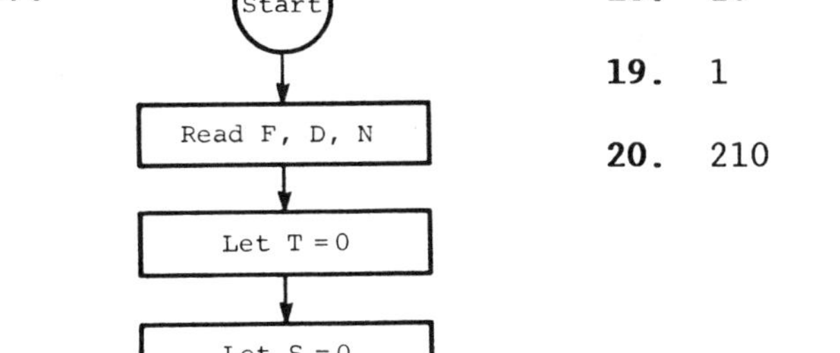

18. 10

19. 1

20. 210

21.

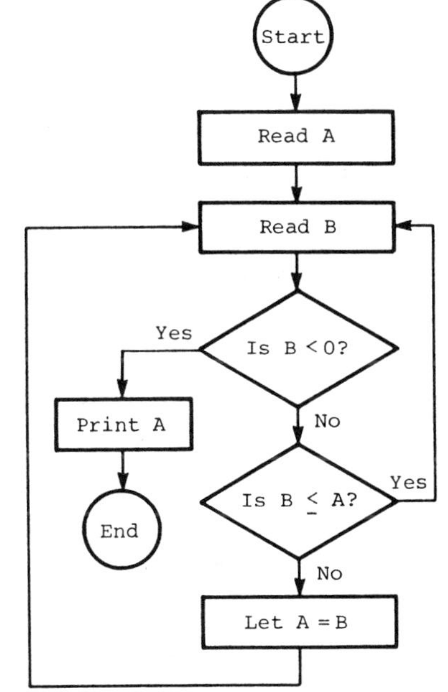

22. The printout would bc: THE LARGEST ITEM IS 13

23. The computer would run out of data in line 20.

24. It identifies and prints the largest number from a list of positive numbers.

25. Just change the DATA line as follows: 80 DATA 25,21,32,26,28,30,26,33,29,31,-1

26. Just change two more lines in the program MAX (and maybe change its name to MIN).

```
40  IF B>=A THEN 20
70  PRINT "THE SMALLEST ITEM IS"; A
```

27. Only the numbers preceding the first negative would be compared, and the largest of those would be printed.

28. 65 IF N>100 THEN 80

29. Change line 20 only: 20 FOR I = 1 TO 200

30. The sum of the squares of the first 100 counting numbers is also found and printed.

31. 5 **32.** 1 **33.** 2 **34.** 6 **35.** 120

36. It has no effect, since the computer never reads more than the first DATA item anyway.

37. For 8!, change line 70 to: 70 DATA 8
For 12!, change line 70 to: 70 DATA 12

38. 1, 20 **39.** 2

40. 3 **41.** R2, R3 **42.** 3 **43.** 39 **44.** 4 **45.** 210

46. (a)

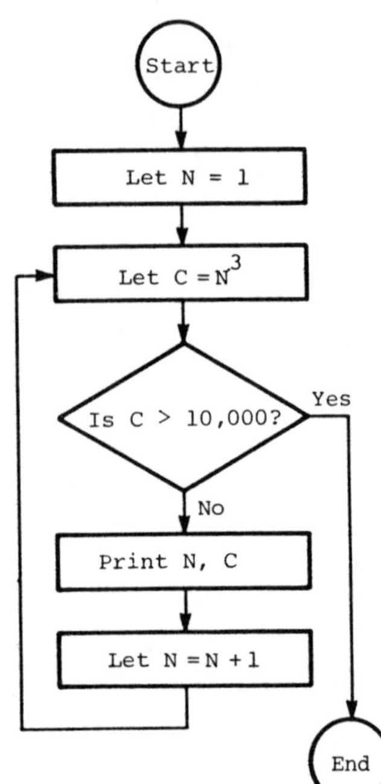

(b)

```
10  LET N = 1
20  LET C = N ↑ 3
30  IF C>10000 THEN 70
40  PRINT N,C
50  LET N = N + 1
60  GO TO 20
70  END
```

47. (a)

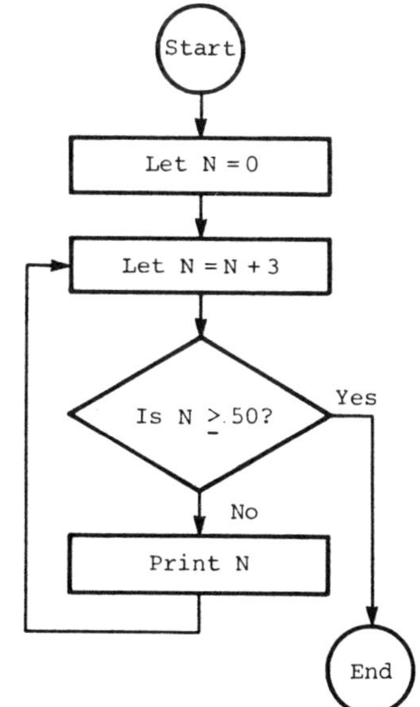

(b)

```
10  LET N = 0
20  LET N = N + 3
30  IF N>=50 THEN 60
40  PRINT N
50  GO TO 20
60  END
```

48. All multiples of 20, from 0 through 1000, together with their squares, would be printed. **49.** All multiples of 5, from 5 through 30, together with their square roots, would be printed.

Chapter 14 Test (page 745)

1. Yes; (c) repetition **2.** Yes; (a) speed **3.** No **4.** Yes; (b) much calculation **5.** Jumbled data following an electrical power surge **6.** A line which instructs the computer to add two numbers that should be multiplied **7.** An unauthorized person gains access to the computerized records of a legal firm **8.** Assuming you have made an error in your check register if it does not agree with the computerized bank statement **9.** Preparing and inputting data **10.** Programming the computer **11.** To get data and instructions into the computer **12.** To store information in the computer **13.** To oversee and coordinate the flow of data within the computer **14.** To perform the necessary arithmetic operations on data within the computer **15.** Business **16.** Scientific **17.** To store information outside the computer, for re-entry later **18.** To store information outside the computer, for re-entry later **19.** To store information outside the computer, for re-entry later **20.** To store information briefly, while it is being processed **21.** To inform the computer of the sequence of steps it must perform to complete a job **22.** To translate the incoming information into the computer's own internal language **23.** To express all information within the computer in a form that the computer can use **24.** 5,380,000 **25.** .0000000000098765 **26.** 9.3748E + 10 **27.** 7.81E - 07 **28.** Valid **29.** Not valid **30.** Valid **31.** Not valid **32.** There is no END statement. **33.** XY is not a valid variable name. **34.** 20

35.

```
NUMBER    SQUARE
   1         1
   2         4
   3         9
   4        16
   5        25
   6        36
   7        49
```

36.

```
 7
12
15
16
15
```

CHAPTER 15

Section 15.1 (page 752)

1. $\begin{bmatrix} 11 & 1 \\ 9 & 4 \end{bmatrix}$ 2. $\begin{bmatrix} -8 & 14 \\ 1 & 7 \end{bmatrix}$ 3. $\begin{bmatrix} 3 & 3 & -3 \\ 4 & -4 & 0 \end{bmatrix}$ 4. $\begin{bmatrix} -3 & 3 & 0 \\ 3 & -3 & -9 \end{bmatrix}$

5. $\begin{bmatrix} -3 & 4 & 2 \\ 8 & 2 & 1 \\ 4 & 3 & 13 \end{bmatrix}$ 6. $\begin{bmatrix} 7 & 2 & 0 \\ 4 & -7 & -6 \\ 5 & -10 & 3 \end{bmatrix}$ 7. Cannot be subtracted - different sizes

8. Cannot be added - different sizes 9. $\begin{bmatrix} 0 \\ 12 \\ 7 \end{bmatrix}$ 10. $\begin{bmatrix} 12 \\ 14 \\ 4 \end{bmatrix}$ 11. $\begin{bmatrix} -14 & -2 \\ 5 & 10 \end{bmatrix}$

12. $\begin{bmatrix} -14 & 6 \\ 10 & 19 \end{bmatrix}$ 13. $\begin{bmatrix} -2 & -1 \\ -1 & -4 \end{bmatrix}$ 14. $\begin{bmatrix} -6 & 1 \\ 7 & -4 \end{bmatrix}$ 15. $\begin{bmatrix} -8 & 0 \\ 6 & -8 \end{bmatrix}$ 16. $\begin{bmatrix} 6 & -3 \\ -12 & 0 \end{bmatrix}$

17. $\begin{bmatrix} -8 & 4 \\ 16 & 0 \end{bmatrix}$ 18. $\begin{bmatrix} 20 & 0 \\ -15 & 20 \end{bmatrix}$ 19. $\begin{bmatrix} -2 & -3 \\ -6 & -8 \end{bmatrix}$ 20. $\begin{bmatrix} 36 & -4 \\ -37 & 28 \end{bmatrix}$ 21. $\begin{bmatrix} 0 & 0 \\ 0 & 0 \end{bmatrix}$

22. $\begin{bmatrix} 2 & 1 & 2 & 1 \\ 3 & 2 & 2 & 1 \\ 4 & 3 & 2 & 1 \end{bmatrix}$ 23. $\begin{bmatrix} 5 & 0 & 7 \\ 0 & 10 & 1 \\ 0 & 15 & 2 \\ 10 & 12 & 8 \end{bmatrix}$ 24. $\begin{bmatrix} 8 \\ 4 \\ 5 \end{bmatrix}$ 25. $\begin{bmatrix} 10 & 12 & 5 \\ 15 & 20 & 8 \end{bmatrix}$

26. $\begin{bmatrix} 55 & 47 & 25 \\ 80 & 60 & 43 \end{bmatrix}$ 27. 60 28. 25 29. $\begin{bmatrix} 97 & 92 & 86 \\ 139 & 121 & 100 \end{bmatrix}$ 30. $\begin{bmatrix} 27 & 27 & 35 \\ 35 & 40 & 28 \end{bmatrix}$

31. y = 3, k = 8, m = 1 32. a = 5, b = 7, c = 8 33. x = 1, y = 8, z = 8

34. m = -1, a = 0, n = 3 35. x = 10, k = 4, y = -4 36. m = 9, a = 1, y = 10, b = 4 37. True 38. False 39. True 40. True 41. True

42. True 43. True 44. True 45. True 46. True 47. Yes

48. Yes

Section 15.2 (page 759)

1. $\begin{bmatrix} 8 & 6 \\ -7 & 3 \end{bmatrix}$ 2. $\begin{bmatrix} 11 & -20 \\ 11 & 4 \end{bmatrix}$ 3. $\begin{bmatrix} -2 & -8 \\ -14 & 34 \end{bmatrix}$ 4. $\begin{bmatrix} -19 & 41 \\ 8 & -2 \end{bmatrix}$ 5. $\begin{bmatrix} 17 & 7 & 9 \\ 13 & 6 & 3 \end{bmatrix}$

6. $\begin{bmatrix} 15 & -19 & 30 \\ -9 & 19 & 20 \end{bmatrix}$ 7. $\begin{bmatrix} 8 & 3 \\ 11 & -2 \\ 4 & 12 \end{bmatrix}$ 8. $\begin{bmatrix} 5 & 0 \\ -16 & 2 \\ -10 & 0 \end{bmatrix}$ 9. Cannot be multiplied

10. Cannot be multiplied 11. $\begin{bmatrix} 14 & 4 & 0 \\ -4 & 4 & 0 \\ -6 & 2 & 0 \end{bmatrix}$ 12. $\begin{bmatrix} 8 & -12 & 12 \\ -2 & 33 & 2 \\ 8 & 5 & 13 \end{bmatrix}$

13. $\begin{bmatrix} 47.5 & 57.75 \\ 27 & 33.75 \\ 81 & 95 \\ 12 & 15 \end{bmatrix}$ **14.** [20 200 50 60]; [220 890 105 125 70]

15. [11,120 13,555] **16.** Yes **17.** Yes **18.** Yes **19.** Yes **20.** No

21. No **22.** Yes **23.** No **24.** Yes **25.** Yes **26.** Yes **27.** No

28. Magic **29.** Magic **30.** Magic **31.** $\begin{bmatrix} 14 & 2 & 14 \\ 10 & 10 & 10 \\ 6 & 18 & 6 \end{bmatrix}$; magic

32. $\begin{bmatrix} 34 & 5 & 36 \\ 27 & 25 & 23 \\ 14 & 45 & 16 \end{bmatrix}$; magic **33.** $\begin{bmatrix} 67 & 67 & 91 \\ 67 & 91 & 67 \\ 91 & 67 & 67 \end{bmatrix}$; magic **34.** $\begin{bmatrix} 91 & 67 & 67 \\ 67 & 91 & 67 \\ 67 & 67 & 91 \end{bmatrix}$; pseudomagic

35. $\begin{bmatrix} 59 & 83 & 83 \\ 83 & 59 & 83 \\ 83 & 83 & 59 \end{bmatrix}$; pseudomagic **36.** $\begin{bmatrix} 150 & 150 & 150 \\ 150 & 150 & 150 \\ 150 & 150 & 150 \end{bmatrix}$; magic

Section 15.3 (page 767)

1. $\begin{bmatrix} -1 & 2 & 1 \\ 3 & -4 & 2 \\ -4 & 0 & 1 \end{bmatrix}$ **2.** $\begin{bmatrix} 2 & -1 & 3 \\ 1 & 3 & -3 \\ -4 & 0 & 1 \end{bmatrix}$ **3.** $\begin{bmatrix} -4 & 0 & 1 \\ -9 & 12 & -6 \\ -1 & 2 & 1 \end{bmatrix}$ **4.** $\begin{bmatrix} -8 & 0 & 2 \\ 3 & -4 & 2 \\ -1 & 2 & 1 \end{bmatrix}$

5. $\begin{bmatrix} 18 & -1 & -1 \\ -4 & 0 & 1 \\ 1 & 3 & -3 \end{bmatrix}$ **6.** $\begin{bmatrix} -4 & 0 & 1 \\ -2 & 6 & 7 \\ -1 & 2 & 1 \end{bmatrix}$ **7.** $\begin{bmatrix} -4 & 0 & 1 \\ 3 & -4 & 2 \\ -13 & 2 & 4 \end{bmatrix}$ **8.** $\begin{bmatrix} 2 & -1 & 3 \\ -5 & -3 & 4 \\ 1 & 3 & -3 \end{bmatrix}$

9. $\begin{bmatrix} 1 & 11 & -5 \\ -1 & -4 & 3 \\ 0 & 5 & -2 \end{bmatrix}$ **10.** $\begin{bmatrix} 6 & -1 & 2 \\ -7 & 4 & -1 \\ 32 & -4 & 6 \end{bmatrix}$ **11.** Exchange rows 1 and 2.

12. Multiply each element of row 3 by 1, and add the results to row 1.

13. Double each element of row 2. **14.** Multiply each element of row 3 by -1/2.

15. Multiply each element of row 1 by 2, and add the results to row 2.

16. Multiply each element of row 3 by -3, and add the results to row 1.

17. Multiply row 2 by -1. Multiply row 2 by -2 and add to row 1.

18. Multiply row 1 by 1/2. Multiply row 1 by -1 and add to row 2. Multiply row 2 by -2/3. Multiply row 2 by -1/2 and add to row 1. **19.** Multiply row 1 by -1/2. Multiply row 1 by -4 and add to row 2. Multiply row 2 by 1/5. Multiply row 2 by 1 and add to row 1. **20.** Exchange rows 1 and 2. Multiply row 1 by -1/2. Multiply row 2 by -1. **21.** Multiply row 1 by 1/6. Multiply row 2 by 1/4. Multiply row 2 by -1/2 and add to row 1. Multiply row 3 by 1/2. **22.** Multiply row 1 by -1/2. Multiply row 1 by -1 and add to row 3. Multiply row 2 by 1 and add to row 1. Multiply row 2 by -2 and add to row 3.

23. $\left[\begin{array}{cc|c} 2 & 3 & 11 \\ 1 & 2 & 8 \end{array}\right]$ **24.** $\left[\begin{array}{cc|c} 3 & 5 & -13 \\ 2 & 3 & -9 \end{array}\right]$ **25.** $\left[\begin{array}{cc|c} 1 & 5 & 6 \\ 3 & -4 & 1 \end{array}\right]$ **26.** $\left[\begin{array}{cc|c} 2 & 7 & 1 \\ 5 & 1 & -15 \end{array}\right]$

27. $\left[\begin{array}{ccc|c} 2 & 1 & 1 & 3 \\ 3 & -4 & 2 & -7 \\ 1 & 1 & 1 & 2 \end{array}\right]$ **28.** $\left[\begin{array}{ccc|c} 4 & -2 & 3 & 4 \\ 3 & 5 & 1 & 7 \\ 5 & -1 & 4 & 7 \end{array}\right]$ **29.** $\left[\begin{array}{ccc|c} 1 & 1 & 0 & 6 \\ 0 & 2 & 1 & 2 \\ 0 & 0 & 1 & 2 \end{array}\right]$

30. $\left[\begin{array}{ccc|c} 1 & 0 & 0 & 6 \\ 0 & 1 & 2 & 2 \\ 1 & 0 & -3 & 2 \end{array}\right]$ **31.** (2, 3) **32.** (-3, 4) **33.** (-3, 0) **34.** (0, -2)

35. (7/2, -1) **36.** (2, -7) **37.** (5, 0) **38.** (1, 1) **39.** No solution

40. No solution **41.** (-2, 1, 3) **42.** (2, 4, 5) **43.** (-1, 23, 16)

44. (1, 0, -1) **45.** (3, 2, -4) **46.** (-1, 2, -2) **47.** (-1, 2, 5, 1)

48. (0, 2, -2, 1) **49.** \$30 for a goat, \$25 for a sheep **50.** \$76 for day laborers, \$80 for concrete finishers **51.** 4 of A, 7 of B **52.** \$5 per pound for dark clay, \$1 per pound for light clay **53.** 6 cm, 6 cm, 9 cm **54.** 74 decals, 96 stickers

55. 6 rhythm, 3 guitarists

Section 15.4 (page 775)

1. $\begin{bmatrix} 1 & 0 \\ 0 & -1 \end{bmatrix}$ **2.** $\begin{bmatrix} 0 & 1 \\ 1 & 0 \end{bmatrix}$ **3.** $\begin{bmatrix} 3/2 & -1/2 \\ -2 & 1 \end{bmatrix}$ **4.** $\begin{bmatrix} -5/3 & -2/3 \\ -2 & -1 \end{bmatrix}$ **5.** $\begin{bmatrix} 13/5 & 6/5 \\ -2 & -1 \end{bmatrix}$

6. $\begin{bmatrix} 1/2 & 1/2 \\ 1/2 & -1/2 \end{bmatrix}$ **7.** No inverse **8.** No inverse **9.** $\begin{bmatrix} -3/2 & 1 \\ 1 & -1/2 \end{bmatrix}$

10. $\begin{bmatrix} 2/11 & -5/11 \\ 1/11 & 3/11 \end{bmatrix}$ **11.** $\begin{bmatrix} 1 & -2 & 0 \\ 0 & 1 & 0 \\ -1 & 3 & 1 \end{bmatrix}$ **12.** $\begin{bmatrix} 1 & 0 & 1 \\ 1 & 0 & 0 \\ 0 & -1/2 & 0 \end{bmatrix}$ **13.** $\begin{bmatrix} 0 & 1/3 & -1 \\ 0 & 1/3 & 0 \\ 1/2 & -5/6 & 2 \end{bmatrix}$

14. $\begin{bmatrix} -1/5 & 4/15 & -2/15 \\ 3/5 & 1/5 & 2/5 \\ 2/5 & 2/15 & -1/15 \end{bmatrix}$ **15.** $\begin{bmatrix} 4 & 3 & 3 \\ -1 & 0 & -1 \\ -4 & -4 & -3 \end{bmatrix}$ **16.** No inverse

17. $\begin{bmatrix} 35 \\ -88 \end{bmatrix} \begin{bmatrix} -4 \\ 0 \end{bmatrix} \begin{bmatrix} 15 \\ -48 \end{bmatrix} \begin{bmatrix} -9 \\ 9 \end{bmatrix} \begin{bmatrix} 35 \\ -97 \end{bmatrix} \begin{bmatrix} 53 \\ -133 \end{bmatrix} \begin{bmatrix} 16 \\ -50 \end{bmatrix} \begin{bmatrix} 5 \\ -15 \end{bmatrix}$

18. $\begin{bmatrix} 39 \\ -98 \end{bmatrix} \begin{bmatrix} -18 \\ 35 \end{bmatrix} \begin{bmatrix} 19 \\ -49 \end{bmatrix} \begin{bmatrix} -25 \\ 49 \end{bmatrix} \begin{bmatrix} 34 \\ -95 \end{bmatrix} \begin{bmatrix} -2 \\ 3 \end{bmatrix} \begin{bmatrix} 5 \\ -24 \end{bmatrix} \begin{bmatrix} 15 \\ -51 \end{bmatrix} \begin{bmatrix} 10 \\ -32 \end{bmatrix} \begin{bmatrix} 33 \\ -85 \end{bmatrix} \begin{bmatrix} 35 \\ -97 \end{bmatrix} \begin{bmatrix} 10 \\ -35 \end{bmatrix} \begin{bmatrix} 39 \\ -105 \end{bmatrix} \begin{bmatrix} 27 \\ -69 \end{bmatrix} \begin{bmatrix} -4 \\ 4 \end{bmatrix}$

19. Santa Claus is fat.

20. $\begin{bmatrix} 76 \\ 77 \\ 96 \end{bmatrix} \begin{bmatrix} 62 \\ 67 \\ 75 \end{bmatrix} \begin{bmatrix} 88 \\ 108 \\ 97 \end{bmatrix} \begin{bmatrix} 141 \\ 160 \\ 168 \end{bmatrix} \begin{bmatrix} 147 \\ 166 \\ 174 \end{bmatrix} \begin{bmatrix} 105 \\ 120 \\ 123 \end{bmatrix} \begin{bmatrix} 111 \\ 131 \\ 119 \end{bmatrix} \begin{bmatrix} 92 \\ 119 \\ 94 \end{bmatrix} \begin{bmatrix} 75 \\ 93 \\ 79 \end{bmatrix} \begin{bmatrix} 181 \\ 208 \\ 208 \end{bmatrix}$

21. Success in dealing with unknown ciphers is measured by these four things in the order named: perseverance, careful methods of analysis, intuition, luck.

22. $\begin{bmatrix} 3/4 & -1/12 \\ -1/3 & 8/9 \end{bmatrix}$ **23.** $\begin{bmatrix} 32/23 & 3/23 \\ 12/23 & 27/23 \end{bmatrix}$

24. 826 metric tons of wheat, 1435 metric tons of oil **25.** 1174 metric tons of wheat, 1565 metric tons of oil **26.** 1018 metric tons of wheat, 1339 metric tons of oil

Section 15.5 (page 781)

1. $\begin{bmatrix} 4 & -1 \\ 3 & 5 \end{bmatrix}$ **2.** $\begin{bmatrix} 2 & -5 \\ -1 & 1 \\ 1 & -3 \end{bmatrix}$ **3.** $\begin{bmatrix} 8 & -7 \\ -2 & 4 \end{bmatrix}$ **4.** $\begin{bmatrix} 6 & 2 \\ -1 & 10 \\ 3 & 5 \end{bmatrix}$ **5.** (3, I); 3

6. (1, I); 7 **7.** (2, III); 2 **8.** (1, III); 1 **9.** (2, III); 0 **10.** (2, II); 3

11. (a) Set up in the stadium (b) Set up in the gym (c) Set up in both

12. (a) Recommend no campaign (b) Recommend campaign for all

(c) Recommend campaign for all

13. (a)

	Better	Not
Market new	50,000	-25,000
Don't	-40,000	-10,000

(b) $5000 and -$22,000; market new

14. Allied should select strategy 1 with probability 10/27 and strategy 2 with probability 17/27. The value of the game is 1/18 million, which represents increased sales of about $55,556. **15.** 1: 1/5, 2: 4/5, I: 3/5, II: 2/5, value = 17/5

16. 1: 7/16, 2: 9/16, I: 9/16, II: 7/16, value = -1/16 **17.** 1: 11/15, 2: 4/15, I: 8/15, II: 7/15, value = 62/15 **18.** The saddle point gives a value of 0. Both players should always select their second strategy. **19.** Both A and B should choose either strategy with a probability of 1/2. The value of the game is 0, a fair game.

Chapter 15 Test (page 784)

1. $\begin{bmatrix} -1 & -1 & 4 \\ 2 & 2 & 0 \\ 3 & 1 & 6 \end{bmatrix}$ **2.** $\begin{bmatrix} 5 & -1 & 2 \\ 2 & -2 & 2 \\ 5 & 1 & 0 \end{bmatrix}$ **3.** $\begin{bmatrix} -9 & -2 & 12 \\ -7 & 0 & 5 \\ -15 & 2 & 12 \end{bmatrix}$ **4.** $\begin{bmatrix} -2 & 4 & -6 \\ 0 & -1 & -1 \\ 10 & 4 & 6 \end{bmatrix}$

5. $\begin{bmatrix} 4 & -2 & 6 \\ 4 & 0 & 2 \\ 8 & 2 & 6 \end{bmatrix}$ **6.** $\begin{bmatrix} 9 & 0 & -3 \\ 0 & -6 & 3 \\ 3 & 0 & -9 \end{bmatrix}$ **7.** $\begin{bmatrix} 2 & -1 & 3 \\ 4 & 1 & 3 \\ 2 & 0 & 1 \end{bmatrix}$ **8.** $\begin{bmatrix} -4 & -1 & 0 \\ 2 & 0 & 1 \\ 4 & 1 & 3 \end{bmatrix}$ **9.** $\begin{bmatrix} -3 \\ 10 \end{bmatrix}$

10. $\begin{bmatrix} 6 & 0 & 12 \\ 26 & 0 & 20 \end{bmatrix}$ **11.** [16] **12.** No product **13.** $\begin{bmatrix} 3 & -1 \\ -5 & 2 \end{bmatrix}$ **14.** No inverse

15. $\begin{bmatrix} 1/2 & 1/2 & -1/2 \\ -1/2 & 1/6 & 1/6 \\ 1/2 & -1/2 & 1/2 \end{bmatrix}$ **16.** $\begin{bmatrix} 2/3 & 0 & -1/3 \\ 1/3 & 0 & -2/3 \\ -2/3 & 1 & 1/3 \end{bmatrix}$ **17.** (-2, 3) **18.** (3, 0)

19. (-1, 0, 2) **20.** (3, 2, 1) **21.** $\begin{bmatrix} 3 & 4 \\ -1 & 5 \end{bmatrix}$ **22.** $\begin{bmatrix} 8 & -3 \\ 0 & 2 \end{bmatrix}$ **23.** 6 **24.** 9

25. Play row one 9/10 of the time and row two 1/10 of the time; value is -31/10.